ELEMENTS OF
FINITE PROBABILITY

HOLDEN-DAY SERIES IN PROBABILITY AND STATISTICS

E. L. Lehmann, Editor

ELEMENTS OF
FINITE PROBABILITY

J. L. Hodges, Jr. and E. L. Lehmann

University of California, Berkeley

HOLDEN-DAY

San Francisco, Cambridge, London, Amsterdam

116863

Preface

After publication of our book *Basic Concepts of Probability and Statistics*, it was suggested to us that "Part I. Probability" be made available separately, to serve as a text for a one quarter or one semester course in probability at the precalculus level. The present book, the result of these suggestions, contains all the material of Part I of the earlier book, supplemented by two new sections at the end of Chapter 6.

A careful treatment of probability without calculus is possible only if attention is restricted to finite probability models, i.e., to models representing experiments with a finite number of outcomes. Fortunately, the basic notions of probability, such as probability model, random variable, expectation and variance, are in fact most easily introduced with finite models. Furthermore, many interesting and important applications lead to finite models, such as the binomial, hypergeometric and sampling models.

More than most branches of mathematics, probability theory retains its connections with the empirical phenomena from which it grew. While it is possible to present probability in a purely abstract manner, divorced from its empirical origins, the subject thereby loses much of its vitality and interest. On the other hand, if the theory is developed in its empirical context, it becomes essential to make clear the distinction between the real world and its mathematical representation. Our treatment is therefore centered on the notion of a probability model and emphasizes its relation to, and distinction from, the underlying random experiment which it represents.

One aspect of this approach is a careful treatment of the independence assumption in building probability models. Many complex experiments are made up of simpler parts, and it is frequently possible to build models for such experiments by first building simple models for the parts, and then combining them into a "product model" for the experiment as a whole. Particular attention is devoted to the realism of this procedure, and in general to the empirical meaning of the independence assumption, which so often is applied invalidly.

While basically we have included only concepts that can be defined and results that can be proved without calculus, there is one exception: we give approximations to certain probabilities whose calculation we have explained in principle, but whose actual computation would be too laborious. Thus, in particular, we discuss the normal approximation to the binomial and hypergeometric distributions and the Poisson approximation to the binomial and Poisson-binomial distributions. Since the limit theorems which underlie these approximations require advanced analytical techniques and are hence not available to us, we give instead numerical illustrations to develop some feeling for their accuracy.

The book contains over 400 problems, some of which provide simple exercises while others extend the ideas and results of the text.* Six of the more important tables are collected at the end of the book as Tables A-F.

A decimal numbering system is used for sections, formulas, examples, tables, problems, and so forth. Thus, Section 5.4 is the fourth section of Chapter 5. To simplify the writing, within Chapter 5 itself we omit the chapter and refer to this section simply as Section 4. Similarly Example 5.4.2 is the second example in Section 5.4. However, within Section 5.4 we omit the chapter and section and refer to the example as Example 2; in other sections of Chapter 5 we omit the chapter and refer to the example as Example 4.2.

J. L. HODGES, JR.
E. L. LEHMANN

Berkeley
January, 1965

---

* Instructors may obtain answer books by writing to the publisher.

Contents

5. RANDOM VARIABLES

6. SPECIAL DISTRIBUTIONS

7. MULTIVARIATE DISTRIBUTIONS

TABLES

CHAPTER 1

PROBABILITY MODELS

1.1 RANDOM EXPERIMENTS

The theory of probability is a mathematical discipline which has found important applications in many different fields of human activity. It has extended the scope of scientific method, making it applicable to experiments whose results are not completely determined by the experimental conditions.

The agreement among scientists regarding the validity of most scientific theories rests to a considerable extent on the fact that the experiments on which the theories are based will yield essentially the same results when they are repeated. When a scientist announces a discovery, other scientists in different parts of the world can verify his findings for themselves. Sometimes the results of two workers appear to disagree, but this usually turns out to mean that the experimental conditions were not quite the same in the two cases. If the same results are obtained when an experiment is repeated under the same conditions, we may say that the result is determined by the conditions, or that the experiment is *deterministic*. It is the deterministic nature of science that permits the use of scientific theory for predicting what will be observed under specified conditions.

However, there are also experiments whose results vary, in spite of all efforts to keep the experimental conditions constant. Familiar examples are provided by gambling games: throwing dice, tossing pennies, dealing from a shuffled deck of cards can all be thought of as "experiments" with unpredictable results. More important and interesting instances occur in many fields. For example, seeds that are apparently identical will produce plants of differing height, and repeated weighings of the same object with a chemical balance will show slight variations. A machine which sews together two pieces of material, occasionally—for no apparent reason—will miss a stitch. If we are willing to stretch our idea of "experiment," length of life may be considered a variable experimental result, since people living under similar conditions will die at different and unpredictable ages. We shall refer to experiments that are not deterministic, and thus do not always yield the same result when repeated under the same conditions, as *random experiments*. Probability theory (and the theory of statistics, which is based on it) are the branches of mathematics that have been developed to deal with random experiments.

Let us now consider two random experiments in more detail. As the first example, we take the experiment of throwing a die. This is one of the simplest random experiments and one with which most people are personally acquainted. In fact, probability theory had its beginnings in the study of dice games.

EXAMPLE *1*. *Throwing a die*. Suppose we take a die, shake it vigorously in a dice cup, and throw it against a vertical board so that it bounces onto a table. When the die comes to rest, we observe as the experimental result the number, say X, of points on the upper face. The experiment is not deterministic: the result X may be any of the six numbers 1, 2, 3, 4, 5, or 6, and no one can predict which of the values will be obtained on any particular performance of the experiment. We may make every effort to control or standardize the experimental conditions, by always placing the die in the cup in the same position, always shaking the cup the same number of times, always throwing it against the same spot on the backboard, and so on. In spite of all such efforts, the result will remain variable and unpredictable.

EXAMPLE *2*. *Measuring a distance*. It is desired to determine the distance between two points a few miles apart. A surveying party measures the distance by use of a surveyor's chain. It is found in practice that the measured distance will not be exactly the same if two parties do the job, or even if the same party does the job on consecutive days. In spite of the best efforts to measure precisely, small differences will accumulate and the final measurement will vary from one performance of the experiment to another.

How is it possible for a scientific theory to be based on indeterminacy? The paradox is resolved by an empirical observation: while the result on any particular performance of such an experiment cannot be predicted, a long sequence of performances, taken together, reveals a stability that can serve as the basis for quite precise predictions. The property of *long-run stability* lies at the root of the ideas of probability, and we shall examine it in more detail in the next section.

1.2 EMPIRICAL BASIS OF PROBABILITY

To obtain some idea about the behavior of results in a sequence of repetitions of a random experiment, we shall now consider some specific examples.

EXAMPLE 1. *Throwing a die.* Figure 1 shows certain results of 5000 throws of a die. In this experiment, we were not interested in the actual value of the number X of points showing, but only in whether X was less

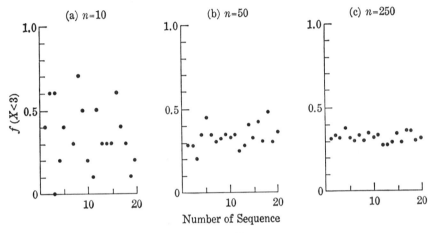

FIGURE 1. DICE

than three $(X < 3)$, or on the contrary was greater than or equal to three $(X \geq 3)$. The values of X on the first ten repetitions or *trials* of the experiment are as follows:

Trial number	1	2	3	4	5	6	7	8	9	10
Value of X	6	3	2	1	5	6	1	3	5	2

The result $(X < 3)$ occurred on trials 3, 4, 7, and 10 and did not occur on trials 1, 2, 5, 6, 8, and 9. Thus, the number of occurrences of the result $(X < 3)$ on the first ten trials was 4: we denote this for brevity by the formula $\#(X < 3) = 4$. Dividing this by the number 10 of trials, we obtain the fraction .4, which will be called the *frequency* of the result $(X < 3)$. This frequency will be denoted by $f(X < 3)$, so that $f(X < 3) = .4$ in the first 10 trials. In general, if a result R occurs $\#(R)$ times in n trials of an experiment, the frequency $f(R)$ of the result is given by

$$f(R) = \frac{\#(R)}{n}.$$

We have been discussing the first sequence of ten trials. In a similar way, 19 other sequences of ten trials were carried out. On the 20 sequences, various values of $f(X < 3)$ were observed, as follows:

Sequence	1	2	3	4	5	6	7	8	9	10	11	12	13	14	15	16	17	18	19	20
$f(X < 3)$	.4	.6	.6	.2	.4	0	.3	.7	.5	.2	.1	.5	.3	.3	.3	.6	.4	.3	.1	.2

Thus, on the second sequence of ten trials, the result $(X < 3)$ occurred six times out of ten, or $f(X < 3) = .6$. The values observed for $f(X < 3)$ varied from 0 (Sequence 6) to .7 (Sequence 8). These observations are displayed in Figure 1a, where each point corresponds to one sequence of ten trials; on this diagram, the horizontal scale shows the number of the sequence, while the vertical scale shows the value of $f(X < 3)$ observed on that sequence.

An examination of Figure 1a shows that while $f(X < 3)$ varies from one sequence to another, it never exceeded .7, and we might perhaps predict that $f(X < 3)$ would not exceed .7 in another sequence of ten trials. Of course $f(X < 3)$ *could* be greater than .7, or even as great as 1, since it is possible that X will be either 1 or 2 every time the die is rolled. However, our experience of 20 sequences suggests that a value of $f(X < 3)$ larger than .7 will not occur very often.

Would the behavior of $f(X < 3)$ be less erratic if a longer sequence of trials were used? If we denote by n the number of trials in the sequence, Figure 1b shows the values of $f(X < 3)$ in 20 sequences of $n = 50$ trials each. These values are still variable, but clearly less so than for $n = 10$, since $f(X < 3)$ now ranges from .20 to .48 instead of from 0 to .7. It appears that, with longer sequences, the frequency of the result $X < 3$ is less variable and hence more predictable than when the sequences are shorter. After studying Figure 1b, even a cautious person might predict that in another sequence of $n = 50$ trials, $f(X < 3)$ is not likely to fall below .15 or above .55. Thus encouraged, we finally turn to Figure 1c, which shows the values of $f(X < 3)$ in 20 sequences of $n = 250$ trials each, based on 5000 throws of the die in all. Again the variation is reduced: now $f(X < 3)$ ranges only from .276 to .372.

EXAMPLE 2. *Random digits.* A rather parallel illustration is provided by a random digit generator. This device, which has been called an "electronic roulette wheel," is designed to produce at random the digits from 0 to 9. (The precise meaning and usefulness of such "random digits" will be made clear in Section 3.4.) In the present experiment we were not interested in the actual value of the digit produced but only in whether it was even, that is, was one of the digits 0, 2, 4, 6, or 8. Figure 2 is analogous to Figure 1. It shows the frequency $f(\text{even})$ with which an even digit occurred, in 20 sequences of $n = 10$, $n = 50$, and $n = 250$ digits. Qualitatively the features of Figure 2 agree with those of Figure 1: it appears that f(even) also stabilizes as n is increased, although the values are placed somewhat higher on the vertical scale.

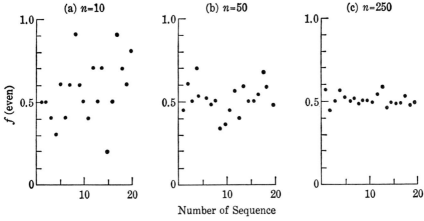

FIGURE 2. RANDOM DIGITS

EXAMPLE 3. *Male births.* The general features of our preceding examples, indeterminacy combined with stability as the sequences get longer, may also appear with sequences of occurrences which at first would not seem to constitute repetitions of an experiment under constant conditions. Figure

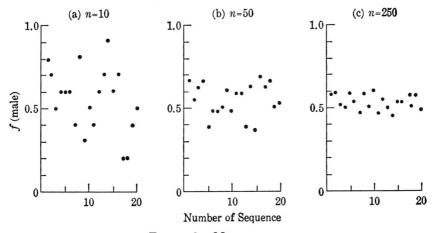

FIGURE 3. MALE BIRTHS

3 relates to the frequency of males in a sequence of human births, showing the frequency f(male) for 20 sequences of $n = 10$, 50, and 250 births.*

* We are indebted to our colleague J. Yerushalmy for the record of sex in 5000 births represented here.

Since the parents in the 5000 cases were of course different, how can we say—even if we agree to regard the sex of a baby as the result of an experiment—that the conditions are constant? Yet, in appearance Figures 2 and 3 are so similar as to suggest that a theory built to deal with one would also work for the other—as indeed it does.

EXAMPLE 4. *Two-letter words.* The data for Figure 4 were obtained by inspecting 5000 lines in a book, and determining for each line whether or not it contained at least one two-letter word. Figure 4 shows the fre-

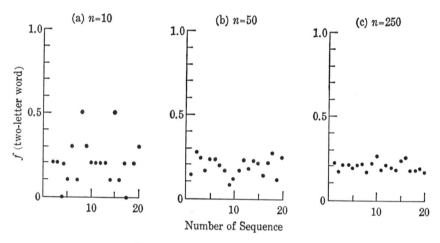

FIGURE 4. TWO-LETTER WORDS

quency f(two-letter word) of getting at least one two-letter word, for 20 sequences of $n = 10$, 50, and 250 lines. Again, we would hardly think of an author, when he sits down to write, as performing an experiment which may result in the appearance of a two-letter word in a line of type, but operationally the sequence of results seem to portray features quite like those of the other cases.

A careful examination of Figures 1–4, or of similar records in other cases, will suggest that the tendency towards stability proceeds at a fairly definite rate as the number n of trials is increased. The table below gives, for each of our four experiments and for each of the three values of n, the difference between the maximum and minimum values observed for f in the 20 sequences. This difference is known as the *range* of f. We see that when the sequences are made five times as long, the ranges become about half as large.

TABLE 1. RANGE OF f

	Dice	Random digits	Male births	Two-letter words
$n = 10$	.7	.7	.7	.5
$n = 50$	.28	.36	.32	.20
$n = 250$	.096	.140	.144	.096

These facts lead to the speculation that we could make f as nearly constant as we please, by taking sufficiently large values for n. In some cases it is possible to see what happens when n is made very large. For example, there has been published a table* giving the number of times each of the ten digits was produced in 20 sequences of $n = 50{,}000$ trials of a random digit generator. If we consider the frequency with which even digits occurred in these sequences, it is found that the lowest value observed among the twenty sequences was .4971 and the highest was .5054, giving a range of only .0083. As a second illustration, let us consider the frequency of males among registered births, which are available from publications of the U.S. Public Health Service. In the twenty years from 1937 to 1956, f(male) for live births in the state of New York varied between .5126 and .5162, giving a range of .0036. (On the average, the number n of these births was about 230,000 per year.)

Data of this kind, gathered from many sources over a long period of time, indicate the following *stability property of frequencies:* for sequences of sufficient length the value of f will be practically constant; that is, if we observed f in several such sequences, we would find it to have practically the same value in each of them. This *long-run frequency* may of course depend on the conditions under which the experiment is performed. The frequency of an ace in a long sequence of throws of a die, for example, may depend on the die that is used, on how it is thrown, on who does the throwing, and so forth. Similarly, the frequency of males in human births has been found to depend, to a greater or lesser extent, on such "conditions of the experiment" as the nationality of the parents and the order of the child in the family. In fact, an active field of research in human biology is concerned with determining just what factors do influence the frequency of males.

It is essential for the stability of long-run frequencies that the conditions of the experiment be kept constant. Consider for example the machine mentioned earlier, which sews together two pieces of material. If the

---

* The RAND Corporation, "A Million Random Digits with 100,000 Normal Deviates," Free Press, Glencoe, Illinois, 1955.

needle that does the stitching gradually begins to blunt, the frequency with which it will miss stitches might increase instead of settling down, in which case a plot of the frequencies would look quite different from Figure 1. Actually, in reality it is of course never possible to keep the conditions of the experiment exactly constant. There is in fact a circularity in the argument here: we consider that the conditions are *essentially* constant as long as the frequency is observed to be stable. As suggested above in connection with the frequency of males, it may be important and useful to study what aspects of the experimental conditions influence the frequency. Thus, special techniques (known as quality control) have been developed to help isolate those conditions of a production process, under which the frequency of defective items is high, in order to change them and thereby improve the quality of the product.

The stability property of frequencies, which we have discussed in this section, is not a consequence of logical deduction. It is quite possible to conceive of a world in which frequencies would not stabilize as the number of repetitions of the experiment becomes large. That frequencies actually do possess this property is an empirical or observational fact based on literally millions of observations. This fact is the experimental basis for the concept of probability with which we are concerned in this book.

PROBLEMS

1. Perform the random experiment of tossing a penny 200 times, and make a plot like Figure 2a. To standardize the experimental conditions, place the penny on the thumb heads up and toss it so that it rotates several times and lands on a hard flat surface. (By combining the results of five such sequences, a figure like 2b can be produced.)

2. In a long sequence of throws of a die as described in Example 1, let $f(1)$, $f(2), \ldots, f(6)$ denote the frequencies with which the upper face shows 1 point, 2 points, $\ldots$, 6 points. Approximately what values would you expect $f(1), f(2)$, $\ldots$ to have if the die is carefully made so that in shape it approximates a perfect cube and if the material is uniform throughout?

3. State qualitatively what changes you would expect in the answer to the preceding problem if the die were loaded by placing a weight in the center of the face with 6 points.

4. State qualitatively what changes you would expect in the answer to Problem 2 if two of the sides of the cube had been shaved so as to bring the sides with 1 point and 6 points closer together.

1.3 SIMPLE EVENTS AND THEIR PROBABILITIES

In Section 1, the theory of probability was stated to be a mathematical discipline dealing with random experiments. Such experiments were illustrated, and some of their basic features described, in Section 2. But how does one deal with them mathematically? Observational phenomena are made accessible to mathematical treatment by constructing *mathematical models* for them. Such a model is an abstraction of the real situation, compared with which it has two important advantages.

(i) Properties and relationships, which in reality hold only approximately, in the model can be postulated to be mathematically precise, and their consequences can then be worked out rigorously (that is, as mathematical theorems). This is for example the case with geometry, where the mathematical theory deals with idealized points, straight lines, etc., satisfying certain postulates. The results which are rigorously deduced from these postulates (for example the theorem of Pythagoras) are then applied to such approximately straight lines as those laid out by a surveyor.

(ii) Each actual situation is in some way unique; results worked out directly in concrete terms would therefore have only very limited applicability. In the model, on the other hand, the situation is stripped of all that is special and irrelevant. The results obtained in the model thus are applicable to all real situations having the same general structure.

It is seen that the construction of a mathematical model involves a two-fold simplification: only the important and relevant features of the actual situation are portrayed in the model; and in this portrayal they are idealized, the "imperfections" of the actual situation being smoothed away. How well a model works depends on how realistic it is in spite of these simplifications. One of the most important tasks in the application of mathematical models is to see that the model employed represents the real situation sufficiently well so that the results deduced from it will have the desired accuracy. For example, consider the model which represents the earth as a sphere. For a rough calculation of the surface in terms of the diameter this may be adequate. For slightly more refined results it may be necessary to take account of the flattening at the poles and to represent the earth as a spheroid.

We now turn to the problem of building a mathematical model for a random experiment. In the experiment, we are interested in the frequencies with which various results occur in the long run. To serve our purpose, the model will have to have features corresponding to these results, and to the frequencies with which they occur. Let us first consider how to represent the results of an experiment.

In any trial of a random experiment, the record of the result could be almost indefinitely detailed. When a die is thrown, we could record how many times it bounces, where on the table it comes to rest, the angle its edge makes with the edge of the table, how many decibels of noise it produces, and so forth. However, if we are concerned with the use of the die in gaming, none of these results is of interest: we just want to know the number of points on the upper face.

It is important, before conducting any experiment, to decide just which features are worth recording, or one may find when the experiment is over that it is not possible to answer the questions of interest. If for example in an investigation of human births the day but not the hour of each birth is recorded, it will be possible to study the distribution of births throughout the year, but not to determine whether more births occur at night than during the day.

Having decided what to observe, we can (at least in principle) make a list of all possible results of our observations in such a way that on each trial of the experiment one and only one of the results on the list will occur. We shall refer to the results on such a list as the *simple results* of the experiment. If in the investigation of human births, for example, we have decided to record just the month of birth because we are only interested in certain seasonal trends, the simple results would be the twelve months of the year. If instead we had decided that both the month of birth and the sex of the child are relevant to the investigation, there would be 24 simple results: (Jan., male), (Jan., female), (Feb., male), . . . , (Dec., female). In an experiment with a die, if we have decided to observe only the number of points showing on the die, the six simple results will be 1 point, 2 points, . . . , 6 points.

According to the above definition, the list must divide the possible outcomes of the experiment into categories, which between them cover all possibilities and which leave no ambiguity as to the category to which the outcome of an experiment belongs. Suppose for example that we are interested in the weather, and are considering a list which classifies each day as sunny, cloudy, rainy. This would not be an adequate list of simple results. It is not complete, since it does not for example include the possibility of it snowing. Also, the list is ambiguous since a day may be rainy in the morning but sunny in the afternoon.

In the model, we shall represent each simple result of the experiment by an element to be called a *simple event*. For example, in the experiment of throwing a die, we may represent the simple result "1 point" by the integer 1, "2 points" by the integer 2, and so forth. The integers 1, . . . , 6 would then constitute the simple events of the model. Equally well, we could use as simple events the words One, . . . , Six. Again, when a penny is tossed we may be interested in whether it falls heads or tails. There are two simple results, and the model correspondingly needs two simple events, which may be labeled H (for heads) and T (for tails).

We shall also want our model to possess features that correspond to the long-run frequencies with which the various simple results occur. To see how these should be specified, consider any particular simple result, say r. Suppose that in a long sequence of n performances or trials of the experiment, the result r occurred $\#(r)$ times. Its frequency is then $f(r) = \#(r)/n$, and this is a number satisfying the two inequalities

$$0 \leq f(r) \leq 1,$$

since $\#(r)$ cannot be less than 0 or greater than n. If e is the simple event corresponding to r, we shall associate with e a number called the *probability of e*, to be denoted by $P(e)$. This number represents in the model the long run frequency $f(r)$ of the corresponding simple result r. Accordingly we shall require that

$$0 \leq P(e) \leq 1$$

for every simple event e.

The probability model for a random experiment will thus contain simple events (corresponding to the simple results of the experiment) to which are assigned probabilities (corresponding to the long-run frequencies of the simple results). We illustrate the construction of such models with two examples.

EXAMPLE 1. *Throwing a die.* As we have suggested above, for the experiment of throwing a die the integers from 1 to 6 may be used as the simple events. If the die is symmetric, one would expect the six faces to occur about equally often in a long sequence of throws. Experience usually bears out this expectation, and the result "1 point" for instance is found to occur in about $\frac{1}{6}$ of the trials; that is, $f(1 \text{ point})$ is usually found to be near $\frac{1}{6}$. This suggests that in the model one should set $P(1) = \frac{1}{6}$, and similarly $P(2) = \frac{1}{6}, \ldots, P(6) = \frac{1}{6}$. The customary probability model for throwing a die thus consists of six simple events, to each of which is assigned the probability $\frac{1}{6}$.

EXAMPLE 2. *Throwing a loaded die.* An amusement store offers for sale dice that are loaded to favor showing the face with one point. The preceding model would not be reasonable for use with such a die, since $f(1 \text{ point})$ will tend to be larger than $\frac{1}{6}$ because of the loading. Suppose that the die is thrown $n = 1000$ times, and that the number of occurrences of each face is as follows:

$\#(1 \text{ point}) = 214,$ $\#(2 \text{ points}) = 152,$ $\#(3 \text{ points}) = 178$
$\#(4 \text{ points}) = 188,$ $\#(5 \text{ points}) = 163,$ $\#(6 \text{ points}) = 105.$

For the probabilities in the model we might reasonably take the corresponding frequencies, putting $P(1) = .214$ and so forth.   As we shall see later, the chance fluctuations in the 1000 throws are so great that there is little or no validity in the third decimal, and the simpler probabilities

$$P(1) = .21, \qquad P(2) = .15, \qquad P(3) = .18,$$
$$P(4) = .19, \qquad P(5) = .16, \qquad P(6) = .11,$$

would serve as well.

   The two examples illustrate the two principal methods of determining probabilities in practice.   Considerations of symmetry, backed up by general experience, will in many problems suggest that certain frequencies should be nearly equal, and one may then reasonably use a model in which the corresponding probabilities are equal.   In other problems one may rely directly on frequencies observed in a long sequence of repeated experiments.   (This corresponds to the way the term is often used in everyday language.   When the probability of twins for example is stated to be 1.3%, it usually means that this was the observed frequency of twins in an extensive series of birth records.)   In more complicated problems, a mixture of observed frequencies and symmetry considerations may be appropriate. Suppose for example that a die is loaded by placing a weight in the center of the face with six points.   This will cause the die to tend to fall with that face down, and hence with the opposite face (which has one point) up. However, the remaining four faces are still symmetric, so that we might want to impose the condition $P(2) = P(3) = P(4) = P(5)$ on the model. If the observed frequencies are those given in Example 2, we would retain the values of $P(1)$ and $P(6)$ assumed there but might replace the probabilities .15, .18, .19, .16 by their average .17, so that the six simple events would be assigned the probabilities

(1) $$P(1) = .21, \qquad P(2) = .17, \qquad P(3) = .17,$$
$$P(4) = .17, \qquad P(5) = .17, \qquad P(6) = .11.$$

EXAMPLE 3.   *Tossing a penny.*   Experience and symmetry suggest that in tossing a penny, heads and tails will tend to occur about equally often, so that in a long series of tosses f(heads) and f(tails) would both be near $\frac{1}{2}$. One might then reasonably form a model consisting of two simple events H and T, with $P(H) = \frac{1}{2}$ and $P(T) = \frac{1}{2}$.

EXAMPLE 4.   *Boy or girl?*   What is the probability that a newborn baby will be a boy?   If we have no detailed knowledge of the frequency of male births, we might feel that there should be about equal numbers of male and female births (this is also suggested by a consideration of the genetic mechanism by which the sex of a child is determined), and hence assign to the two simple events M (for male) and F (for female) the probabilities

(2) $$P(M) = \tfrac{1}{2}, \qquad P(F) = \tfrac{1}{2}.$$

Actually, examination of any sufficiently extensive sequence of birth records shows the frequency of male births to be slightly higher than $\tfrac{1}{2}$. The observations for the state of New York quoted in Section 1, for example, suggest putting

(3) $$P(M) = .514, \qquad P(F) = .486.$$

This example shows again that theoretical considerations are not necessarily completely reliable guides to a correct model. In the present case, of course, the difference between the two models turns out to be rather slight. For many purposes, the simpler model (2) will be quite adequate, and we shall in fact later in the book occasionally use it because of its simplicity.

The various simple events taken together form a collection that will be called the *event set* and denoted by ε. Thus in both Examples 1 and 2, ε consists of the first six positive integers; in Example 3 it consists of the two letters H and T; and in Example 4 of the two letters M and F.

PROBLEMS

1. In an investigation concerned with age, decide for each of the following whether it would be a possible list of simple results.

   (i) $r_1 =$ young : less than 25 years
      $r_2 =$ middle : 20–55 years
      $r_3 =$ old   : more than 55 years

  (ii) $r_1 =$ young : less than 20 years
      $r_2 =$ middle : 20–55 years
      $r_3 =$ old   : more than 55 years

 (iii) $r_1 =$ young : less than 20 years
      $r_2 =$ middle : 20–55 years
      $r_3 =$ old   : 56–80 years

2. An event set ε consists of the 3 simple events e_1, e_2, and e_3. Explain for each of the following why it cannot be a probability model:

   (i) $P(e_1) = .3$, $P(e_2) = .6$, $P(e_3) = 1.2$
  (ii) $P(e_1) = .6$, $P(e_2) = .9$, $P(e_3) = -.5$.

3. A die is thrown twice; if you are interested in the numbers of points on both the first and on the second throws, what would you take as your list of simple results? How many simple results are there in this list?

4. If a penny and nickel are tossed, make a list of simple results, in such a way that all of them might be expected to occur with approximately equal frequency.

5. A box contains three marbles, one blue, one red, and one white. Make a list of simple results for an experiment consisting of a selection of two of these marbles.

6. In the preceding problem make a list of simple results if the two marbles are drawn out one after the other (without replacing the first marble before the second one is drawn) and if the order in which the two marbles are obtained is relevant to the experiment.

7. Make a list if in the preceding problem the two marbles are drawn out with replacement, that is, if the first marble is put back into the box before the second marble is drawn.

8. A pyramid has as its base an equilateral triangle ABC, and its three sides ABD, BCD, CAD are congruent isosceles triangles. Assuming that in 1000 throws the pyramid fell on its base 182 times, use the symmetry with respect to the three sides to build a model for the four possible results of a throw.

9. The base of a prism is an equilateral triangle. In 2000 throws, the prism fell 1506 times on its rectangular sides, and the remaining 494 times on its upper and lower ends. Use the symmetries of the prism to build a model for the five possible results of a throw.

10. In an amusement park one can shoot 100 times at a circular target with a bull's-eye. If for a certain person the target shows 8 bull's-eyes and 23 hits which are not bull's-eyes, build a probability model with the three simple events: bull's-eye, hit (but not a bull's eye), miss.

1.4 DEFINITION OF PROBABILITY MODEL

As is easily checked in all examples considered in the preceding section, the probabilities of the simple events in the event set add up to 1. To see why this should be true in general, suppose that the simple results of an experiment are labeled $r_1, r_2, \ldots$. On each performance of the experiment exactly one simple result occurs. In a sequence of n performances we must therefore have

$$\#(r_1) + \#(r_2) + \ldots = n.$$

On dividing both sides by n, this equation becomes

$$f(r_1) + f(r_2) + \ldots = 1.$$

Let $e_1, e_2, \ldots$ denote the simple events that in the model correspond to the simple results $r_1, r_2, \ldots$. Since the probabilities $P(e_1), P(e_2), \ldots$ are to represent the frequencies $f(r_1), f(r_2), \ldots$ when n is large, it seems reasonable to require that the probabilities in the model should satisfy

$$P(e_1) + P(e_2) + \ldots = 1.$$

The model would not give a satisfactory picture of the experimental situation if the probabilities were defined so as not to add up to 1.

We can now give a formal definition of a probability model, and describe its identification with the random experiment.

Definition. By a *probability model* we mean the following:

(i)   there is an *event set* $\mathcal{E}$, which is a set of elements called *simple events*;

(ii)   to each simple event e is attached a number $P(e)$ called the *probability* of the event e; the probabilities must satisfy $0 \leq P(e) \leq 1$ for each e, and their sum must be equal to 1.

In using the model to represent a random experiment, we identify the simple events of the model with the simple results of the experiment, and the probability of a simple event with the frequency of the corresponding result in a long sequence of trials of the experiment. This relationship may be summarized in the following "dictionary" for translating from the real world to the model and back:

Real World	Model
random experiment	probability model
simple result	simple event
list of simple results	event set
long-run frequency	probability

A probability model can be exhibited by listing its simple events together with their probabilities, for example in the form

$$e_1, \quad e_2, \ldots$$
$$P(e_1), P(e_2), \ldots$$

In Example 3.2, for instance, the probability model may be specified by

1	2	3	4	5	6
.21	.15	.18	.19	.16	.11.

The simple results of an experiment are essentially the "atoms" from which other results can be built up. Any result consisting of more than one simple result is said to be *composite*. Consider for instance the situation mentioned in the preceding section, in which the simple results are the month of birth and sex of a child. The following are some examples of composite results together with the simple results of which they are composed.

(a)   The composite result "The child is a male born during the first three months of the year" is composed of the simple results (Jan., male), (Feb., male), (Mar., male).

(b) The composite result "The child is a male" is composed of the simple results (Jan., male), (Feb., male), . . . , (Dec., male).

(c) The composite result "The child is born in January" is composed of the simple results (Jan., male), (Jan., female).

Suppose now that R is the composite result composed, say, of the two simple results r_1 and r_2. This may be indicated by writing $R = \{r_1, r_2\}$. Since on each trial of the experiment exactly one simple result occurs, we must have $\#(R) = \#(r_1) + \#(r_2)$, and hence

$$f(R) = f(r_1) + f(r_2).$$

In general the frequency of a composite result is the sum of the frequencies of the simple results that make it up.

To a composite result R of the experiment, there corresponds in the model a *composite event*, say E. This consists of the simple events that correspond to the simple results making up R. For example, if $R = \{r_2, r_6, r_8\}$ consists of the simple results r_2, r_6, and r_8, then the composite event E corresponding to R in the model consists of the simple events e_2, e_6, and e_8. Since the frequency of R would then be given by $f(R) = f(r_2) + f(r_6) + f(r_8)$, we should have in the model $P(E) = P(e_2) + P(e_6) + P(e_8)$. Generalization of this example motivates the following definition of the probability of a composite event.

Definition. The probability of a composite event E is the sum of the probabilities of the simple events of which E is composed.

As an illustration, consider the experiment of throwing a die, and the composite result that the number of points on the upper face is even. This composite result consists of the three simple results: 2 points, 4 points, 6 points. In the models of Examples 3.1 and 3.2, the corresponding composite event (even) will then consist of the integers 2, 4, and 6, so that

$$P(\text{even}) = P(2) + P(4) + P(6).$$

In the model of Example 3.1 we thus have

$$P(\text{even}) = \tfrac{1}{6} + \tfrac{1}{6} + \tfrac{1}{6} = \tfrac{1}{2} = .5,$$

while in the model of Example 3.2

$$P(\text{even}) = .15 + .19 + .11 = .45.$$

Since the probabilities of all simple events are nonnegative and add up to 1, it is clear that for any event E,

$$0 \leqq P(E) \leqq 1.$$

In presenting probability models, we have so far been very careful to distinguish between the results of real experiments and the events that represent them in the model. However, it is sometimes convenient to be less careful and to employ the same terms for the results and for the corresponding events in the model. Thus, we may for example write P(die falls with six points showing) rather than $P(6)$, where 6 denotes the event representing the result that the die falls with six points showing, as we did in Examples 3.1 and 3.2. When discussing applicational examples, we shall usually adopt this simpler terminology.

We shall conclude this section with an important example, in which the values of the probabilities are obtained mainly on the basis of extensive experience.

EXAMPLE 1. *Life table.* Consider the "experiment" that consists in observing the length of a human life. It is usual to think of life span as a continuous variable, but for our present purpose it will suffice to observe merely the decade A in which the individual dies, so that the simple results are "dies before 10th birthday" ($A = 1$), "survives 10th birthday but dies before 20th" ($A = 2$), etc. Can we regard such an experiment as random? It is clearly not repeatable unless we agree that the identity of the individual is not essential to the constancy of the conditions. If we observe the life spans of a number of similar individuals, we might perhaps regard them as trials of the same experiment. The entire life insurance industry is founded on the observation that the property of stability does indeed hold in this case: the fraction of a large number of similar individuals who die in a specified decade of their lives will be nearly constant and can therefore be predicted on the basis of past experience.

The probability model for life span is known as a *life table*, the earliest example of which was given by Graunt in 1662. The simple events correspond to the age of the individual at death. The probability assigned to one of these events correspond to the frequency with which such individuals die in the decade in question. An example of a life table is shown below, where for simplicity we assume there is no chance of reaching age 100.

TABLE 1. LIFE TABLE

Decade A	Probability of death	Decade A	Probability of death
1	.064	6	.127
2	.013	7	.211
3	.022	8	.269
4	.032	9	.170
5	.064	10	.028

The meaning of the entry .032 opposite decade 4 is that among a large number of individuals, of the kind for whom the table is appropriate, approximately 3.2% will die between their 30th and 40th birthdays.

According to the above table, what is the probability of reaching the age of 60? This is a composite result, consisting of the simple results of dying in the 7th, 8th, 9th, or 10th decade. The probability of reaching 60 is therefore $.211 + .269 + .170 + .028 = .678$.

It is important when using a life table to be sure that the table represents the life spans of individuals of the kind to whom it is to be applied. For example, women in our culture live considerably longer than men. The table above is based on experience of white males living in the United States at the present time—it should not be used for a woman, a Negro, a resident of Pakistan, or someone in the twenty-first century.

PROBLEMS

1. An event set ε consists of the four simple events e_1, e_2, e_3, e_4. Determine for each of the following whether it satisfies the conditions of a probability model:

(i) $P(e_1) = .01$, $P(e_2) = .03$, $P(e_3) = .11$, $P(e_4) = .35$.

(ii) $P(e_1) = .3$, $P(e_2) = .6$, $P(e_3) = .9$, $P(e_4) = -.8$.

(iii) $P(e_1) = .01$, $P(e_2) = .04$, $P(e_3) = .06$, $P(e_4) = .89$.

(iv) $P(e_1) = .2$, $P(e_2) = .3$, $P(e_3) = 0$, $P(e_4) = .5$.

2. An event set ε consists of five simple events $e_1, \ldots, e_5$. If $P(e_1) = .01$, $P(e_2) = .02$, $P(e_3) = .03$, $P(e_4) = .04$, determine $P(e_5)$.

3. An event set ε consists of 10 simple events $e_1, \ldots, e_{10}$. Determine the probabilities of these events if their probabilities are all equal.

4. With the model of Example 3.1, find the probability of the following events.

(i) The number of points is at least three.

(ii) The number of points is at most two.

(iii) The number of points is more than four.

5. Find the probabilities of the events (i)–(iii) of the preceding problem for model (1) of Example 3.2.

6. With model (1) of Example 3.2 would you (at even money) prefer to bet for or against the die showing an even number of points?

7. A person driving to work every day on a route with four traffic lights has observed the following to be a suitable probability model for the number of red lights encountered on a trip:

$$P(0 \text{ red lights}) = .05$$
$$P(1 \text{ red light}) = .25$$
$$P(2 \text{ red lights}) = .36$$
$$P(3 \text{ red lights}) = .26$$
$$P(4 \text{ red lights}) = .08.$$

Find the probabilities of his encountering

(i) at least 2 red lights

(ii) more than 2 red lights

(iii) at most 2 red lights.

8. In a population for which Table 1 is appropriate, find approximately the *median* age of death; that is, the age such that the probability is $\frac{1}{2}$ of dying before that age and $\frac{1}{2}$ of surviving beyond it.

9. In a long sequence of observations on length of life of male rats, it was found that 98 percent still survived 200 days after birth, 83 percent survived 400 days, 40 percent survived 600 days, 8 percent survived 800 days, and that there were no survivors after 1000 days. On the basis of this information, construct a probability model with the simple events "death within the first 200 days," "death between 200 and 400 days," etc.

1.5 UNIFORM PROBABILITY MODELS

A reasonable probability model for throwing a die or tossing a coin is frequently obtained by assigning equal probability to all simple events. In general, if all simple events are assigned the same probability, we say that the probability model is *uniform*. For the case of a die or a coin we have discussed this model in Examples 3.1 and 3.3. Surprisingly, such models, which are of course realistic only if the simple results of the experiment tend to occur about equally often, are appropriate in a great many interesting and important cases.

We shall in the next chapter take up applications of the uniform model to sampling theory, and it will be applied in many other situations throughout the rest of the book. For the moment we mention only that gambling devices other than dice or coins also provide simple illustrations of the uniform model. Thus, when drawing a card from a standard deck containing 52 cards, it is customary to assign equal probability $\frac{1}{52}$ to each card of the deck. Similarly, for a roulette wheel one would assign equal probability to the simple events that correspond to the ball coming to rest in any particular slot. In fact, the use of such devices for gaming depends on the equal frequency of the outcomes. If, for example, a roulette wheel favored one slot over the others, gamblers would soon discover this and break the bank.

The calculation of probabilities is particularly simple when the model is uniform. Suppose the event set $\mathcal{E}$ consists of $\#(\mathcal{E})$ simple events. If each simple event is to have the same probability, and if the sum of the probabilities is to be 1, then the probability of each simple event must be $1/\#(\mathcal{E})$. Consider now a composite event E consisting of $\#(E)$ simple events. Then, by the definition of the probability of a composite event, the probability of E is the sum of $\#(E)$ terms, each equal to $1/\#(\mathcal{E})$, so that

$$(1) \qquad\qquad P(E) = \frac{\#(E)}{\#(\mathcal{E})}.$$

To compute the probability, it is therefore only necessary to count how many simple events there are in E and $\mathcal{E}$, and to take the ratio.

EXAMPLE *1. Drawing a card.* A standard bridge deck contains 13 cards of each of four different suits: two red suits (hearts and diamonds) and two black suits (clubs and spades). The 13 cards of each suit are Ace, King, Queen, Jack and cards numbered from 2 to 10. The deck is shuffled and a card is drawn. What is the probability that it will be a spade, if the uniform model is assumed? In the present case, there are 52 simple events corresponding to the 52 cards, and hence $\#(\mathcal{E}) = 52$. Of these 52 events, 13 (namely those corresponding to the 13 spades) make up the event E = spade. Hence $P(E) = \#(E)/\#(\mathcal{E}) = \frac{13}{52} = \frac{1}{4}$.

High school algebra books often include a section on probability, which is usually devoted to the uniform model. The simple events are called "equally likely cases," and the simple events that make up the composite event whose probability is sought are called "favorable cases." The probability of the event is defined as the ratio of the number of favorable cases to the number of equally likely cases. This of course is in agreement with formula (1).

The uniform model was used much more freely in the past than it is today, the simple results of an experiment being often quite uncritically treated as equally likely. The practice was justified by citing the Principle of Insufficient Reason, which declared that cases were equally likely unless reasons to the contrary were known. Unfortunately, the results were often quite unrealistic, since events might occur with quite different frequencies even though the model builder was unaware of the reasons for the difference. In modern practice, the burden of proof is shifted: it is up to the model builder to advance reasons for using the uniform model. Sometimes the model is justified on grounds of the symmetry of the results, as in the case of the die. The final test, however, is empirical: do the results occur in practice with nearly equal frequency?

The inadequacy of the Principle of Insufficient Reason is made clear by the fact that the list of simple results of an experiment may be drawn up in many different ways. When the uniform model is used with the different lists, different answers are obtained all of which according to the Principle of Insufficient Reason are equally valid. We illustrate the point with a simple example.

EXAMPLE *2. Probability of a boy.* What is the chance that a two-child family will have at least one boy? If the number of boys is denoted by B, there are three possible results: $B = 0$, $B = 1$, $B = 2$. Of these three cases, the last two are favorable to the family having at least one boy, so that the use of the uniform model gives the value $\frac{2}{3}$ for the desired probability.

But we could list the results differently, recording the sex of the first and second children separately. Then there would be four cases: MM,

MF, FM, FF; where for example MF means "first child male, second child female." Of the four cases, the first three imply that there is at least one boy, so that we get $\frac{3}{4}$ for the desired probability if the uniform model is used with this list.

Which answer is right, $\frac{2}{3}$ or $\frac{3}{4}$? Both are correctly deduced from the premises, and no amount of theoretical argument could prove or disprove either. To find out which model is the more realistic, it is necessary to observe the sex distributions actually occurring in two-child families. When this is done, it is found that the second model is the more realistic, although even moderately large samples would convince us that it too does not give an adequate description. For example, MM occurs somewhat more frequently than FF, reflecting the fact that boys constitute about 51.4% of all births. That boys are more frequent than girls could not have been predicted by theoretical arguments, and the reason for it is still not fully understood.

To drive home the point that the test of a model must in the last analysis be empirical, we will mention two circumstances in which the second model would be quite wrong. Identical twins are always of the same sex, which tends to increase the frequency of MM and FF families. The frequency of identical twins is in fact low, but if they constituted about $\frac{1}{3}$ of the two-child families, then the first model would fit much better than the second. Again, in some cultures it is thought essential that a family have a son. Suppose that in such a society, families were terminated as soon as a boy was born. This would mean that only FM and FF could occur in two-child families, so that both models would be quite wrong.

We conclude the section by giving two further examples of the use of uniform models.

EXAMPLE 3. *Sum of points on two dice.* In many dice games, the player throws two dice, and the outcome of the game depends on the total number T of points showing. As in Example 2, there are two rather natural ways to make out the list of simple results. We might observe that T may take on the 11 different values 2, 3, . . . , 12, and take these as our equally likely cases. This would, for example, imply $P(T = 7) = \frac{1}{11}$. Alternatively, we might record the results of the two dice separately, writing for example (4, 3) if the first die showed 4 points and the second 3 points. This record has the following 36 possible values:

(2)

(1, 1)	(1, 2)	(1, 3)	(1, 4)	(1, 5)	(1, 6)
(2, 1)	(2, 2)	(2, 3)	(2, 4)	(2, 5)	(2, 6)
(3, 1)	(3, 2)	(3, 3)	(3, 4)	(3, 5)	(3, 6)
(4, 1)	(4, 2)	(4, 3)	(4, 4)	(4, 5)	(4, 6)
(5, 1)	(5, 2)	(5, 3)	(5, 4)	(5, 5)	(5, 6)
(6, 1)	(6, 2)	(6, 3)	(6, 4)	(6, 5)	(6, 6)

Of these the following six give $T = 7$: $(1, 6)$, $(2, 5)$, $(3, 4)$, $(4, 3)$, $(5, 2)$ and $(6, 1)$. With the second model, $P(T = 7) = \frac{6}{36} = \frac{1}{6}$, which is nearly twice as large as $\frac{1}{11}$. Which if either of these radically different results is correct, can be determined only by experience, though analogy with Example 2 may lead one to guess that the second model will work better. Extensive experience justifies attributing equal probability to the 36 simple events displayed above, provided the dice are sufficiently well made.

EXAMPLE 4. *Floods.* When building a dam to protect a valley against the spring flood, the engineers consult the records of the past 50 years and make the dam just high enough to contain the worst flood recorded. How likely is it that the dam will hold for the next twenty-five years? As always, the answer depends on the model. If the climate and vegetation are not changing, then it seems plausible to assume that the worst flood is as likely to occur in one year as in another, of the 75 years consisting of the last 50 and the next 25. With this model, the probability that a larger flood will occur in the next 25 years than in the past 50, is $\frac{25}{75} = \frac{1}{3}$.

PROBLEMS

1. If a card is drawn under the assumptions of Example 1, find the probability that it is (i) red; (ii) an ace; (iii) a red ace.

2. A box contains 10 marbles, of which 2 are white, 3 red, and 5 black. A marble is drawn at random, that is, in such a way that each marble has the same chance of being selected.
   (i) Construct a probability model for this experiment.
   (ii) Find the probability that the marble drawn will be white.

3. In Example 3, find the probabilities of the following events.
   (i) The numbers of points on both dice are even.
   (ii) The number of points on at least one of the two dice is even.
   (iii) The sum of the points on the two dice is even.

4. In Example 3, find the probabilities
$$P(T = 2), P(T = 3), \ldots, P(T = 12).$$

5. In order to decide which of three persons will pay for a round of drinks, each tosses a penny. If the result of one toss differs from those of the other two (i.e., one head and two tails, or one tail and two heads), the "odd man" has to pay. Assuming the 8 possible results HHH, HHT, HTH, HTT, THH, THT, TTH, TTT to be equally likely, what is the probability that one toss will differ from the other two?

6. Assuming that in three-child families the 8 cases MMM, MMF, ..., FFF are equally likely, find the probabilities of the following events:
   (i) at least one boy   (iv) exactly two boys
   (ii) at least two boys   (v) at most one boy
   (iii) exactly one boy   (vi) more boys than girls

(vii) at least one girl and one boy   (ix) the oldest a boy and the youngest a girl
(viii) the oldest a boy   (x) no girl younger than a boy.

7. Twelve keys, of which only one fits, are tried one after another until a door opens. Let e_1 correspond to the result that the door opens on the first try; e_2 to the result that it opens on the second try; etc., and suppose that the 12 simple events $e_1, \ldots, e_{12}$ are equally likely. Find the probability that the door will be opened
   (i) on the twelfth try,
   (ii) on none of the first three tries,
   (iii) on either the first or the twelfth try.

8. Suppose that a random digit generator produces two digits in such a way that all 100 cases 00, . . . , 09; 10, . . . , 19; . . .; 90, . . . , 99 are equally likely. Interpreting 00 to be 0, 01 to be 1, . . . , 09 to be 9, the machine produces a number between 0 and 99. What is the probability that this number is (i) positive and divisible by 11, (ii) less than 20?

9. In a surprise quiz, you are given two multiple choice questions, one with three possible answers a, b, c and the other with five possible answers A, B, C, D, E. Let (a, C) denote the event that you give answer a for the first and answer C for the second question, etc. Suppose that you have no idea as to the right answers and decide to write all possible combinations

$$(a, A), \ldots, (a, E); (b, A), \ldots, (b, E); (c, A), \ldots, (c, E)$$

on separate slips of paper of which you then draw one at random; that is, so that each has the same chance of being selected. Suppose the correct answers are b in the first and A in the second problem. What is the probability that you will give:
   (i) the correct answer on both questions,
   (ii) the incorrect answer on both questions,
   (iii) at least one correct answer,
   (iv) at most one correct answer,
   (v) the correct answer on the first question,
   (vi) the correct answer on the first but an incorrect answer on the second question?

10. In throws with three dice, the sum $T = 9$ can be produced in six ways, namely as $1 + 2 + 6, 1 + 3 + 5, 1 + 4 + 4, 2 + 2 + 5, 2 + 3 + 4, 3 + 3 + 3$. (i) Determine the number of ways in which the sum $T = 10$ can be produced. (ii) Would you conclude that $P(T = 9) = P(T = 10)$?

11. Assume that the $6^3 = 216$ different outcomes of throws with three dice: $(1, 1, 1), (1, 1, 2), \ldots, (6, 6, 6)$ are all equally likely. Under this assumption, compute $P(T = 9)$ and $P(T = 10)$, and discuss the difference between this result and that suggested by the preceding problem.

1.6 THE ALGEBRA OF EVENTS

Returning now to the consideration of probability models in general, we shall in the present section study certain relations that may exist between events, and certain operations that may be performed on them. These will enable us in the next section to derive desired probabilities from others that are given or assumed. We shall be working here within the mathematical model, with definitions as precise and proofs as rigorous as those of plane geometry or any other branch of pure mathematics, but we shall keep the random experiment in view as motivation for definitions and proofs.

Together with any result R that may occur on a trial of a random experiment, one may consider another result, namely "R does not occur." These two results are said to be *complements*, or complementary to one another. For example, the complement of the result that a three-child family has at least one boy is that all three children are girls. Again, if X is the number of points showing when a die is thrown, the results "X is even" and "X is odd" are complementary. We shall denote the complement of a result by placing a bar above it, so that $\overline{X \leq 2}$ means the same as $X > 2$. We shall employ the same terminology in the model.

Definition. The *complement* of an event E is the event $\overline{E}$ which consists just of those simple events in $\mathcal{E}$ that do not belong to E.

It follows from this definition that the sets E and $\overline{E}$ have no common member, and that between them they contain all simple events of the event set $\mathcal{E}$. The situation is illustrated in Figure 1, where E consists of

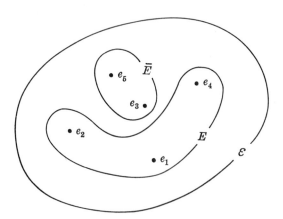

FIGURE 1. COMPLEMENTARY EVENTS

the simple events e_1, e_2, e_4, and $\overline{E}$ consists of the remaining simple events in $\mathcal{E}$, namely e_3, e_5.

An interesting special case is the complement of the event set $\mathcal{E}$ itself. By definition, $\mathcal{E}$ consists of all simple events of the model under discussion, so that $\overline{\mathcal{E}}$ is a set without members. This set is known as the *empty set*.

If we think in terms of results, $\bar{\mathcal{E}}$ corresponds to a result that cannot occur, such as the result $X = 7$ when rolling a die.

Related to any two given results R, S is the result which occurs when both the result R and the result S occur, and which will be called the result "R and S." For example, if with two-child families R denotes the result that the first child is a boy and S that the second child is a boy, then "R and S" denotes the result that both children are boys. Similarly, if R indicates that a card drawn from a deck is a heart while S indicates that it is a face card, then the result "R and S" will occur if a heart face card is drawn.

Suppose the results R, S are represented in the model by the events E, F respectively. What event in the model then corresponds to the result "R and S" ? To answer this question notice that the result "R and S" occurs whenever the experiment yields a simple result, which is a simple result both of R and of S. Therefore the event in the model corresponding to "R and S" will consist of those simple events that belong both to E and to F. The situation is illustrated in Figure 2a, where $E = \{e_1,\ e_3,\ e_4,\ e_6\}$

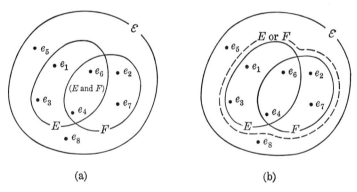

(a)   (b)

FIGURE 2. INTERSECTION AND UNION

corresponds to the result R consisting of the simple results r_1, r_3, r_4, r_6, and where $F = \{e_2,\ e_4,\ e_6,\ e_7\}$ corresponds to the result S consisting of the simple results r_2, r_4, r_6, r_7. Here "R and S" will occur whenever the experiment yields one of the simple results r_4 or r_6. The event corresponding to the result "R and S" consists therefore of the simple events e_4, e_6. It is the common part or intersection of the two events E, F.

Definition. The *intersection* $(E$ and $F)$ of two events E, F is the event which consists of all simple events that belong both to E and to F.

It may of course happen that two events E, F have no simple events in common. The intersection $(E$ and $F)$ is then the empty set.

Definition. Two events E, F are said to be *exclusive* if no simple event belongs to both E and to F.

The results corresponding to two exclusive events will be such that not both of them can happen on the same trial of the random experiment. For example, when throwing a die, the results $X \leq 2$ and $X > 4$ are exclusive, but the results "X is even" and "X is divisible by 3" are not, since both occur when $X = 6$. Again, for two-child families, the results "first child is a boy" and "both children are girls" are exclusive, but the results "first child is a boy" and "second child is a boy" are not, since both children may be boys. The case of two exclusive events E and F is illustrated in Figure 3.

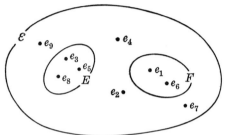

FIGURE 3.   EXCLUSIVE EVENTS

Another result related to the given results R, S is the result "R or S" which occurs when either the result R occurs or the result S occurs, or both occur. If for example R denotes the result that the first child of a two-child family is a boy while S denotes that the second child is a boy, then "R or S" will occur if at least one of the children is a boy. Similarly, if R denotes that a card drawn from a deck is a heart, while S denotes that it is a face card, then "R or S" will occur if the card is a heart or a face card, including the case when it is a heart face card.

What event in the model corresponds to the result "R or S"? To answer this question, notice that the result "R or S" occurs whenever the experiment yields one of the simple results of R or of S or both. Therefore the event in the model corresponding to "R or S" will consist of those simple events belonging to E or to F or both. The situation is illustrated in Figure 2b, where as before $E = \{e_1, e_3, e_4, e_6\}$ corresponds to the result R consisting of the simple results r_1, r_3, r_4, r_6, while $F = \{e_2, e_4, e_6, e_7\}$ corresponds to the result S consisting of the simple results r_2, r_4, r_6, r_7. Here "R or S" will occur whenever the experiment yields one of the simple results r_1, r_2, r_3, r_4, r_6, r_7. The composite event corresponding to "R or S" consists therefore of the simple events e_1, e_2, e_3, e_4, e_6, e_7. It is obtained by combining or uniting the simple events of E with those of F, producing the set (E or F) enclosed by the dashed line in Figure 2b.

Definition. The *union* (E or F) of two events E, F is the event which consists of all simple events that belong to E, or to F, or to both E and F.

EXAMPLE 1. *Two dice.* In the model for throwing two dice of Example 5.3, let E correspond to the result "first die shows one point," so that E consists of the first row of tableau (5.2). Similarly, let F correspond to "second die shows one point," consisting of the first column of (5.2). Then (E or F) consists of the eleven simple events in the top and left margins of (5.2), and corresponds to the result "at least one die shows one point." On the other hand, (E and F) consists only of the simple event (1, 1) and corresponds to the results "both dice show one point."

EXAMPLE 2. *Complementation.* Consider an event E and its complement $\overline{E}$. Since E and $\overline{E}$ have no simple event in common, they are exclusive. By the definition of complement, any simple event not in E belongs to $\overline{E}$, so that every simple event belongs either to E or to $\overline{E}$. It follows that the union of E and $\overline{E}$ is the entire event set $\mathcal{E}$: (E or $\overline{E}$) = $\mathcal{E}$.

The reader should be warned of a confusion that sometimes arises due to connotations of the word "and" in other contexts. From the use of "and" as a substitute for "plus," it might be thought that (E and F) should represent the set obtained by putting together or uniting the sets E and F. However, in the algebra of events (E and F) corresponds to the result "R and S" which occurs only if both R and S occur, and thus (E and F) is the common part or intersection of E and F.

In many books the notation ($E \cup F$) is used for (E or F) while ($E \cap F$) is used for (E and F).

PROBLEMS

1. An experiment consists of ten tosses with a coin. Give a verbal description of the complement of each of the following events:
   (i) at least six heads
   (ii) at most six heads
   (iii) no heads.

2. In Problem 5.6 give a verbal description of the complements of the events described in parts (i), (ii), (v), and (viii).

3. In Problem 5.9 give verbal descriptions of the complements of the events described in parts (i)–(v).

4. In Problem 5.6 give verbal descriptions of the intersections of each of the following pairs of events:
   (i) the events (i) and (ii)   (iii) the events (ii) and (iii)
   (ii) the events (i) and (iii)   (iv) the events (i) and (iv)

(v) the events (i) and (v)   (viii) the events (iii) and (vi)

(vi) the events (i) and (vi)   (ix) the events (iv) and (vii)

(vii) the events (ii) and (vi)   (x) the events (vi) and (vii).

5. In Problem 5.6 determine for each of the following pairs whether they are exclusive:

(i) the events (i) and (iii)   (v) the events (iv) and (vi)

(ii) the events (ii) and (iii)   (vi) the events (v) and (vi)

(iii) the events (iii) and (v)   (vii) the events (v) and (vii)

(iv) the events (iv) and (v)   (viii) the events (vi) and (vii).

6. In Problem 5.9 pick out three pairs from the events described in parts (i)–(vi) that are exclusive.

7. Give verbal descriptions of the unions of each of the pairs of events of Problem 4.

8. In Problem 5.9, give verbal descriptions of the unions of each of the following pairs of events:

(i) the events (i) and (iii)

(ii) the events (ii) and (iii).

9. For each of the following statements determine whether it is correct for all E, F, and G.

(i) If E, F are exclusive, and F, G are exclusive, then E, G are exclusive.

(ii) If E, F are exclusive, and E, G are exclusive, then E, $(F$ or $G)$ are exclusive.

(iii) If E, $(F$ or $G)$ are exclusive, then E, F are exclusive.

10. From a class of ten, an instructor selects a student to answer a certain question; if the first student cannot answer, he selects one of the remaining students; etc. Let E denote the event that the first student knows the answer, and F the event that the first student does not know the answer but the second one does. Are E and F exclusive?

11. Suppose that the event set ε is broken up into exclusive pieces $E_1, E_2, \ldots, E_a$. Is it true that then any event F can be written as

(1) $$F = (E_1 \text{ and } F) \text{ or } (E_2 \text{ and } F) \text{ or } \ldots (E_a \text{ and } F)?$$

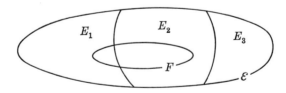

12. Draw diagrams to illustrate the facts (known as De Morgan's Laws) that, for any sets E and F

(i) $(\overline{E \text{ or } F}) = \overline{E} \text{ and } \overline{F}$

(ii) $(\overline{E \text{ and } F}) = \overline{E} \text{ or } \overline{F}$.

1.7 SOME LAWS OF PROBABILITY

In the preceding section we have defined three operations on events: complementation, intersection, and union. We shall now consider how probabilities behave under union and complementation. The probabilities of intersections will be studied in Chapters 3 and 4.

A law connecting the probability of the union (E or F) with the probabilities of E and of F is obtained most easily in the special case that E and F are exclusive. If R and S are two exclusive results, then not both can happen on the same trial of the experiment, and therefore in a sequence of trials

$$\#(R \text{ or } S) = \#(R) + \#(S).$$

For example, in an evening of poker, the number of red flushes dealt to a player will be the sum of the number of heart flushes and the number of diamond flushes that he receives. Dividing both sides of the displayed equation by the total number of trials we see that

$$f(R \text{ or } S) = f(R) + f(S) \qquad \text{if } R, S \text{ are exclusive.}$$

Since probability is supposed to represent long-run frequency, this suggests that in the model we should have the equation

(1) $\qquad P(E \text{ or } F) = P(E) + P(F) \qquad \text{if } E, F \text{ are exclusive.}$

The proof of this *addition law for exclusive events* may be illustrated on Figure 6.3. There (E or F) consists of the five simple events e_1, e_3, e_5, e_6, e_8, so by the definition of the probability of a composite event (Section 4),

$$P(E \text{ or } F) = P(e_1) + P(e_3) + P(e_5) + P(e_6) + P(e_8).$$

The right side may be written as

$$[P(e_3) + P(e_5) + P(e_8)] + [P(e_1) + P(e_6)]$$

which is just $P(E) + P(F)$. It is clear that the argument would hold in general.

EXAMPLE 1. *Two dice.* Suppose that in throwing two dice, the 36 simple events displayed in (5.2) are equally likely. If T denotes the sum of the points on the two dice, then, as shown in Example 5.3, $P(T = 7) = \frac{6}{36}$. The probabilities of the other values of T are as follows (Problem 5.4).

TABLE 1. PROBABILITIES OF VALUES OF T

t	2	3	4	5	6	7	8	9	10	11	12
$P(T = t)$	$\frac{1}{36}$	$\frac{2}{36}$	$\frac{3}{36}$	$\frac{4}{36}$	$\frac{5}{36}$	$\frac{6}{36}$	$\frac{5}{36}$	$\frac{4}{36}$	$\frac{3}{36}$	$\frac{2}{36}$	$\frac{1}{36}$

Let us now find the probability of the event G that the sum T will be divisible by 5. Since this occurs if and only if T is either equal to 5 or to 10, G is the union of the exclusive events $E: T = 5$ and $F: T = 10$. Hence

$$P(G) = P(E) + P(F) = \tfrac{4}{36} + \tfrac{3}{36} = \tfrac{7}{36}.$$

A special case of the addition law (1) is obtained by taking for F the complement $\overline{E}$ of E. Since E and $\overline{E}$ are exclusive and their union is the event set $\mathcal{E}$, it follows that

$$P(E) + P(\overline{E}) = P(E \text{ or } \overline{E}) = P(\mathcal{E}) = 1.$$

This establishes the important *law of complementation*

(2) $$P(E) = 1 - P(\overline{E}).$$

As we shall see later, the main usefulness of this relation resides in the fact that it is often easier to calculate the probability that something does not happen than that it does happen.

As an illustration of (2), consider once more the model of Example 1 and suppose we wish to determine the probability of the event E: the sum T of the points showing on the two dice is three or more. The complement of E is the event $\overline{E}: T = 2$, which has probability $\tfrac{1}{36}$. Hence

$$P(E) = 1 - \tfrac{1}{36} = \tfrac{35}{36}.$$

The concept of exclusive events extends readily to more than two events.

Definition. The events $E_1, E_2, \ldots$ are said to be *exclusive* if no simple event belongs to more than one of them.

The addition law also extends in the obvious manner:

(3) $$P(E_1 \text{ or } E_2 \text{ or } \ldots) = P(E_1) + P(E_2) + \ldots$$
                                        if $E_1, E_2, \ldots$ are exclusive.

If E, F are not exclusive, law (1) will in general not be correct, as may be seen by examining Figure 6.2b. Here

$$P(E) = P(e_1) + P(e_3) + P(e_4) + P(e_6)$$
$$P(F) = \qquad\qquad P(e_4) + P(e_6) + P(e_2) + P(e_7)$$

so that

$$P(E) + P(F) = P(e_1) + P(e_3) + 2P(e_4) + 2P(e_6) + P(e_2) + P(e_7)$$

while

$$P(E \text{ or } F) = P(e_1) + P(e_3) + P(e_4) + P(e_6) + P(e_2) + P(e_7).$$

Since $P(e_4)$ and $P(e_6)$ occur twice in $P(E) + P(F)$ but only once in $P(E \text{ or } F)$, it follows that $P(E) + P(F)$ is greater than $P(E \text{ or } F)$ (except in the trivial case when both $P(e_4)$ and $P(e_6)$ are equal to zero).

A correct law must allow for the double counting of the probabilities of those simple events which belong both to E and to F, that is to the intersection $(E$ and $F)$. In Figure 6.2a the event $(E$ and $F)$ consists of e_4 and e_6, so that

$$P(E \text{ and } F) = P(e_4) + P(e_6).$$

It follows that

(4) $$P(E \text{ or } F) = P(E) + P(F) - P(E \text{ and } F).$$

This addition law holds for all events E, F whether or not they are exclusive. If they happen to be exclusive (as in Figure 6.3), $(E$ and $F)$ will be empty and have probability 0, in which case (4) reduces to (1).

EXAMPLE 1. *Two dice (continued)*. In Example 6.1 we considered for two dice the events E, F corresponding to the results "first die shows one point" and "second die shows one point" respectively. If the 36 simple events displayed in (5.2) are equally likely, it is seen that

$$P(E) = \tfrac{6}{36}, \quad P(F) = \tfrac{6}{36}, \quad \text{and} \quad P(E \text{ and } F) = \tfrac{1}{36}.$$

The probability of the event $(E$ or $F)$ corresponding to the result that at least one of the dice shows one point is then, by (4), equal to $\tfrac{6}{36} + \tfrac{6}{36} - \tfrac{1}{36} = \tfrac{11}{36}$. This can also be seen directly from the fact that the event $(E$ or $F)$ consists of 11 simple events each having probability $\tfrac{1}{36}$.

It is important to keep in mind that law (3) requires the assumption that the events are exclusive. When they are not, it is necessary to correct for multiple counting, as is done in law (4) for the case of two events. The formulas for nonexclusive events become rapidly more complicated as the number of events is increased (see Problem 12).

PROBLEMS

1. In Problem 5.6, find the probabilities of the complements of the events described in parts (i), (ii), (v), and (vii).

2. In Problem 5.9, find the probabilities of the complements of the events described in parts (i)–(v).

3. In Problem 5.8, use the law of complementation to find the probabilities of the following events.
  (i) At least one of the two digits is greater than zero.
  (ii) At least one of the two digits is even.

4. In Example 1, use the results of Table 1 and the addition law (3) to find the probabilities of the following events:
  (i) $T \geq 10$
  (ii) $T < 5$
  (iii) T is divisible by 3.

5. In Problem 5.6 let B be the number of boys. Make a similar table to Table 1 showing the probabilities of B taking on its various possible values 0, 1, 2, and 3.

6. Use the table of the preceding problem and the addition law (3) to find the probabilities of the following events:

  (i) $B \geq 2$
  (ii) $B > 2$
  (iii) $B \leq 1$.

7. A manufacturer of fruit drinks wishes to know whether a new formula (say B) has greater consumer appeal than his old formula (say A). Each of four customers is presented with two glasses, one prepared from each formula, and is asked to state which he prefers. The results may be represented by a sequence of four letters; thus ABAB would mean that the first and third customers preferred A, while the second and fourth preferred B. Suppose that the $2^4 = 16$ possible outcomes of the experiment are equally likely, as would be reasonable if the two formulas are in fact equally attractive. If S denotes the number of consumers preferring the new formula, make a table similar to Table 1, showing the probabilities of S taking on its various possible values.

8. Use the table of the preceding problem and the addition law (3) to find the probabilities of the following events.

  (i) At least two of the customers prefer the new product.
  (ii) At most two of the customers prefer the new product.
  (iii) More than two of the customers prefer the new product.

9. Let ε consist of the six simple events $e_1, \ldots, e_6$, and let $P(e_1) = P(e_2) = .1$, $P(e_3) = .2$, $P(e_4) = .25$, $P(e_5) = .3$, $P(e_6) = .05$. If

$$E = \{e_1, e_2\}, \ F = \{e_2, e_3, e_4\}, \ G = \{e_2, e_3, e_5\},$$

find

  (i) $P(\overline{E})$ (iv) $P(F \text{ or } G)$
  (ii) $P(\overline{F})$ (v) $P(E \text{ or } F \text{ or } G)$.
  (iii) $P(E \text{ or } F)$

10. Let ε consist of the six simple events $e_1, \ldots, e_6$, and let $P(e_1) = .01$, $P(e_2) = .05$, $P(e_3) = .14$, $P(e_4) = .1$, $P(e_5) = .2$, $P(e_6) = .5$. If

$$E = \{e_1, e_4, e_6\}, \ F = \{e_3, e_4, e_5\}, \ G = \{e_2, e_5\},$$

check for each of the following equations whether it is true by computing both the right- and left-hand sides:

  (i) $P(E \text{ or } F) = P(E) + P(F)$
  (ii) $P(E \text{ or } G) = P(E) + P(G)$
  (iii) $P(F \text{ or } G) = P(F) + P(G)$.
Explain your results.

11. Check equation (4) for the events E and F of Problem 9.

12. Check the following generalization of equation (4) by computing both sides when E, F, G are the events of Problem 9:

$$P(E \text{ or } F \text{ or } G) = [P(E) + P(F) + P(G)]$$
$$- [P(E \text{ and } F) + P(E \text{ and } G) + P(F \text{ and } G)]$$
$$+ P(E \text{ and } F \text{ and } G)$$

CHAPTER 2

SAMPLING

2.1 A MODEL FOR SAMPLING

The notion that information about a population may be obtained by
examining a *sample* drawn from the population has been made familiar to
everyone in recent years.   Public opinion polling organizations predict
how millions of people will vote, on the basis of interviews with a few
thousands.   Advertisers decide to support or to drop television programs
on the basis of popularity ratings that rest on the viewing practices of a
sample of much less than one percent of the audience.   The quality of the
product of large factories is controlled by inspection of a small fraction of
the output.   Newspapers carry stories reporting on the cost of living, the
number of unemployed, the acreage planted in certain crops, and many
other economic variables which are estimated from the examination of a
sample.   Like anything else sampling may be done well or badly, and it
is desirable for everyone to understand the theoretical basis for an activity
that has become so important to our society.   In its application, sampling
involves many complications of detail, but the idea is essentially simple,
and is in fact based on the uniform model.

Since the purpose behind taking a sample is to get information about
the population, it seems natural to select a sample so that it will be repre-
sentative of the population.   For instance, a fruit grower trying to estimate the harvest from a grove of lemon trees might pick out a few trees
that he judges to be typical of the grove as a whole, count the fruit on the
selected trees, and then assume that the average number of fruit per tree
in the whole orchard is about equal to the average for the sampled trees.
Again, in trying to forecast an election, we might select counties that have
voted like the country as a whole in recent elections, and conduct interviews with voters in these counties.   While this method of "purposive"
sampling is superficially attractive, it has not worked well in practice.

Biases of the selector creep in too easily when the items for the sample are selected purposively by the exercise of judgement.   Also, items that are typical of the population in some respects need not be typical in others. For instance, counties that vote like the country on the last election may well not do so on the next, when the issues will be different.

Most sampling experts have come to the conclusion that they cannot rely on samples selected purposively, and that the only safe practice is to have the sample chosen by the operation of chance.   Dice, pennies, and random number generators have the virtue of complete impartiality, and a sample selected by their operation is not subject to the bias of human judgement.   Great ingenuity has been exercised in devising efficient ways to use chance mechanisms in picking the sample, some of which will be mentioned in later chapters.   We shall here consider only the simplest case, in which the sample is chosen so that all possible samples of the same size have the same probability of being chosen.   Such a sample is known as a *random sample*.   The concept can best be presented by means of an example.

EXAMPLE *1*.   *The delegation*.   A city is governed by a council consisting of a mayor and six councilmen.   It is necessary to send three members to testify in Washington.   All seven want to go, and the Mayor proposes that the three delegates be selected by lot.   He places in a box seven marbles, similar in size, weight, etc., and labeled with the integers 1 through 7.   A list of the seven men is made, and the names on the list are similarly numbered.   The Mayor's secretary is blindfolded, the marbles shaken up, and she draws three.   The delegation will consist of the three men whose numbers are the same as those of the three marbles drawn.

The above procedure of selecting the sample by lot seems to be completely fair and impartial.   Because the marbles are alike and are thoroughly mixed, and because the drawing is done blindfold, there appears to be no means whereby one possible three-man delegation could be favored over another.

We shall now build a probability model for this experiment.   The simple results are the possible three-man delegations, or the possible sets of three marbles.   They may be denoted by triples of integers, as follows:

	123	134	146	234	246	345	367
	124	135	147	235	247	346	456
(1)	125	136	156	236	256	347	457
	126	137	157	237	257	356	467
	127	145	167	245	267	357	567

It is seen that there are 35 possible samples of three marbles that the secretary might draw.   Since the experiment is arranged so that none of the samples is favored over any other, it seems reasonable to regard all samples as equally likely.

Let us generalize the idea of the example. Suppose that it is desired to draw a sample of s items from a population of N items. We shall denote by $\binom{N}{s}$ the number of different samples of size s that can be formed from a population of N items. For example, $\binom{7}{3}$ is the number of different samples of three items that can be chosen from a given set of seven items; tableau (1) shows that $\binom{7}{3} = 35$.

Definition. If a sample of size s is drawn from a population of size N in such a way that each of the $\binom{N}{s}$ possible samples has the same probability of being drawn, we say that it is a *random sample.*

Thus, if the drawing is at random, the probability of any particular sample is $1 \Big/ \binom{N}{s}$.

Table 1 shows all values of $\binom{N}{s}$ for populations of size $N \leqq 10$. A more extensive table, which is discussed in the next section, is given as Table A at the end of the book. In principle, any entry of these tables could be computed by writing out a tableau similar to (1). However, much more convenient methods for obtaining the numerical values of $\binom{N}{s}$ will be presented in the next section.

TABLE 1.   THE NUMBER $\binom{N}{s}$ OF SAMPLES

s / N	1	2	3	4	5	6	7	8	9	10
1	1									
2	2	1								
3	3	3	1							
4	4	6	4	1						
5	5	10	10	5	1					
6	6	15	20	15	6	1				
7	7	21	35	35	21	7	1			
8	8	28	56	70	56	28	8	1		
9	9	36	84	126	126	84	36	9	1	
10	10	45	120	210	252	210	120	45	10	1

EXAMPLE *1. The delegation (continued)*. Suppose that the Mayor and three members of the council are Conservatives, while the other three are Liberals. It turns out that the delegation, although supposedly chosen by lot, consists entirely of Conservatives. Is this so unlikely, under random sampling, that the Liberals have good reason for believing the drawing was rigged? Since there are four Conservatives on the Council, there are $\binom{4}{3}$ possible three-man delegations consisting entirely of Conservatives, and from Table 1 we see that $\binom{4}{3} = 4$. If the drawing is fair, so that the $\binom{7}{3} = 35$ delegations are equally likely, the probability of getting a delegation without Liberals is $\frac{4}{35} = .11$, or about one chance in nine. This is not small enough to make a strong case for rigging.

EXAMPLE *2. Quality control.* A box of ten fuses contains three that will not work. If a random sample of four fuses is examined, what is the chance that no defective fuse will be found? From Table 1 we see that there are $\binom{10}{4} = 210$ possible samples of size $s = 4$. By assumption, the sample is random; that is, all 210 possible samples are equally likely. Since the box contains seven good fuses, there are $\binom{7}{4} = 35$ samples consisting entirely of good fuses. The probability that no defective fuse will be found in the sample is therefore $\frac{35}{210} = .167$.

EXAMPLE *3. Lunch counter.* Three persons occupy the seven seats at a small lunch counter. It is noticed that no two of them are sitting next to each other. Is this fact evidence that the customers tend to avoid taking a stool next to one already occupied? If the customers seat themselves without regard to whether the adjacent seat is occupied, we may think of them as choosing their places at random. Since three of the seven seats may be chosen in $\binom{7}{3} = 35$ different ways, we have only to count the number of choices which do not bring two customers together. There are 10 such arrangements:

OEOEOEE,   OEOEEOE,   OEOEEEO,   OEEOEOE,   OEEOEEO
OEEEOEO,   EOEOEOE,   EOEOEEO,   EOEEOEO,   EEOEOEO

The probability of the observed event is therefore $\frac{10}{35} = \frac{2}{7}$ if the customers seat themselves at random. This probability is too large for the observed seating to be very strong evidence in favor of the avoidance theory.

EXAMPLE 4. *The diseased poplars.* Of a row of ten poplar trees, four adjacent trees are affected with a disease. Is there reason for thinking that the disease is spreading from one tree to another? This problem is much like the preceding. If the disease strikes at random, there are $\binom{10}{4} = 210$ possible sets of four that might be affected. Of these arrangements, only seven consist of four adjacent trees. Thus P(affected trees adjacent) $= \frac{7}{210} = \frac{1}{30}$, if the choice is random. This is rather a small probability, so there is some ground for thinking that a causal relation underlies the adjacency of the diseased trees.

The method of drawing a random sample by means of numbered marbles, described in Example 1, is feasible only if the population size N is sufficiently small. For larger N, a more convenient method utilizes a table of random numbers (see Section 3.4). An essential step in both these methods, or any others, is the construction of a numbered list of the items in the population. It is often difficult and expensive to make such a list. However, to draw a random sample one cannot do without it or some other equivalent method of numbering the items. Thus, a random sample of the houses in a block may be obtained by making a sketch map of the block and numbering the houses on this map. If light bulbs are packed in cartons in a regular pattern, one may devise a systematic numbering scheme that attaches to each bulb a different integer, thereby making it unnecessary actually to write down the list. Sampling experts have developed many devices to obtain the equivalent of a list at less expense and trouble.

PROBLEMS

1. In Example 1, find the probabilities of the following events.
   (i) The delegation consists of Liberals only.
   (ii) The delegation consists of two Conservatives and one Liberal.
   (iii) There are at least two Conservatives on the delegation.
   (iv) The Mayor is a member of the delegation.

2. Check the entries $\binom{5}{2}$ and $\binom{5}{3}$ in Table 1 by listing all possible samples of sizes two and three that can be drawn from the five persons A, B, C, D, E.

3. Use the definition of $\binom{N}{s}$ to find the value of

   (i) $\binom{N}{N}$,   (ii) $\binom{N}{1}$,   (iii) $\binom{N}{N-1}$.

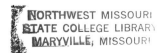

4. Of a group of seven children, four are selected at random to receive instruction by method A, while method B will be used on the remaining three. Find the probability of the following events.

    (i) The four most intelligent children are all assigned to method A.

    (ii) The three most intelligent children are all assigned to method A.

    (iii) The most intelligent child is assigned to method A.

[Hint: In counting the numbers of samples having the properties in question, it may be helpful to label the children $1, 2, \ldots, 7$ in order of intelligence.]

5. Find the probabilities of the three events (i)–(iii) of the preceding problem assuming that five of the seven children are selected at random to be instructed by method A, the remaining two receiving instruction by method B.

6. Suppose that of the seven children in Problem 4, four are boys and three girls. Two of the four boys and two of the three girls are selected at random to be instructed by method A.

    (i) How many possible samples of two boys and two girls are there?

    (ii) Assuming all these samples to be equally likely, find the probability that the most intelligent boy and the most intelligent girl both receive instruction by method A.

7. A batch of ten items contains two defectives. If two items are drawn at random, what is the probability that both are nondefective?

8. In Example 4, what is the probability that no two diseased trees are adjacent?

9. By inspection of Table 1, formulate a rule for obtaining each entry as the sum of two entries in the row above it. Use the rule to add a new row to the table.

10. It appears in Table 1 that certain pairs of entries in each row are equal. Formulate a rule that specifies when two entries are equal.

11. A square field is divided into nine square plots, arranged in three rows and three columns. Three plots are chosen at random. What is the probability that of the chosen plots

    (i) all are in the same row,

    (ii) one is in each column,

    (iii) one is in each row and one is in each column?

12. In order to select a law firm at random, it is suggested to draw a lawyer from an available list of all N lawyers in the city and then select the firm to which he belongs. Suppose there are in the city 50 firms consisting of only one lawyer, ten firms consisting of two lawyers each, two firms consisting of three lawyers each, and one firm consisting of four lawyers. Find the probability that the selected firm consists of (i) four lawyers, (ii) one lawyer.

    Has the law firm been selected at random?

2.2 THE NUMBER OF SAMPLES

The number $\binom{N}{s}$ of different samples of size s that can be drawn from a population of size N is of great importance in probability and statistics, and also in other branches of mathematics. It is known as the *number of combinations* of N things taken s at a time. The numbers $\binom{N}{s}$ are also referred to as *binomial coefficients*. We shall now point out several features of these quantities, and show how a table of values of $\binom{N}{s}$ may easily be computed.

An inspection of Table 1.1 shows that, at least in all cases covered by the table,

$$(1) \qquad\qquad \binom{N}{1} = N \quad \text{and} \quad \binom{N}{N} = 1.$$

These relations hold quite generally. Suppose that a sample of size $s = 1$ is to be drawn. Then each of the N items may serve as this sample, so that there are N possible samples of size 1. At the other extreme, if the sample is to have size $s = N$, the "sample" must consist of the entire population, and this is possible in just one way.

To discover another property of these numbers, let us look at one of the rows of Table 1.1, for example the last row:

$$(2)$$

s	1	2	3	4	5	6	7	8	9	10
$\binom{10}{s}$	10	45	120	210	252	210	120	45	10	1

The entries are arranged symmetrically about the largest value, $\binom{10}{5} = 252$. Thus $\binom{10}{4} = 210 = \binom{10}{6}$, $\binom{10}{3} = 120 = \binom{10}{7}$, and so forth. A similar symmetry holds in the other rows. This phenomenon is easily explained. For example, when a sample of size $s = 3$ is drawn from a population of size $N = 10$, there is left in the population a remnant of size $N - s = 10 - 3 = 7$. We can think of these seven items as a sample of size 7. Thus to each sample of size 3 that may be removed, there corresponds a sample of size 7 that is left. Therefore the number of samples of size $s = 3$ equals the number of samples of size $N - s = 7$, or $\binom{10}{3} = \binom{10}{7}$. The same argument shows that quite generally

(3)
$$\binom{N}{N-s} = \binom{N}{s},$$

which is the formal expression of the observed symmetry.

Equation (3) makes it possible to cut in half the size of any table of the quantities $\binom{N}{s}$. A table utilizing this fact and giving all entries with $N \leq 26$ and $s \leq 13$ is given as Table A at the end of the book. If we wish to use this table for example to obtain the value of $\binom{24}{15}$, we look up instead the value of $\binom{24}{24-15}$ to find

$$\binom{24}{15} = \binom{24}{9} = 1{,}307{,}504.$$

For values beyond the range of the table, there exist a variety of formulas and approximations. One such formula will be derived in Section 4.

Equation (3) breaks down in one case, namely when s is equal to 0. The left side then becomes $\binom{N}{N}$, which by (1) has the value 1; but the right side becomes $\binom{N}{0}$, which is meaningless. Whenever a mathematical expression is meaningless because it is undefined, we are free to attach to it any meaning that we like. Usually, it is convenient to do this in such a way that certain formulas remain valid for the previously undefined case. This suggests that we *define*

(4)
$$\binom{N}{0} = 1,$$

so that equation (3) will continue to be valid when $s = 0$. With this definition it is possible to complete the symmetry of the rows of Table 1.1; by adding the entry for $s = 0$, the row for $N = 7$ for example will become:

s	0	1	2	3	4	5	6	7
$\binom{7}{s}$	1	7	21	35	35	21	7	1

Finally, we shall discuss a relation which permits much easier computation of the table than direct enumeration. Inspection of Table 1.1 shows that any entry is the sum of the entry above it and the entry to the left of the latter. The entry above $\binom{N}{s}$ is $\binom{N-1}{s}$, and the entry to the left of this is $\binom{N-1}{s-1}$. The suggested relation is therefore

(5)
$$\binom{N}{s} = \binom{N-1}{s} + \binom{N-1}{s-1},$$

and this does in fact hold quite generally.

To see how to prove equation (5), let us consider once more the problem of choosing a three-man delegation from a seven-man council (Example 1.1).   The $\binom{7}{3}$ = 35 possible delegations may be divided into two types: those to which the Mayor belongs, and those to which he does not.   There are just $\binom{6}{2}$ = 15 of the former, since if the Mayor belongs, there are still two members to be chosen from among the six other councilmen.   On the other hand, the number of three-man delegations without the Mayor is $\binom{6}{3}$ = 20, since for these delegations all three must be chosen from the six ordinary council members.   This proves (5) for the case $N = 7$, $s = 3$, and the argument can easily be extended to give a proof of the general case.

Relation (5) can be used to compute a table of $\binom{N}{s}$ by obtaining successively each row from the preceding one.   To illustrate the method, let us get the value $\binom{8}{3}$ from the entries listed above for $N = 7$.   The entry above $\binom{8}{3}$ is $\binom{7}{3}$ = 35; the entry to the left of this is $\binom{7}{2}$ = 21, and their sum gives $\binom{8}{3}$ = 35 + 21 = 56.   In this manner it is possible to build up the table quickly.   The triangular scheme that is built up in this way is known as *Pascal's triangle*.   Table 1.1 may easily be checked by this device.

The method outlined above has been used on an automatic computer to compute the values up to $N = 200$, and the resulting table has been published.*   The values increase very rapidly; it may interest the reader to know that $\binom{200}{100}$ = 90,548,514,656,103,281,165,404,177,077,484,163,874, 504,589,675,413,336,841,320, which is a number of 59 digits!   Values sometimes quoted are the number of possible hands at poker, $\binom{52}{5}$ = 2,598,960, and the number of possible hands at bridge, $\binom{52}{13}$ = 635,013,559,600.

EXAMPLE 1.   *Poker.*   What is the chance that a poker hand will be a heart flush (i.e. consist only of hearts)?   A poker hand consists of 5 cards dealt from a deck of 52 cards.   Before they are dealt, the cards are shuffled, and if the shuffling is sufficiently thorough it is natural to assume that no one poker hand is more likely to be dealt than any other.   This assumption cannot be directly checked, because the number of poker hands is so large

* *Table of Binomial Coefficients*, Cambridge University Press, 1954.

that it is not feasible to deal enough hands to show whether or not they all arise with equal frequency. It is possible however to check certain consequences of the assumption of the uniform model, and experiments of this sort have been carried out. The general conclusion is that much more thorough shuffling than is customary among card players would be needed before the uniform model could be safely used.

Suppose, however, that we are willing to assume that all hands are equally likely. It is then easy to compute the probability of a heart flush. The number of favorable cases is the number of hands that can be chosen from the 13 hearts in the deck, and this is just $\binom{13}{5} = 1287$. Therefore, $P(\text{heart flush}) = 1287/2,598,960 = .000495$, which is about 1 in 2000. The same argument shows this also to be the probability of each of the other types of flush.

EXAMPLE 2. *Inclusion of a specified item.* A term paper consists of 24 problems. In order to save time, the instructor corrects only eight of them which he selects at random. If in your assignment only one problem is wrong, what is the probability that it will be among those selected for correction? The total number of possible samples of eight problems is $\binom{24}{8} = 735,471$. The number of these including the one incorrect problem is $\binom{23}{7} = 245,157$, since this is the number of ways in which the remaining seven problems needed for the sample can be chosen from the 23 correct problems. The desired probability is therefore

$$\frac{245,157}{735,471} = \frac{1}{3}.$$

This example illustrates a fact which holds quite generally: the probability that a random sample of size s includes any specified item of the population of N items from which the sample is taken is s/N. (In the example $s = 8$, $N = 24$ so that $s/N = \frac{1}{3}$; for a general proof see Problem 12.) It follows that the method of random sampling is "fair" in the sense that each item has the same probability (namely s/N) of being included in the sample.

PROBLEMS

1. Use Table A and relation (3) to find $\binom{25}{17}$.

2. Use Table A and relation (5) to find $\binom{27}{6}$.

3. Using Table A and making repeated use of relation (5), find $\binom{28}{6}$.

4. A batch of 20 items contains four defectives. If three items are drawn at random, find the probability that
  (i) all three are nondefective,
  (ii) at least one is defective.

5. A batch of 25 items contains five defectives. If three items are drawn at random, what is the probability that at least one is defective?

6. A group of 20, one of whom acts as secretary, selects at random a delegation of five. What is the probability that the secretary is included in the delegation?

7. In a poker hand, what is the probability of a "flush" (i.e., all five cards from the same suit)?

8. A lot of 25 fuses contains five defectives. How large a sample must one draw so that the probability of getting at least one defective fuse in the sample will exceed $\frac{1}{2}$?

9. A box contains four red and five white marbles. In how many ways can a sample be drawn consisting of
  (i) one red and one white marble?
  (ii) one red and two white marbles?

10. From the box of Problem 9, a sample of size two is drawn at random. What is the probability that it consists of one red and one white marble?

11. (i) Show that the total number of ways of selecting a committee of s from a group of N and naming one as chairman is $\binom{N}{s}\binom{s}{1}$. [Hint: Select first the committee; then from the committee members a chairman.]

  (ii) Show that an alternative answer to (i) is $\binom{N}{1}\binom{N-1}{s-1}$. [Hint: select first the chairman from the whole group; then select the $s-1$ ordinary members.]

  (iii) By comparing the answers to (i) and (ii) show that

(6)
$$\binom{N}{s} = \frac{N}{s}\binom{N-1}{s-1}.$$

12. Using the result of Problem 11, show that the probability that a specified item is included in a sample of size s taken at random from a population of N is

$$\frac{\binom{N-1}{s-1}}{\binom{N}{s}} = \frac{s}{N}.$$

13. By successive application of (6) and the fact that $\binom{k}{1} = k$, find (i) $\binom{5}{2}$, (ii) $\binom{6}{3}$, (iii) $\binom{7}{4}$.

14. Use (6) to show that

$$\text{(i)} \quad \binom{N}{2} = \frac{N(N-1)}{2}; \qquad \text{(ii)} \quad \binom{N}{3} = \frac{N(N-1)(N-2)}{6}.$$

2.3 ORDERED SAMPLING

In Section 1, we presented the following method for obtaining a random sample of the desired size from a population of items: let the N items in the population be numbered from 1 to N, and let a box contain N marbles similarly numbered. After thorough mixing, s marbles are taken from the box, and the sample consists of those s items in the population whose numbers appear on these s marbles.

Unless s is quite small, it is difficult to grab exactly s marbles at once. An obvious method to insure that the desired number of marbles is obtained, is to take them one at a time until just s have been drawn from the box. The result of this procedure is a sample of s marbles *arranged in a particular order*. One of the marbles in the sample was obtained on the first draw, another on the second draw, and so forth.

Definition: A sample arranged in order is called an *ordered sample*.

To distinguish between an ordered sample and the kind discussed previously to which we may now refer as "unordered," we shall adopt in this section a notational convention. A sample will be indicated by listing its items, in parentheses when the sample is ordered, in braces when it is unordered. Thus an unordered sample consisting of the two items A and B may be denoted indifferently by {A, B} or by {B, A}. On the other hand, (A, B) and (B, A) denote two different ordered samples consisting of the items A and B. In (A, B) item A is first and B second; in (B, A) the order of the two items is reversed.

To illustrate the relation between ordered and unordered samples, consider a population of $N = 4$ marbles labeled A, B, C, D (they could equally well be labeled 1, 2, 3, 4, but the use of letters will provide a clearer notation). An ordered sample of size $s = 2$ is drawn. The 12 possible ordered samples are displayed below, arranged in columns corresponding to the six possible unordered samples of the same size.

(1)

Unordered sample	{A, B}	{A, C}	{A, D}	{B, C}	{B, D}	{C, D}
Corresponding ordered samples	(A, B) (B, A)	(A, C) (C, A)	(A, D) (D, A)	(B, C) (C, B)	(B, D) (D, B)	(C, D) (D, C)

As a second illustration, suppose that from the same set of marbles we draw an ordered sample of size $s = 3$. Each of the $\binom{4}{3} = 4$ unordered samples may be arranged in six different orders, giving the $4 \cdot 6 = 24$ ordered samples shown below.

	Unordered sample	{ABC}	{ABD}	{ACD}	{BCD}
(2)	Corresponding ordered samples	(ABC)	(ABD)	(ACD)	(BCD)
		(ACB)	(ADB)	(ADC)	(BDC)
		(BAC)	(BAD)	(CAD)	(CBD)
		(BCA)	(BDA)	(CDA)	(CDB)
		(CAB)	(DAB)	(DAC)	(DBC)
		(CBA)	(DBA)	(DCA)	(DCB)

It will be convenient to introduce the symbol $(N)_s$ to represent the number of different ordered samples of size s that can be drawn from a population of size N. (This quantity is also known as the *number of permutations* of N things taken s at a time.) The illustrations above show that

$$(4)_2 = 12 \quad \text{and} \quad (4)_3 = 24.$$

Table 1 gives the values of $(N)_s$ for populations of size 10 and less. These values are in general much larger than the corresponding values of $\binom{N}{s}$ shown in Table 1.1, as is reasonable since each sample of several items corresponds to many different ordered samples of these items. While the small entries of the present table could be obtained by making systematic lists of all ordered samples for the given values of N and s, this would be too cumbersome for the large entries. All values were actually computed from the simple formula for $(N)_s$ given in the next section.

TABLE 1. THE NUMBER $(N)_s$ OF ORDERED SAMPLES

N \ s	1	2	3	4	5	6	7	8	9	10
1	1									
2	2	2								
3	3	6	6							
4	4	12	24	24						
5	5	20	60	120	120					
6	6	30	120	360	720	720				
7	7	42	210	840	2520	5040	5040			
8	8	56	336	1680	6720	20160	40320	40320		
9	9	72	504	3024	15120	60480	181440	362880	362880	
10	10	90	720	5040	30240	151200	604800	1814400	3628800	3628800

Let us now build a probability model for the random experiment of drawing an ordered sample of size s from a population of size N. It is natural to take as the simple events all possible different ordered samples. What probabilities should be attached to them? If the N marbles are of similar size and weight and are thoroughly mixed, and if the drawing is done blindfold, we would expect each of the ordered samples to appear with about equal frequency, and actual experiments with small populations bear out this expectation. Accordingly we shall treat all $(N)_s$ ordered samples as equally likely, and assign to each of them the probability $1/(N)_s$. When an ordered sample is drawn so that this model may reasonably be applied, we shall refer to it as a *random* ordered sample.

The usefulness of ordered sampling for obtaining a random (unordered) sample rests on the following important fact:

(3)   to obtain a random sample of size s from a population of size N, we may first draw an ordered random sample and then disregard the order.

We shall prove this first for the special case of a sample of size $s = 3$ drawn from a population consisting of $N = 4$ items. If the items are numbered A, B, C, D, let us find for example the probability that the sample, without regard to order, is {A, B, D}. Each of the ordered samples shown in the tableau (2) has the same probability $\frac{1}{24}$, and it is therefore only necessary to count the number of ordered samples corresponding to {A, B, D}. These are just the six cases listed in the second column of the tableau, and the desired probability is therefore $\frac{6}{24} = \frac{1}{4}$.

Extending this argument, it is seen that each of the $\binom{4}{3} = 4$ possible unordered samples

$$\{A, B, C\}, \quad \{A, B, D\}, \quad \{A, C, D\}, \quad \{B, C, D\}$$

appears just six times in the tableau (2) of ordered samples. Each of the four possible unordered samples that can be obtained by first drawing an ordered sample of size three and then disregarding the order has probability $\frac{1}{4}$, and the unordered sample obtained in this manner is therefore random.

The above argument can be used to show quite generally that the sample obtained from a random ordered sample by disregarding the order is random. Notice that each unordered sample may be arranged in the same number, in fact $(s)_s$, of different orders. Therefore, in the model for ordered sampling, all (unordered) samples have the same probability $(s)_s/(N)_s$, as was to be proved

We know, from Section 1, that the probability of each unordered sample is $1/\binom{N}{s}$. Equating this with the expression $(s)_s/(N)_s$ just obtained for the same probability, we see that

(4) $$(N)_s = \binom{N}{s} \cdot (s)_s.$$

That is, the number of ordered samples is the number of unordered samples multiplied by the number of ways in which each sample can be ordered.

To discover another important property of ordered sampling, let us suppose once more that a random ordered sample of size $s = 3$ is drawn from the population of four marbles labeled A, B, C, D and find the probability that marble D appears on the second draw. Inspection of tableau (2) shows the following six ordered samples to have marble D in the second position:

(A, D, B)   (B, D, A)   (A, D, C)   (C, D, A)   (B, D, C)   (C, D, B)

The desired probability is therefore $\frac{6}{24} = \frac{1}{4}$.

In the same manner it is easily checked that each of the four marbles has the same chance of appearing on the second draw (Problem 8). How could it be otherwise, since there is nothing to favor any marble over any other as a candidate for the second spot? This result generalizes to the following *equivalence law of ordered sampling:*

(5)
    if a random ordered sample of size s is drawn from a population of size N, then on any particular one of the s draws each of the N items has the same probability $1/N$ of appearing.

As an illustration, suppose that an instructor has announced that he will call at random on three students to present solutions of the three home-work problems at the board. One of the ten students is unable to solve Problem 2, and wonders what his chances are of being found out. In effect, the instructor will draw an ordered random sample of size $s = 3$ from a population of size $N = 10$. By the equivalence law, the worried student has probability $1/N = \frac{1}{10}$ of being the person sampled on the second draw, and hence being asked to work Problem 2.

The equivalence law asserts that each item in the population is equally likely to be obtained on any specified draw. It is also true that each *pair* of items in the population is equally likely to be obtained on any *two* specified draws. For example, if we give equal probability to each of the ordered samples in tableau (2), what is the probability that the items {A, B} will be obtained on draws 2 and 4? This event occurs with the following four samples

(C, A, D, B),   (D, A, C, B),   (C, B, D, A),   (D, B, C, A),

so that the desired probability is $\frac{4}{24} = \frac{1}{6}$. The same probability attaches to each of the six (unordered) pairs. The result also extends beyond two items: each (unordered) triple of items has the same chance $1 \Big/ \binom{N}{3}$ of

being obtained on any three specified draws, etc.   We shall call this the
"generalized equivalence law of ordered sampling."

PROBLEMS

1.   Check the values $(5)_2$ and $(5)_3$ of Table 1 by enumeration from tableaus similar
to (1) and (2).

2.   (i) Check the values $(3)_1$ and $(4)_4$ of Table 1 by enumeration.
  (ii) Explain why it is always true that $(N)_N = (N)_{N-1}$.
  (iii) Is it true that the total number of ways in which N items can be arranged
  in order is $(N)_N$?

3.   Check the values $(3)_1$ and $(4)_1$ by enumeration, and explain why it is always
true that $(N)_1 = N$.

4.   From Table 1, calculate $(N)_2/(N)_1$ for $N = 2, 3, \ldots, 10$, and conjecture a
general formula for $(N)_2$.

5.   From Table 1, calculate $(N)_N/(N - 1)_{N-1}$ for $N = 2, 3, \ldots, 10$, and conjecture a general formula for $(N)_N$.

6.   In an essay contest, there are three prizes worth $500, $200, and $100 re-
spectively.   In how many different ways can these be distributed among nine
contestants?

7.   A newly formed club of ten members decides to select its officers by lot.   From
the ten names, four are drawn out one by one.   The first one drawn will serve as
President, the second as Vice-President, the third as Treasurer, and the fourth as
Secretary.
  (i) How many different possible outcomes are there to this lottery?
  (ii) What is the probability that the only girl in the club will become Vice-
  President?
  (iii) What is the probability that the four oldest members will be chosen for the
  four offices (not necessarily in order of importance)?

8.   From tableau (2), check that in a random ordered sample of $s = 3$ drawn from
a population of four items labeled A, B, C, D, each of the four items has the same
probability of being obtained on the second draw.

9.   From the tableau of Problem 1, check that in a random ordered sample of
$s = 3$ drawn from a population of five items, each of the five items has the same
probability of being obtained on the second draw.

10.   A lottery contains one grand prize of $1000; the winning number will be
announced after all customers have drawn their tickets.   Two customers arrive
simultaneously, and customer A is permitted to draw a ticket first.   Customer B
complains that he is at a disadvantage since if A has drawn the grand prize, B will
have no chance to get it.   Is B's complaint justified?

11.   Four runners in a ski race, wearing numbers 1, 2, 3, 4 on their backs, are started one after another in random order. Make a tableau of all possible starting orders and find the probabilities of the following events.

(i) Runner No. 1 is started first, then runner No. 2, then No. 3, and lastly No. 4.

(ii) Runner No. 1 is started first.

(iii) The starting position of at least two of the runners coincides with the numbers on their backs.

(iv) The starting position of exactly one runner coincides with the number on his back.

(v) The starting positions of exactly two runners agree with the numbers on their backs.

12. A magazine prints the photographs of four movie stars and also (in scrambled order) a baby picture of each. What is the probability that a reader by purely random matching of the pictures gets at least two right?

13. An ordered sample of $s = 5$ is drawn from ten items numbered 1 to 10. What is the probability that the items drawn will appear in order of increasing (not necessarily consecutive) numbers?

14. Consider an ordered sample of size s drawn at random from a population of N items. Let E represent the result that a specified item is included in the sample. Find $P(E)$ by noting that $E = (E_1$ or E_2 or $\ldots$ or $E_s)$, where $E_1, E_2, \ldots$ represent the events that the specified item is obtained on the 1st draw, on the 2nd draw, $\ldots$.

2.4 SOME FORMULAS FOR SAMPLING

In the preceding sections we introduced the methods of ordered and unordered random sampling. If the size of the population is N and that of the sample s, we denoted by $(N)_s$ the number of possible ordered samples and by $\binom{N}{s}$ the number of possible samples without regard to order. We shall first develop general formulas for these quantities and then give some applications of these formulas.

Let us begin by obtaining a formula for $(N)_2$, the number of ordered samples of size two that can be drawn from a population of N items numbered $1, \ldots, N$. Consider the process of drawing such a sample. On the first draw there are N items to choose from. Whichever item is first chosen, there will remain $N - 1$ possibilities for the second draw. Therefore the number of ordered samples of size two is

(1) $$(N)_2 = N(N - 1).$$

For example, there are $(5)_2 = 5 \cdot 4 = 20$ ordered samples of size two that can be drawn from a population of five items. These 20 items may be displayed as follows:

	(1, 2)	(1, 3)	(1, 4)	(1, 5)
(2, 1)		(2, 3)	(2, 4)	(2, 5)
(3, 1)	(3, 2)		(3, 4)	(3, 5)
(4, 1)	(4, 2)	(4, 3)		(4, 5)
(5, 1)	(5, 2)	(5, 3)	(5, 4)	

where the five rows correspond to the five possible choices on the first draw, and the four entries in each row to the four choices remaining for the second draw after one item has been chosen.

What about $(N)_3$, the number of ordered samples of size three? Again there will be N possibilities on the first draw, and $N - 1$ possibilities on the second draw regardless of the choice on the first one. Finally, however the first two choices are made, there will remain $N - 2$ possibilities for the third draw. Thus the total number of samples is $(N)_3 = N(N - 1)(N - 2)$. For example, when $N = 10$ there are $10 \cdot 9 \cdot 8 = 720$ different ordered samples of size three.

In a quite similar way it can be argued that the number of ordered samples of size four is $N(N - 1)(N - 2)(N - 3)$, and in general that the number of ordered samples of size s will be the product of s factors, starting with N and decreasing one each time. What is the last factor? By the time the sth factor has been reached, the original N will have been reduced by one $s - 1$ times, so the last factor is $N - (s - 1) = N - s + 1$. The final formula for the number of ordered samples of size s from a population of size N is

$$(2) \qquad (N)_s = N(N - 1)(N - 2) \cdots (N - s + 1).$$

For example, the number of ordered samples of size five from a population of size ten is $10 \cdot 9 \cdot 8 \cdot 7 \cdot 6 = 30{,}240$.

An important and interesting special case of formula (2) arises when $s = N$, that is, when the entire population is taken into the sample. The expression (2) then becomes

$$(3) \qquad (N)_N = N(N - 1)(N - 2) \cdots 2 \cdot 1$$

or just the product of the first N positive integers. This quantity is known as N *factorial* and is written $N!$ Thus, $(N)_N = N!$ is the number of ways in which N elements can be arranged in order.

By substituting (2) and (3) into formula (3.4), we obtain

$$(4) \qquad \binom{N}{s} = \frac{N(N - 1) \cdots (N - s + 1)}{1 \cdot 2 \cdots s}.$$

An easy way to remember this formula is to notice that the numerator is the product of s decreasing factors starting with N, while the denominator contains s increasing factors starting with 1. As an example we compute

$$\binom{10}{4} = \frac{10 \cdot 9 \cdot 8 \cdot 7}{1 \cdot 2 \cdot 3 \cdot 4} = 10 \cdot 3 \cdot 7 = 210,$$

which agrees with the value given in Table 1.1.

Formula (2) can be used to prove the equivalence law of ordered sampling stated in the preceding section. To prove this law, we must show that on any particular draw, each of the N items has the same probability $1/N$ of being drawn. To fix ideas, consider the probability of obtaining a particular item, say item A, on the second draw. There are $(N)_s$ equally likely ordered samples. How many of these will have item A in second place? If item A is specified to occupy second place, there will remain $N - 1$ other items for the $s - 1$ other places. The remaining places can then be filled in $(N - 1)_{s-1}$ different ways. The desired probability is therefore

$$\frac{(N - 1)_{s-1}}{(N)_s} = \frac{(N - 1)(N - 2) \cdots (N - s + 1)}{N(N - 1)(N - 2) \cdots (N - s + 1)} = \frac{1}{N}.$$

Clearly, the argument would work equally well for any item and any place, which proves the desired result. A similar argument leads to the generalized equivalence law.

PROBLEMS

1. Use formula (2) to check in Table 3.1 the entries for (i) $(7)_3$, (ii) $(7)_4$, (iii) $(10)_5$.

2. Use formula (4) to check that the number of possible poker hands is 2,598,960.

3. Prove the following alternative expression for $\binom{N}{s}$:

$$(5) \qquad \binom{N}{s} = \frac{N!}{s!(N - s)!}.$$

4. Give a meaning to 0! in such a way that (5) will remain valid when $s = 0$ and when $s = N$.

5. Use (5) to prove the relations (2.1), (2.3), (2.5), and (2.6).

6. (i) What is the probability that in three throws with a fair die, different numbers occur on all three throws?
(ii) What is the probability that at least two of the throws show the same number? [Hint: Assume that all $6^3 = 216$ possible results of the three throws are equally likely.]

7. What is the probability that in six throws with a fair die all six faces occur? [Hint: Assume that all 6^6 possible results of the six throws are equally likely.]

8. What is the probability that in a group of $s = 5$ persons at least two have their birthday on the same day? [Hint: Neglect Feb. 29 and assume that all $(365)^5$ possible sets of five birthdays are equally likely.]

Note: It is a surprising fact that for $s = 23$, the desired probability is greater than $\frac{1}{2}$.

9. The *binomial theorem* states that

$$(a + b)^N = \binom{N}{0} a^N + \binom{N}{1} a^{N-1}b + \binom{N}{2} a^{N-2}b^2 + \ldots + \binom{N}{N} b^N.$$

By choosing appropriate values for a and b, prove that

$$\binom{N}{0} + \binom{N}{1} + \ldots + \binom{N}{N} = 2^N$$

and

$$\binom{N}{0} - \binom{N}{1} + \binom{N}{2} - \binom{N}{3} + \ldots = 0.$$

10. Prove the binomial theorem. [Hint: In multiplying out $(a + b)(a + b) \ldots (a + b)$, the terms $a^s b^{N-s}$ arise if a is selected from s of the parentheses and b from the remaining $N - s$. How many such terms are there?]

CHAPTER 3

PRODUCT MODELS

3.1 PRODUCT MODELS FOR TWO-PART EXPERIMENTS

Random experiments often consist of two or more parts: for example, several throws of a die or throws of several dice; drawing two or more marbles from a box; observing the weather on consecutive days or the sexes of successive children in a family; etc. Frequently it is relatively easy to build a satisfactory model for each of the parts separately. The problem then arises: how should the separate models for the various parts be combined to provide a model for the experiment as a whole? The present chapter is devoted to one type of combined model for the whole experiment, which we shall call the "product model." Very many of the probability models used in practice are of this type.

EXAMPLE 1. *Stratified sampling.* We have discussed in Chapter 2 some aspects of random sampling. Frequently the population from which the sample is drawn is made up of a number of different subpopulations or *strata*. Human populations may for example be stratified according to religion or age, sex, party registration, etc. It may be desirable to avoid samples which are too unrepresentative, such as samples consisting mainly of items coming from a single stratum. This can be achieved by the method of *stratified sampling*, according to which a random sample of specified size is drawn from each of the strata. The separate samples drawn from the different strata then constitute parts of the whole experiment, and each part may be represented by the kind of model considered in Section 2.1. The problem is how to combine these models to produce a model for the whole experiment.

EXAMPLE 2. *Two loaded dice.* In Example 1.3.2 we developed a model for the throw of a loaded die. In many dice games two dice are thrown, both of which may be loaded. If we regard the throw of each die as a part of the whole experiment, the problem arises how to combine two models like that of Example 1.3.2 into a model for the experiment of throwing two loaded dice.

We shall begin by considering product models for experiments consisting of only two parts. Let us first see how to choose an event set for a two-part experiment for both parts of which the event sets have already been selected. Suppose that part A has an event set $\mathcal{E}_A$ consisting of simple events $e_1, e_2, \ldots, e_a$ corresponding to the simple results $r_1, r_2, \ldots, r_a$, while part B has an event set $\mathcal{E}_B$ consisting of simple events $f_1, f_2, \ldots, f_b$ corresponding to the simple results $s_1, s_2, \ldots, s_b$. When the whole experiment is performed, we shall want to record the results of both parts. If, for example, the result of part A is r_2 and the result of part B is s_1, the result of the whole experiment is "r_2 and s_1." Since any of the a simple results $r_1, r_2 \ldots, r_a$, of part A may occur in combination with any of the b simple results $s_1, s_2, \ldots, s_b$ of part B, there will be $a \cdot b$ possibilities for the experiment as a whole. (Thus, in Example 2, die A may show any of its $a = 6$ faces and die B may also show any of its $b = 6$ faces, so that there will be $6 \cdot 6 = 36$ simple results for the experiment of throwing both dice.)

The event set for the whole experiment will need $a \cdot b$ simple events, corresponding to the $a \cdot b$ simple results. These simple events may be conveniently displayed in a tableau of a rows and b columns:

(1)

e_1 and f_1	e_1 and f_2	$\ldots$	e_1 and f_b
e_2 and f_1	e_2 and f_2	$\ldots$	e_2 and f_b
$\ldots$			
e_a and f_1	e_a and f_2	$\ldots$	e_a and f_b.

Here, for example, (e_1 and f_2) is the simple event corresponding to the simple result "r_1 and s_2." We shall refer to (1) as the *product* of the event sets $\mathcal{E}_A$ and $\mathcal{E}_B$, and denote it by $\mathcal{E}_A \times \mathcal{E}_B$.

To complete the model, we must assign probabilities to each of the $a \cdot b$ simple events in $\mathcal{E}_A \times \mathcal{E}_B$. Suppose that for parts A and B of the experiment separately, probability models $\mathcal{Q}$ and $\mathcal{B}$ are given with the following probabilities:

(2)

Model $\mathcal{Q}$	*Model* $\mathcal{B}$
$e_1, e_2, \ldots, e_a$	$f_1, f_2, \ldots, f_b$
$p_1, p_2, \ldots, p_a$	$q_1, q_2, \ldots, q_b$

where of course

(3) $p_1 + p_2 + \ldots + p_a = 1$ and $q_1 + q_2 + \ldots + q_b = 1.$

The probabilities to be assigned to the simple events (1) of $\mathcal{E}_A \times \mathcal{E}_B$ must be nonnegative and add up to one. This can be done in many different ways. One simple method, which turns out to be realistic in many cases, consists of assigning to each of the simple events of (1) the *product* of the corresponding probabilities of models α and $\mathcal{B}$. Thus, to the simple event (e_1 and f_2) we assign the probability p_1q_2, and so forth. The tableau of probabilities is then as follows:

$$
\begin{array}{llll}
P(e_1 \text{ and } f_1) = p_1q_1 & P(e_1 \text{ and } f_2) = p_1q_2 & \ldots & P(e_1 \text{ and } f_b) = p_1q_b \\
P(e_2 \text{ and } f_1) = p_2q_1 & P(e_2 \text{ and } f_2) = p_2q_2 & \ldots & P(e_2 \text{ and } f_b) = p_2q_b \\
\quad \ldots & \quad \ldots & & \quad \ldots \\
P(e_a \text{ and } f_1) = p_aq_1 & P(e_a \text{ and } f_2) = p_aq_2 & \ldots & P(e_a \text{ and } f_b) = p_aq_b
\end{array}
$$

(4)

It is easy to check that tableau (4) does specify a probability model, as defined in Section 1.4. The probabilities are obviously not negative, and they add up to 1, as the following argument proves. Consider the sum of the probabilities in the first row of (4); using (3) we find that

$$(5) \quad p_1q_1 + p_1q_2 + \ldots + p_1q_b = p_1(q_1 + q_2 + \ldots + q_b) = p_1 \cdot 1 = p_1.$$

Similarly the probabilities in the second row of (4) add up p_2, and so forth. The sum of the rows is therefore $p_1 + p_2 + \ldots + p_a$, which by (3) equals 1.

The above discussion leads to the following formal definition.

Definition. The model defined by (1) and (4) will be called the *product* of models α and $\mathcal{B}$, and will be denoted by $\alpha \times \mathcal{B}$. The models α and $\mathcal{B}$ will be called the *factors* of model $\alpha \times \mathcal{B}$.

EXAMPLE 3. *Multiple-choice quiz.* A quiz has two multiple choice questions, the first offering three choices a, b, c, and the second five choices A, B, C, D, E. A student guesses at random on each question. Let us consider the guess on the first question as part A, and the guess on the second question as part B, of a two-part experiment. Model α has three simple events a, b, c, and the statement that the student "guesses at random" justifies assigning probabilities $\frac{1}{3}$ to each. Similarly model $\mathcal{B}$ has the five simple events $A, \ldots, E$, to each of which probability $\frac{1}{5}$ is assigned. The product model $\alpha \times \mathcal{B}$ will then have $3 \cdot 5 = 15$ simple events:

a and A	a and B	a and C	a and D	a and E
b and A	b and B	b and C	b and D	b and E
c and A	c and B	c and C	c and D	c and E

(6)

to each of which is assigned the probability $\frac{1}{3} \cdot \frac{1}{5} = \frac{1}{15}$.

EXAMPLE 2. *Two loaded dice (continued).* An experiment consists of throwing two dice. Suppose that for each throw separately the model (1.3.1) is satisfactory. Let $e_1, \ldots, e_6$ represent the result of getting one, $\ldots$, six points on the first die. Then $p_1 = .21$, $p_2 = \ldots = p_5 = .17$, $p_6 = .11$. Similarly, let $f_1, \ldots, f_6$ represent the results on the second die, with $q_1 = .21$, $q_2 = \ldots = q_5 = .17$, $q_6 = .11$. Then the product model

PROBABILITIES OF THROWS OF TWO LOADED DICE

$P(e_1$ and $f_1) =$ $.21 \times .21 = .0441$	$P(e_1$ and $f_2) =$ $.21 \times .17 = .0357$	$P(e_1$ and $f_3) =$ $.21 \times .17 = .0357$	$P(e_1$ and $f_4) =$ $.21 \times .17 = .0357$	$P(e_1$ and $f_5) =$ $.21 \times .17 = .0357$	$P(e_1$ and $f_6) =$ $.21 \times .11 = .0231$
$P(e_2$ and $f_1) =$ $.17 \times .21 = .0357$	$P(e_2$ and $f_2) =$ $.17 \times .17 = .0289$	$P(e_2$ and $f_3) =$ $.17 \times .17 = .0289$	$P(e_2$ and $f_4) =$ $.17 \times .17 = .0289$	$P(e_2$ and $f_5) =$ $.17 \times .17 = .0289$	$P(e_2$ and $f_6) =$ $.17 \times .11 = .0187$
$P(e_3$ and $f_1) =$ $.17 \times .21 = .0357$	$P(e_3$ and $f_2) =$ $.17 \times .17 = .0289$	$P(e_3$ and $f_3) =$ $.17 \times .17 = .0289$	$P(e_3$ and $f_4) =$ $.17 \times .17 = .0289$	$P(e_3$ and $f_5) =$ $.17 \times .17 = .0289$	$P(e_3$ and $f_6) =$ $.17 \times .11 = .0187$
$P(e_4$ and $f_1) =$ $.17 \times .21 = .0357$	$P(e_4$ and $f_2) =$ $.17 \times .17 = .0289$	$P(e_4$ and $f_3) =$ $.17 \times .17 = .0289$	$P(e_4$ and $f_4) =$ $.17 \times .17 = .0289$	$P(e_4$ and $f_5) =$ $.17 \times .17 = .0289$	$P(e_4$ and $f_6) =$ $.17 \times .11 = .0187$
$P(e_5$ and $f_1) =$ $.17 \times .21 = .0357$	$P(e_5$ and $f_2) =$ $.17 \times .17 = .0289$	$P(e_5$ and $f_3) =$ $.17 \times .17 = .0289$	$P(e_5$ and $f_4) =$ $.17 \times .17 = .0289$	$P(e_5$ and $f_5) =$ $.17 \times .17 = .0289$	$P(e_5$ and $f_6) =$ $.17 \times .11 = .0187$
$P(e_6$ and $f_1) =$ $.11 \times .21 = .0231$	$P(e_6$ and $f_2) =$ $.11 \times .17 = .0187$	$P(e_6$ and $f_3) =$ $.11 \times .17 = .0187$	$P(e_6$ and $f_4) =$ $.11 \times .17 = .0187$	$P(e_6$ and $f_5) =$ $.11 \times .17 = .0187$	$P(e_6$ and $f_6) =$ $.11 \times .11 = .0121$

assigns to its 36 simple events the probabilities shown in the tableau on page 58.

As these examples show, it is very easy to construct the product of two given factor models. However, product models provide realistic representations of two-part experiments only if certain conditions are satisfied, and one should not be tempted into indiscriminate use of such models by the simplicity of their construction. We shall investigate in the next section the conditions under which product models may be expected to be appropriate.

For simplicity we have so far restricted the consideration of product models to experiments with only two parts, but the ideas extend to experiments with three or more parts. In analogy with (1) the simple events of the product model will then be of the form

$$(7) \qquad\qquad e \text{ and } f \text{ and } g \text{ and } \ldots$$

where e, f, g are simple events in the models for the separate parts. As in (4), the product model assigns to the event (7) the product of the corresponding probabilities of the factor models, that is,

$$(8) \qquad P(e \text{ and } f \text{ and } g \text{ and } \ldots) = P(e) \cdot P(f) \cdot P(g) \ldots.$$

It is again not difficult to check that the probabilities (8) add up to 1 as $e, f, g, \ldots$ range independently over the simple events of the factor models, so that (7) and (8) define a probability model.

We conclude with some remarks on the logical consistency of the notation employed for product models. We have used, for example, $(e_1 \text{ and } f_2)$ to denote the simple event corresponding to the result of getting r_1 on part A and s_2 on part B. Previously (Section 1.6) the word "and" was used to represent the intersection of two events. Can we regard $(e_1 \text{ and } f_2)$ as the intersection of e_1 with f_2? At first glance, it would seem that this is not possible, since e_1 is an event in model $\mathfrak{A}$ while f_2 is an event in model $\mathfrak{B}$. However, these two uses of "and" can be reconciled as follows.

Consider the composite event made up of the simple events in the first row of (1)·

$$(9) \qquad\qquad \{(e_1 \text{ and } f_1), (e_1 \text{ and } f_2), \ldots, (e_1 \text{ and } f_b)\}.$$

This event corresponds to the occurrence of one of the results $(r_1 \text{ and } s_1)$, $(r_1 \text{ and } s_2)$, $\ldots$, $(r_1 \text{ and } s_b)$; that is, to the occurrence of the result r_1 on part A (regardless of what happens on part B). In model $\mathfrak{A}$, r_1 is represented by e_1, so it would not be unreasonable to use e_1 also to represent r_1 in model $\mathfrak{A} \times \mathfrak{B}$; that is, to use e_1 to denote the event (9). The symbol e_1 would then denote two different events: a simple event in A, and a composite event in $\mathfrak{A} \times \mathfrak{B}$, but both corresponding to the same result r_1. Similarly, f_2 could be used to denote the event in $\mathfrak{A} \times \mathfrak{B}$ consisting of the second column of (1). With this notation, the intersection of e_1 (first row) and f_2 (second column) is just the event denoted in (1) by $(e_1 \text{ and } f_2)$.

With the above convention, two different events are denoted by e_1, and it is then desirable that the same probability be assigned to these two events.   This is in fact the case.   According to (2) the simple event e_1 of model α has been assigned probability p_1, while (5) shows that the same probability p_1 has been assigned to the composite event e_1 of model $\alpha \times \mathfrak{B}$.

PROBLEMS

1. Build a product model for the experiment of throwing two fair dice.   Compare this with the model of Example 1.7.1.

2. Build a product model for the sexes of two children in a family, assuming a boy or girl equally likely for both the first and second child.   Compare this with the model of Example 1.5.2.

3. Compare the model assumed in Problem 1.5.9 with the product model of Example 3.

4. Suppose model α is a uniform model with simple events $e_1, \ldots, e_a$, and model $\mathfrak{B}$ is a uniform model with simple events $f_1, \ldots, f_b$.   Show that the product model $\alpha \times \mathfrak{B}$ is again a uniform model.

5. Suppose that models α and $\mathfrak{B}$ each have three simple events with probabilities

$$P(e_1) = .1 \quad P(e_2) = .2 \quad P(e_3) = .7$$
$$P(f_1) = .2 \quad P(f_2) = .3 \quad P(f_3) = .5;$$

construct the product model $\alpha \times \mathfrak{B}$.

6. Determine which of the following two models is a product model and find its factor models:

$$\begin{array}{llll}
\text{(i)} & P(e_1 \text{ and } f_1) = 0 & P(e_1 \text{ and } f_2) = .1 \\
& P(e_2 \text{ and } f_1) = .2 & P(e_2 \text{ and } f_2) = .5 \\
& P(e_3 \text{ and } f_1) = .2 & P(e_3 \text{ and } f_2) = 0 \\
\text{(ii)} & P(e_1 \text{ and } f_1) = .04 & P(e_1 \text{ and } f_2) = .06 \\
& P(e_2 \text{ and } f_1) = .28 & P(e_2 \text{ and } f_2) = .42 \\
& P(e_3 \text{ and } f_1) = .08 & P(e_3 \text{ and } f_2) = .12
\end{array}$$

7. Using the model of Example 2, compute the probability that the total number of points showing on the two dice is four.

8. Let models α, $\mathfrak{B}$, $\mathfrak{C}$ each have two simple events with probabilities $\frac{1}{2}$.   Construct the product model $\alpha \times \mathfrak{B} \times \mathfrak{C}$.

9. If models α, $\mathfrak{B}$, $\mathfrak{C}$ have a, b, c simple events respectively, how many simple events are there in the product model $\alpha \times \mathfrak{B} \times \mathfrak{C}$?

3.2 REALISM OF PRODUCT MODELS

Suppose that α and $\mathfrak{B}$ are realistic models for parts A and B of a two-part experiment.   It is now necessary to investigate under what conditions the product model $\alpha \times \mathcal{B}$ will then be realistic for the experiment as a whole.

Let us consider to this end a simple event e of α corresponding to a simple result r of part A of the experiment, and suppose that probability p has been assigned to e. Since α is assumed to be a realistic model for part A, it follows that the probability p is at least approximately equal to the long-run frequency with which r occurs; that is, if $f(r)$ is the frequency with which r occurs in a large number n of trials, then

(1) $$p \sim f(r),$$

where the symbol $\sim$ means that the two sides are approximately equal. Similarly, if f is one of the simple events of $\mathcal{B}$, corresponding to the simple result s of part B, with probability q, the assumed realism of model $\mathcal{B}$ implies that

(2) $$q \sim f(s).$$

Consider now the simple event (e and f) in the product model. By (1.4), the product model $\alpha \times \mathcal{B}$ assigns to the event (e and f) the probability

(3) $$P(e \text{ and } f) = pq.$$

This assignment will be realistic if, and only if, the frequency of the corresponding result "r and s" is approximately equal to pq; that is, if

(4) $$f(r \text{ and } s) \sim pq.$$

Substituting (1) and (2) into (4) gives

(5) $$f(r \text{ and } s) \sim f(r)f(s).$$

Recalling that the frequency of a result is the number of occurrences of the result, divided by the number n of trials, requirement (5) may be written as

(6) $$\frac{\#(r \text{ and } s)}{n} \sim \frac{\#(r)}{n} \cdot f(s).$$

If both sides are multiplied by $n/\#(r)$, equation (6) becomes

(7) $$\frac{\#(r \text{ and } s)}{\#(r)} \sim f(s).$$

This is the form of the requirement which is often most convenient to apply.

What is the meaning of the ratio on the left-hand side of (7)? In a long sequence of n trials of the whole experiment, certain trials will produce the result r on part A of the experiment, and $\#(r)$ is the number of trials that do so. Restrict attention to these $\#(r)$ trials. Some of them may also happen to produce the result s on part B; these trials are just the ones which produce result r on part A and result s on part B. Their number is $\#(r \text{ and } s)$. The ratio on the left-hand side of (7) is therefore the fraction of the trials producing r which also produce s. In other words, it is the frequency of s among those trials which produce r. We shall refer to this ratio as the *conditional frequency* of s, given that r has occurred, and denote it by

(8) $$f(s|r) = \frac{\#(r \text{ and } s)}{\#(r)}.$$

EXAMPLE 1. *Penny and dime.* Suppose that an experiment consists of tossing a penny and a dime and recording for each coin whether it falls heads or tails. If we regard the toss of the penny as part A of the experiment, and the toss of the dime as part B, then $a = b = 2$. In $n = 1000$ trials of the whole experiment, suppose that the number of occurrences of the $2 \cdot 2 = 4$ simple results are as follows:

#(penny heads and dime heads) = 238,

#(penny heads and dime tails) = 247

#(penny tails and dime heads) = 267,

#(penny tails and dime tails) = 248.

The penny fell heads in $238 + 247 = 485$ of the trials. On 238 of these 485 trials, the dime also fell heads. Therefore the conditional frequency of "dime heads" given "penny heads" is f(dime heads|penny heads) = $\frac{238}{485} = .491$.

In the notation of conditional frequency, the requirement (7) may be written as

(9) $$f(s|r) \sim f(s).$$

In words, the product model is realistic only if the frequency $f(s)$ of s in the whole long sequence of trials is approximately equal to the conditional frequency $f(s|r)$ of s among those trials which produce r. In our illustration, f(dime heads) = $(238 + 267)/1000 = .505$, which is approximately equal to f(dime heads|penny heads) = .491. We would of course not expect exact equality because of chance fluctuations.

In a product model the two factors play symmetrical roles, and it is easy to show (Problem 3) that in fact relation (9) is equivalent to

(10) $$f(r|s) \sim f(r).$$

The equivalent relations (9) and (10) assert that the frequency of a simple result in one part of the experiment is not much altered by the fact that a specified simple result has occurred in the other part.

Definition. The parts of a two-part experiment are said to have *unrelated frequencies* or, for short, to be *unrelated*, if the long-run frequency of any result in one part of the experiment is approximately equal to the long-run conditional frequency of that result, given that any specified result has occurred in the other part of the experiment.

In terms of this definition we can answer the question raised at the beginning of the section. Assuming always that the factor models are realistic, the argument leading to (9) and (10) shows that the product model will be realistic if, and only if, formulas (9) and (10) hold for all simple results r and s, that is, if the two parts of the experiment are unrelated in the sense of our definition.

EXAMPLE 2. *Two draws from a box.* A box contains six marbles, alike except for color: one is red, two are white, and three are green. An ordered sample of size two is drawn from the box, and the colors of the marbles are noted. The two drawings may be considered as two parts of the experiment.

Let us consider the first drawing separately, as part A of the whole experiment. The marble drawn must be one of three colors, which in model α may be represented by the three simple events r_A (for red), w_A (for white), g_A (for green). If the marbles are thoroughly mixed and the drawing is done blindfold, it seems reasonable to suppose that the six marbles would occur with about equal frequency, and to complete model α by assigning to these events the probabilities $\frac{1}{6}$, $\frac{2}{6}$, $\frac{3}{6}$ respectively.

Now consider part B of the experiment, which consists of the second drawing. It is represented by model $\mathcal{B}$, for which we shall also need three simple events, say r_B, w_B, g_B. Because of the equivalence law of ordered sampling (Section 2.3) the six marbles should also show up with about equal frequency on the second draw, so that in model $\mathcal{B}$ we should wish to assign probabilities $\frac{1}{6}$, $\frac{2}{6}$, $\frac{3}{6}$ to the events r_B, w_B, g_B respectively.

The product of the two models gives us model $\alpha \times \mathcal{B}$ in which there are $3 \cdot 3 = 9$ simple events, with probabilities as follows:

$$P(r_A \text{ and } r_B) = \tfrac{1}{6} \cdot \tfrac{1}{6} = \tfrac{1}{36} \qquad P(r_A \text{ and } w_B) = \tfrac{1}{6} \cdot \tfrac{2}{6} = \tfrac{2}{36}$$

(11) $\quad P(w_A \text{ and } r_B) = \tfrac{2}{6} \cdot \tfrac{1}{6} = \tfrac{2}{36} \qquad P(w_A \text{ and } w_B) = \tfrac{2}{6} \cdot \tfrac{2}{6} = \tfrac{4}{36}$

$$P(g_A \text{ and } r_B) = \tfrac{3}{6} \cdot \tfrac{1}{6} = \tfrac{3}{36} \qquad P(g_A \text{ and } w_B) = \tfrac{3}{6} \cdot \tfrac{2}{6} = \tfrac{6}{36}$$

$$P(r_A \text{ and } g_B) = \tfrac{1}{6} \cdot \tfrac{3}{6} = \tfrac{3}{36}$$

$$P(w_A \text{ and } g_B) = \tfrac{2}{6} \cdot \tfrac{3}{6} = \tfrac{6}{36}$$

$$P(g_A \text{ and } g_B) = \tfrac{3}{6} \cdot \tfrac{3}{6} = \tfrac{9}{36}.$$

Would the product model be realistic for the experiment as a whole? Obviously not, for consider the event (r_A and r_B). Since the box contains only one red marble, we cannot get red on both draws, and the realistic probability for (r_A and r_B) is not $\frac{1}{36}$ but 0. In this experiment, the long-run frequency of "red on second draw" among all trials (which is $\frac{1}{6}$) is not the same as the conditional frequency of "red on second draw" given "red on first draw" (which is zero), so that the two parts of the experiment are not unrelated.   In fact, the result of the first draw changes the conditions under which the second marble is drawn.   In this case, the result of part A exerts a direct influence on part B.

EXAMPLE 3. *Sex of twins.*   Consider the "experiment" of observing the sex of the first-born and second-born of two twins.   We may regard the sex of the first-born twin as part A, and that of the second-born as part B, of a two-part experiment.   Part A has two possible results, which in model α may be represented by events M_A and F_A, corresponding to "first-born is male" and "first-born is female," respectively.   Similarly, model $\mathcal{B}$ has the two simple events M_B and F_B, and model $\alpha \times \mathcal{B}$ for the whole experiment has $2 \cdot 2 = 4$ simple events: M_A and M_B, M_A and F_B, F_A and M_B, F_A and F_B.

Would a product model be realistic here?   That is, would the frequency of, say, "second-born is male" in a long sequence of observations be about the same as its frequency among those births on which "first-born is male"?   One might say "the first-born cannot exert any influence on the second-born, whose sex is already determined, and therefore the answer is Yes." But experience would not bear this out: actual observations show that "second-born is male" occurs about 52% of the time among all twin births, while it occurs about 67% of the time among those twin births for which the first-born is male.   It is true that the sex of the first-born does not exert any direct influence on the sex of the second-born, but in some cases the sex of both twins is subject to a common influence.   In about one third of all twin births, the two twins originate from a single egg (identical twins), and in these cases both are always of the same sex.   If we were to change the experiment by restricting the observations to two-egg (or fraternal) twins, then a product model would be found to work reasonably well.

This example illustrates the possibility that there may be a relation between the frequencies of the two parts of an experiment, arising not from the direct influence of the result of the first part on the chances of the second part (as in Example 2), but indirectly from the fact that both parts are subject to influence from a common "outside" factor.   The outside factor in many cases is not known to the experimenter, who may then be tempted to assume a product model in cases where it is quite unrealistic.

Let us now give an example for which a product model is realistic.

EXAMPLE 4. *Sampling with replacement.*   Consider once more two draws from the box of Example 2, but carried out in a different way.   After the first marble has been drawn and its color noted, it is returned to the box, and the marbles are stirred again before the second draw.   When a sample is drawn in this way, with the box restored to its original condition after each draw, we say that the sampling is *with replacement*.

In sampling with replacement, it seems reasonable to suppose that the result of the first draw will not in any way alter the chances on the second draw, since the box is restored to its original condition before the second marble is drawn.   One may expect that the conditional frequency of "red on second draw" given "red on first draw" would be about the same as the frequency of "red on second draw" among all trials.   Consequently, the product model (11) should be realistic for the present experiment.   Of course, such speculations can never be definitive, and the final test of the realism of any model must be experimental.

Since product models are so simple, it is fortunate that in many two-part experiments experience shows the frequencies to be unrelated, so that the product of realistic factor models is realistic for the experiment as a whole. These cases are characterized by the fact that there is no connection, direct or indirect, between the parts.   In addition to the present Example 4, Examples 1, 2 and 3 of the preceding section illustrate situations in which product models are appropriate.

Product models are characterized by the fact that

$$(12) \qquad P(e \text{ and } f) = P(e)P(f)$$

for any simple events e pertaining to the first factor and f pertaining to the second factor.   It follows from (12), (see Problem 11) that

$$(13) \qquad P(E \text{ and } F) = P(E)P(F)$$

where E and F are any events (simple or composite) pertaining respectively to the first and second factors of a product model.   Equation (13) has an interpretation in terms of unrelated frequencies exactly analogous to that given earlier in the section for equation (3).

It is customary to refer to events E and F for which (13) holds as "independent."

Definition.   In any probability model, two events E and F satisfying (13) are said to be *independent*.

The independent events that we shall have occasion to discuss will nearly always pertain to separate factors of a product model, but the terminology is used also in other cases (see Section 4.2).

The results of the present section extend in a natural way to experiments with more than two parts.   Suppose that $\mathfrak{C}$, $\mathfrak{B}$, $\mathfrak{C}$, ... are realistic models for parts A, B, C, ... of an experiment.   Then the product model $\mathfrak{C} \times \mathfrak{B} \times \mathfrak{C} \times \cdots$ defined by (1.7) and (1.8) will be realistic provided the parts are unrelated according to the following definition.

Definition. The different parts of an experiment with several parts are said to have *unrelated frequencies* or, for short, to be *unrelated* if the long-run frequency of occurrence of any result on one part is approximately equal to the long-run conditional frequency of that result, given that any specified results have occurred on the other parts.

Analogously to the case of two factors it follows from (1.8) (see Problem 12) that

(14) $P(E \text{ and } F \text{ and } G \cdots) = P(E)P(F)P(G) \cdots$

for any events (simple or composite) E, F, G, . . . pertaining respectively to the first, second, third, $\cdots$ factor of a product model.

Throughout this section we have assumed that the factor models α and $\mathcal{B}$ are realistic for parts A and B of the experiment. To complete the discussion, we shall prove below that model $\alpha \times \mathcal{B}$ cannot be realistic unless the factor models α and $\mathcal{B}$ are realistic. Combining this fact with the earlier result of this section, we can then state that the product model $\alpha \times \mathcal{B}$ is realistic if, and only if, (i) the factor models α and $\mathcal{B}$ are realistic, and (ii) the two parts of the experiment have unrelated frequencies.

To prove that model $\alpha \times \mathcal{B}$ can be realistic only if both α and $\mathcal{B}$ are realistic, consider once more a simple event e of model α corresponding to the simple result r of part A, and suppose that model α assigns probability p to e. We have then seen (at the end of Section 1 in small print) that model $\alpha \times \mathcal{B}$ assigns probability p to the composite event e which represents the result r in model $\alpha \times \mathcal{B}$. Realism of model $\alpha \times \mathcal{B}$ then requires $p \sim f(r)$ and hence that the probability assigned to e in model α be realistic. This shows that realism of $\alpha \times \mathcal{B}$ implies that α is realistic and the same argument applies to $\mathcal{B}$.

PROBLEMS

1. The following table shows the number of students in a class of 50 getting 0–10 points, 11–20 points, 21–30 points respectively on the first and second problems of a test.

Prob. 1 \ Prob. 2	0–10	11–20	21–30
0–10	7	4	2
11–20	4	15	5
21–30	1	3	9

   (i) Find the conditional frequency with which students get 21–30 points on the second problem, given that they got 21–30 points on the first problem.
   (ii) Find the frequency with which students get 21–30 points on the second problem among the totality of students.

(iii) Describe in words analogous to (i) the frequency given by $2/(7 + 4 + 2)$.

2. The following table gives the distribution of 100 couples being married, according to their marital status.

Bride \ Groom	single	widowed	divorced
single	70	2	5
widowed	1	3	2
divorced	6	2	9

(i) Find the conditional frequency with which the bride is a divorcee given that the groom is a widower.
(ii) What is the frequency with which the groom is a widower among all cases?
(iii) Describe in words analogous to (i) the frequency given by $6/(6 + 2 + 9)$.

3. Show that relation (9) implies relation (10).

4. For each of the experiments whose results are described
(i) in Problem 1
(ii) in Problem 2,
check whether the two parts appear to be unrelated. Do your findings agree with what you would expect?

5. In a table giving the age distribution of all married couples in a city, would you expect the frequencies of the results "husband over 60" and "wife over 50" to be related or unrelated?

6. (i) In a table giving the frequency distribution for pairs of consecutive letters in works of English prose, would you expect the frequencies of the results "first letter is a vowel" and "second letter is a consonant" to be related or unrelated?
(ii) Make a frequency count of the first 100 pairs of letters of this section to illustrate the point.

7. Would you expect a product model to be appropriate for an experiment whose two parts consist of
(i) one throw each with two dice,
(ii) two successive throws with the same die?

8. State whether you would expect a product model to fit well an experiment whose two parts consist in observing the weather (rain or shine)
(i) on February 1 and 2 of the same year,
(ii) on February 1 of two successive years.

9. Build a realistic model for the sex of the first and that of the second born of identical twins. Is this a product model?

10. Use the results of Section 2.3 to build a realistic model for Example 2. Is this a product model?

11. Let E consist of the simple events (e_1, e_3) of model $\mathfrak{a}$, and F of the simple events (f_2, f_3, f_5) of model $\mathfrak{B}$.

(i) List the simple events in model $\mathfrak{a} \times \mathfrak{B}$ which make up the event $(E$ and $F)$.

(ii) If $P(e_1) = p_1$, $P(e_3) = p_3$, $P(f_2) = q_2$, $P(f_3) = q_3$, $P(f_5) = q_5$, find $P(E$ and $F)$.

(iii) Show that $P(E$ and $F) = P(E)P(F)$.

[Hint for (iii): collect together the terms of $P(E$ and $F)$ involving p_1 and those involving p_3, and factor out p_1 from the first and p_3 from the second of these sums. Note that the resulting factors of p_1 and p_3 are the same.]

12. Let E consist of the simple events (e_1, e_3) of model $\mathfrak{a}$, F of the simple events (f_2, f_5) of model $\mathfrak{B}$, and G of the simple events (g_1, g_4) of model $\mathfrak{c}$. If $P(e_1) = p_1$, $P(e_3) = p_3$, $P(f_2) = q_2$, $P(f_5) = q_5$, $P(g_1) = r_1$, $P(g_4) = r_4$, find $P(E$ and F and $G)$ and show that it is equal to $P(E)P(F)P(G)$. [Hint: Use the method of Problem 11.]

3.3 BINOMIAL TRIALS

We shall now consider a simple but very important application of product models. Suppose that a sequence of trials is performed, on each of which a certain result may or may not happen. The occurrence of the result is called a *success*, its nonoccurrence a *failure*. In a sequence of tosses of a penny, for example, "heads" might be designated a success in which case "tails" would constitute a failure. This terminology is purely conventional, and the result called success need not be desirable.

Each trial may be considered as one part of the whole experiment. If the trials are unrelated, in the sense of the preceding section, a product model is appropriate. Each factor model corresponding to a particular trial then has two simple events corresponding to success and failure. In the simplest case, in which success has the same probability, say p, and hence failure has the same probability $q = 1 - p$, in each factor model, the product model is called the *binomial trials model*.

EXAMPLE 1. *Three throws with a die.* Consider a dice game in which the player wins each time the die shows either 1 or 2 points (success) and loses each time it shows 3, 4, 5, or 6 points (failure). If the experiment consists of three throws, the results may be represented in the model by the events

SSS   SSF   SFS   SFF   FSS   FSF   FFS   FFF

with SFS, for example, representing the result that the player wins on the first and third throws but loses on the second. The binomial trials model assigns to these events the probabilities

$$p \cdot p \cdot p \quad p \cdot p \cdot q \quad p \cdot q \cdot p \quad p \cdot q \cdot q \quad q \cdot p \cdot p \quad q \cdot p \cdot q \quad q \cdot q \cdot p \quad q \cdot q \cdot q.$$

The probability of the player winning, for example, in exactly two of the three throws is then

$$P(\text{SSF}) + P(\text{SFS}) + P(\text{FSS}) = 3p^2q.$$

If the die is assumed to be fair, then $p = \frac{1}{3}$, $q = \frac{2}{3}$, and the desired probability is $\frac{2}{9}$.

Under what conditions is the binomial trials model realistic for a sequence of trials? Since it is a product model, the various trials (parts) should have unrelated frequencies in the sense of the preceding section. Thus if for example the occurrence of success on one trial tends to increase or decrease the chance of success on the next trial to a material degree, a product model would not be realistic. In addition, the binomial trials model assumes that the probability of success is the same on each trial.

When considering whether to use the model for a sequence of trials, the following two questions must therefore be asked.

(a) Is the chance of success the same on each trial?

(b) Will the chance of success on any trial be affected by success or failure on the others?

We shall now consider several examples, and discuss for each whether the binomial trials model might be expected to work.

EXAMPLE 2. *Sex of children in three-child families.* Consider a family with three children. Each birth may be considered a trial (especially by the mother) that produces either a male (M) or female (F) child. When the records of thousands of such families are assembled, it is found (a) that the frequency of male on each of the three births is very nearly the same, being about .514, and (b) that there is little or no relation between the frequency of males on the different births. For example, among the families in which the first child is of a specified sex (say female), the frequency of males on the second birth is still about .514. Thus, a binomial trials model with $p = .514$ is quite realistic. Using this model, we find that the probability that all three children are female is about $(.486)(.486)(.486) = .115$; while the probability that all three are male is about $(.514)^3 = .136$.

When very large numbers of records are assembled, slight departures from this model become apparent. For example, the frequency of male births differs slightly in different populations. In general, no mathematical model corresponds exactly to reality, and any probability model will show deficiencies when a sufficiently great body of data is collected.

EXAMPLE 3. *Defectives in lot sampling.* Suppose an ordered sample of ten items is drawn from a lot of 50 items, and each sampled item is inspected to see if it is defective. Would it be realistic to use a binomial model? It follows from the equivalence law for ordered sampling (2.3.5) that, if the sampling is random, the probability of a defective is the same on each draw, so that condition (a) is met. But condition (b) fails, since the results on the earlier draws will influence the chances on the later ones. To make this point concrete, suppose the lot contains exactly one defective item. Then each of the ten draws has the same probability $\frac{1}{50}$ of producing a defective, but if the first-drawn item is defective, there is no possibility of getting a defective on any subsequent draw.

If the sampling were done with replacement, however, the ten trials would be unrelated, and the binomial trials model would serve very well. Furthermore, if the size of the lot instead of being 50 were very large compared with the size of the sample, sampling with or without replacement would nearly always lead to the same result (since the chance of drawing the same item more than once would then be very small even when sampling with replacement). In this case, the binomial model would therefore be quite satisfactory.

EXAMPLE 4. *Winning at tennis.* The games played by two tennis players may be thought of as a sequence of trials, on which player A either wins or loses. Typically, the server has a considerable advantage, so that the frequency of wins by A will be materially higher when he serves than when he receives. Condition (a) fails, and the binomial trials model does not work.

EXAMPLE 5. *Rain on successive days.* We may regard successive days as trials, on each of which it either does or does not rain in a certain city. To be specific, consider the Saturday, Sunday, and Monday of the first weekend in July. If we regard the successive years as repetitions of this three-part experiment, examination of the record may show that the frequency of rain is about the same on the Saturday, Sunday, and Monday; thus condition (a) is met. However, the frequencies may be found to be heavily related. A possible explanation is that in some areas rain tends to come in storms that last for several days. If it rains on a Saturday, this means that a storm is occurring, and the risk of rain on the next day is considerably greater than if the Saturday were fair.

EXAMPLE 6. *Red at roulette.* A roulette wheel has 37 slots, of which 18 are red. Can a binomial trials model be used for the occurrence or non-occurrence of red on, say, five successive spins of the wheel? Records kept over long periods of the play at Monte Carlo and elsewhere can be broken up into successive sequences of five spins to provide data of repetitions of the experiment. Such data justify the use of the binomial model, since the five spins turn out to be unrelated in the frequency sense, and the frequency of red is the same (about $\frac{18}{37}$) on each of the five trials.

This finding contradicts the intuitive belief of many gamblers, who play according to systems that imply a relationship among the frequencies. For example, a gambler may wait until the wheel has shown non-red four times and then bet on red. He feels that "the law of averages" will force the wheel to tend to show red after a run of non-red; or he will argue that a run of five non-reds is so unlikely that after four non-reds the next spin should give red. But the wheel has no memory, and (except where the wheel is dishonestly controlled by a magnet or other device) the record supports the assumption of unrelated frequencies.

EXAMPLE 7. *Defective items in mass production.* Suppose an automatic machine produces certain items one after the other. Occasionally the machine turns out a defective item. Frequency counts appear to justify the use of a binomial trials model for many such experiments. Over a very long period of time, however, an essential part of the machine may gradually wear out. In this case the frequency of defectives rises and condition (a) fails if a long sequence of trials is considered.

The simple events in a sequence of n binomial trials are sequences of successes (S) and failures (F). If $n = 5$, the outcome of the experiment might for example be SSFSF or SSSSF, etc. Since the binomial trials model is a product model, the probabilities of these events are obtained by multiplying together the probabilities of the indicated events of the individual trials. Thus the probability of SSFSF, for example, is

$$P(\text{SSFSF}) = p \cdot p \cdot q \cdot p \cdot q = p^3 q^2.$$

Similarly

$$P(\text{FFSSS}) = q \cdot q \cdot p \cdot p \cdot p = p^3 q^2.$$

In this manner we see that the probability of three successes and two failures in any specified order will be equal to $p^3 q^2$.

More generally, in a sequence of n binomial trials the probability of any specified sequence of b successes and $n - b$ failures is a product of b factors equal to p and $n - b$ factors equal to $q = 1 - p$, and hence is equal to

(1) $$p^b q^{n-b}.$$

EXAMPLE 8. *Comparing two drugs.* To compare two drugs A and B a doctor decides to give some of his patients drug A and some drug B. In order to rule out the possibility of his assigning the drugs to the patients in a manner which might favor one or the other, he selects for each patient one of the drugs at random, that is with probabilities $\frac{1}{2}$. If the experiment involves ten patients, let us find the probability that all will get the same drug so that no comparison is possible. The ten patients constitute ten binomial trials with probability $\frac{1}{2}$ of success (being assigned drug A). The probability of getting either ten successes or ten failures is

$$P(10 \text{ successes}) + P(10 \text{ failures})$$

since the two events are exclusive. The first of these terms is $p^{10} = (\frac{1}{2})^{10}$ since $p = \frac{1}{2}$; the second one is $q^{10} = (\frac{1}{2})^{10}$ since $q = \frac{1}{2}$. The desired probability is therefore $(\frac{1}{2})^{10} + (\frac{1}{2})^{10} = 2(\frac{1}{2})^{10} = (\frac{1}{2})^9 = \frac{1}{512}$.

EXAMPLE 9. *The shooting gallery.* At a fair, a prize is offered to any person who in a sequence of four shots hits the target three times in a row. What is the probability of a person getting the prize if his probability of hitting on any given shot is $\frac{3}{4}$? If the shots can be considered to be unrelated, they constitute four binomial trials with probability $p = \frac{3}{4}$ of success (hitting the target). The prize will be won in the cases SSSS, SSSF, FSSS, and in no others. The probabilities of these cases are

$$P(\text{SSSS}) = (\tfrac{3}{4})^4 = \tfrac{81}{256}; \quad P(\text{SSSF}) = P(\text{FSSS}) = (\tfrac{3}{4})^3 \tfrac{1}{4} = \tfrac{27}{256}.$$

Since the three cases are exclusive, the desired probability is

$$\tfrac{81}{256} + \tfrac{27}{256} + \tfrac{27}{256} = \tfrac{135}{256} = .527.$$

The binomial trials model extends in a natural way to situations like those of Examples 4 and 7, where the trials are unrelated but have unequal probabilities. To see what becomes of formula (1) in this case, consider three unrelated trials with success probabilities p_1, p_2, p_3 and failure probabilities $q_1 = 1 - p_1$, $q_2 = 1 - p_2$, $q_3 = 1 - p_3$. There are then eight possible patterns of successes and failures, with the following probabilities:

$$P(\text{SSS}) = p_1 p_2 p_3, \ P(\text{SSF}) = p_1 p_2 q_3, \ P(\text{SFS}) = p_1 q_2 p_3, \ P(\text{SFF}) = p_1 q_2 q_3$$

$$P(\text{FSS}) = q_1 p_2 p_3, \ P(\text{FSF}) = q_1 p_2 q_3, \ P(\text{FFS}) = q_1 q_2 p_3, \ P(\text{FFF}) = q_1 q_2 q_3.$$

This model easily generalizes to more than three trials.

Another extension of the idea of binomial trials is to unrelated trials with more than two possible outcomes, the probabilities of which do not change from trial to trial. In the next section we shall consider an example of such *multinomial* trials. More general aspects will be taken up in Section 7.3.

PROBLEMS

1. In Example 1, find the probability that the player who uses a fair die will win (i) at least two of the three throws; (ii) at most two of the three throws; (iii) exactly two of the three throws.

2. In a sequence of five tosses with a fair penny, find the probability of the following events: (i) HHHHT (four Heads then one Tail); (ii) HHHHH; (iii) HTHTH; (iv) HTTTH.

3. In four binomial trials with success probability p, find the probability of (i) four successes; (ii) four failures; (iii) exactly one success; (iv) exactly two successes; (v) exactly three successes; (vi) exactly one failure; (vii) at most two successes; (viii) at least one success.

4. In Example 8, what is the probability that as a result of the random assignment the two drugs will be used alternately?

5. In a sequence of five tosses with a fair penny,
(i) what is the probability of observing a run of four successive heads?
(ii) what is the probability of never having a head after a tail?

6. A farmer wishes to determine the value of a fertilizer. He divides his field into 15 plots, five rows of three plots each. In each row he selects one of the three plots at random and applies the fertilizer to it, while giving no fertilizer to the other two in the row. What is the probability
(i) that all five fertilized plots are in the first column?
(ii) that all fertilized plots are in the same column?

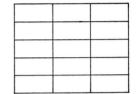

7. In a tennis match suppose that the individual games are unrelated, and that player A has probability $\frac{2}{3}$ of winning a game in which he serves and probability $\frac{1}{2}$ of winning a game in which he receives. The players alternate in serving. What is the probability that player A will win the first six games?

8. A set in tennis is won by the first player who wins six games provided by that time his opponent has won at most four games. Under the assumptions of Problem 7, find the probability that player A will win the set with a score of 6:1 if
(i) he serves in the first game;
(ii) he receives in the first game.

9. Suppose that in training new workers to perform a delicate mechanical operation, the probabilities that the worker will be successful on his first, second, and third attempt are $p_1 = .03$, $p_2 = .06$, $p_3 = .11$ respectively, and that the three attempts may be considered to be unrelated. Find to three decimals the probabilities that the worker will be successful (i) all three times; (ii) exactly twice; (iii) exactly once; (iv) on none of his three attempts.

3.4 THE USE OF RANDOM NUMBERS TO DRAW SAMPLES

In Section 2.1 we emphasized the desirability of drawing samples at random and mentioned that this is most commonly done with the aid of a table of random numbers. We shall now explain how such tables can be made, and how they may be used to obtain random samples.

Suppose a box contains ten marbles, identical except that each is labeled with a different one of the ten digits $0, 1, 2, \ldots, 9$. The marbles are stirred, one of them is drawn from the box, and the digit on it is written down—suppose it happens to be "1." The marble is returned to the box, and the process repeated—perhaps "0" is obtained on the second trial, and then "0," "9," "7," and so forth. The results of 1000 drawings might look like the following table.

TABLE 1. RANDOM DIGITS

10097	32533	76520	13586	34673	54876	80959	09117	39292	74945
37542	04805	64894	74296	24805	24037	20636	10402	00822	91665
08422	68953	19645	09303	23209	02560	15953	34764	35080	33606
99019	02529	09376	70715	38311	31165	88676	74397	04436	27659
12807	99970	80157	36147	64032	36653	98951	16877	12171	76833
66065	74717	34072	76850	36697	36170	65813	39885	11199	29170
31060	10805	45571	82406	35303	42614	86799	07439	23403	09732
85269	77602	02051	65692	68665	74818	73053	85247	18623	88579
63573	32135	05325	47048	90553	57548	28468	28709	83491	25624
73796	45753	03529	64778	35808	34282	60935	20344	35273	88435
98520	17767	14905	68607	22109	40558	60970	93433	50500	73998
11805	05431	39808	27732	50725	68248	29405	24201	52775	67851
83452	99634	06288	98083	13746	70078	18475	40610	68711	77817
88685	40200	86507	58401	36766	67951	90364	76493	29609	11062
99594	67348	87517	64969	91826	08928	93785	61368	23478	34113
65481	17674	17468	50950	58047	76974	73039	57186	40218	16544
80124	35635	17727	08015	45318	22374	21115	78253	14385	53763
74350	99817	77402	77214	43236	00210	45521	64237	96286	02655
69916	26803	66252	29148	36936	87203	76621	13990	94400	56418
09893	20505	14225	68514	46427	56788	96297	78822	54382	14598

This is a *table of random digits*. Because the ten marbles are alike, it is reasonable to assume that, in any given place in the table, each of the ten digits has the same probability $\frac{1}{10}$ of appearing. Furthermore, because the drawn marble is replaced and the marbles are restirred after each drawing, it may be assumed that the frequencies of the digits appearing in the various places are unrelated. The digits therefore constitute the results of a sequence of multinomial trials, where each trial has ten possible outcomes. Large random digit tables are produced by electronic machines rather than by hand drawing. The table* from which our Table 1 is taken contains one million digits, which have been carefully examined by various frequency counts to check empirically the assumptions of unrelatedness and equal probability.

We shall explain how random numbers are used in drawing random samples by taking up a sequence of examples, starting with the simplest case of a sample of size one.

* "A Million Random Digits with 100,000 Normal Deviates," by The RAND Corporation. The Free Press (1955). (Table 1 reproduced by permission.)

EXAMPLE 1. *Choosing one of ten items.* A poll taker wishes to choose at random one of the ten houses on a certain street. After making a sketch map on which the houses are labeled 0, 1, 2, . . . , 9, he opens his random number table and reads off the first digit, "1." The house to be sampled is then the one labeled "1" on the map. This house may be assumed to have been drawn at random since each house had the same chance $\frac{1}{10}$ to be selected.

EXAMPLE 2. *Choosing one of one hundred items.* The digits appearing in two consecutive places in the table form a two-digit number—for example "10" occupies the first two places in our table. There are 100 two-digit numbers that might occupy the two places, beginning with 00 and going up to 99. The assumptions of randomness and unrelatedness of the digits imply that each of these 100 numbers has the same probability $\frac{1}{100}$ of appearing.

Suppose the Census Bureau wishes to choose at random one of the 100 counties of the State of North Carolina. A list of the counties is obtained, and the counties labeled successively 00, 01, 02, . . . , 99. The random number table is consulted—let us use the second line this time—and the number "37" read off. From the county list, the county bearing the number 37 is selected.

EXAMPLE 3. *Choosing one of an arbitrary number of items.* Suppose we wish to choose at random one of the 876 students attending a certain college. The registrar provides a list of the students, and they are numbered consecutively from 000 to 875. By an easy extension of the argument in Example 2, it appears that a three-place entry in the table has probability $\frac{1}{1000}$ of being any of the digits from 000 to 999. Suppose we use the fourth line, getting the number "990." Unfortunately the highest number on the list is 875, so we continue along the line, taking the next number, "190" which is usable. The student whose name is opposite 190 on the list is therefore selected.

The above procedure will always eventually yield one of the 876 usable numbers. Since all 1000 three-digit numbers are equally likely, it is plausible that each of the 876 usable numbers has the same probability $\frac{1}{876}$ of being selected in this way. However, a proof of this fact is beyond the scope of this book.

The procedure illustrated in this example easily generalizes to a method for selecting one of an arbitrary number of items. One continues drawing from the table numbers of the appropriate length until one is found that appears on the list. With this method, each item on the list has the same chance of being drawn.

EXAMPLE 4. *Choosing two of ten items.* Let us modify Example 1 by requiring the poll taker to choose two of the ten houses. He takes two digits from the table—say "1" and "0" if the first line is used—and then proceeds to the houses labeled "0" and "1" on his map.

A difficulty would arise if the second digit had also been "1." In that case it would be necessary to continue until a digit appears that differs from the first digit obtained. It is intuitively clear that the first digit found to be different from "1" has the same chance, $\frac{1}{9}$, of being each of the 9 digits other than "1." However, a formal argument that justifies regarding the two houses thus drawn as forming a random sample will again have to be omitted.

Let us now summarize in a general rule the procedure for drawing a random sample of s items from a population of N items. A list of the N items is made and the items are numbered consecutively. Random numbers of the required length are read from the table, until s distinct numbers of the list are obtained. The items having these s numbers form the sample.

EXAMPLE 5. *Choosing ten of the fifty American states.* Number the 50 states of the United States in an alphabetical list beginning with Alabama 01 and ending with Wyoming 50. It is desired to select ten of them at random. For illustration, let us begin with the ninth row of the table, getting the two-digit numbers

$$63, 57, 33, 21, 35, 05, 32, 54, 70, 48, 90,$$

$$55, 35, 75, 48, 28, 46, 82, 87, 09, 83, 49.$$

Ignoring 00 and numbers above 50, as well as repeats, we obtain the following ten distinct usable numbers:

$$33, 21, 35, 05, 32, 48, 28, 46, 09, 49.$$

From the alphabetical list we now read off the ten state names; these are a random sample of size 10:

California (05), Florida (09), Massachusetts (21), Nevada (28), New York (32), North Carolina (33), Ohio (35), Virginia (46), West Virginia (48), Wisconsin (49).

As in the above examples, it is customary in practice to use a different line or page of the random number table for each application. Otherwise, the user may remember that the first digit in the table happens to be a "1," and may use this information to destroy the randomness of the sample. The poll taker of Example 1, for example, may number the houses on his sketch map so as to avoid attaching "1" to a house he does not wish to visit, perhaps because he noticed a large dog in the yard. This obviously leads to bias—dog owners will tend to be underrepresented in the sample!

CHAPTER 4

CONDITIONAL PROBABILITY

4.1 THE CONCEPT OF CONDITIONAL PROBABILITY

It sometimes happens that we acquire partial knowledge of the way a random experiment is turning out before the complete result becomes known. During the course of the experiment we may see that certain results are precluded by what has happened so far, or the experiment may be completed but its result revealed to us only in part. Examples will make it clear that when such partial information is obtained, the original probability model should be modified.

EXAMPLE 1. *Poker hands*. Suppose a poker player happens, by accident, to catch a glimpse of the hand dealt to an opponent. The glimpse is too fleeting for individual cards to be distinguishable, but the player does perceive that all the cards are red. It is then certain that the opponent cannot have "four of a kind," as that would require him to have at least two black cards. In our earlier model for poker hands (Example 2.2.1), every hand is assigned a positive probability; this model will no longer be realistic, since it assigns positive probability to an event we know to be impossible. One also feels that the chance of the opponent holding a "heart flush" is now higher than it was before the new information was obtained.

EXAMPLE 2. *Life table*. Suppose we are observing a life span for which Table 1.4.1 is appropriate, and that the individual in question has just celebrated his 20th birthday. The experiment is still in progress, but we know that neither of the results $A = 1$ or $A = 2$ (death in the first or second decade) can happen. These results are assigned probabilities .064 and .013 in Table 1.4.1, as was appropriate at birth, but we now want to give them probability zero since they are impossible. On the other hand, we should want to assign a higher probability to $A > 6$ than at birth, since the individual has now survived the dangers of childhood and adolescence.

In each of these examples, the new information serves to rule out certain of the simple results that were originally possible. Let us denote by R the set of simple results that are still possible on the basis of what is now known: in the first example, R consists of all poker hands formed of red cards only while in the second example R consists of death in any decade from the third to the tenth. We shall denote by E the set of simple events that correspond to the simple results in R. It is clear that the original probability model, according to which events in $\overline{E}$ have positive probability, should be replaced by a new model.

We have emphasized in Section 1.2 that the frequency of a result depends on the conditions of the experiment. Our basic idea is that the probability attributed to a result on a particular trial of an experiment should correspond to the frequency of the result in a long sequence of trials of the experiment *carried out under essentially the same conditions* as the particular experiment under consideration. We may think of the new information as serving to change the experimental conditions: in addition to the requirements previously given, we now require that the result must be one of those in R. Any trial that gives a result in $\overline{R}$ is not considered a proper trial under the new conditions and is thrown out. The original sequence of trials is reduced to the sequence consisting of those trials that gave a result in R, and it is the frequency of results in this sequence that we want to represent in the new model. In the terminology of Section 3.2, what is now of interest is the conditional frequency, given that R has occurred. The relation between the probabilities in the two models will depend on the relation between the frequencies in the two sequences. This can best be explained by a simple example.

EXAMPLE 3. *Is the other child a boy?* A new family with two children is going to move into the neighborhood. It is learned that at least one of the children is a boy. A boy living in the same block hopes that the other child will also be a boy. What is the chance of his hope being fulfilled?

In order to keep the arithmetic simple, let us ignore the slight tendency for boys to outnumber girls, and assume that boys and girls are equally frequent. If we regard the two births in the family as unrelated, a product model would be appropriate. It would assign probability $\frac{1}{4}$ to each family type:

Family type	Probability
MM	$\frac{1}{4}$
MF	$\frac{1}{4}$
FM	$\frac{1}{4}$
FF	$\frac{1}{4}$

where for example MF represents "First child male, second child female."

This model was reasonable when it was known only that the family had two children, but as soon as we acquire the additional information that there is at least one boy in the family, the model is no longer realistic. The new information rules out the result that both children are girls. In building a new model, we shall therefore want to assign probability zero to the event FF.

What about the other three events? Originally, they were assigned equal probabilities, corresponding to the empirical fact that the three family types MM, MF, FM occur with approximately equal frequencies. Ruling out the type FF will not alter the fact that the other three types occur with nearly equal frequency among all families except those with two girls. Therefore it is realistic to continue to assign equal probabilities to the three remaining types. But in any probability model, the sum of the probabilities of the simple events must be 1. We are thus led to the following new model:

Family type	Probability
MM	$\frac{1}{3}$
MF	$\frac{1}{3}$
FM	$\frac{1}{3}$
FF	0

This will be realistic when we are dealing with a two-child family *known to contain at least one boy*. In terms of this model, the answer to the original question is easily seen to be $\frac{1}{3}$: the "other child will also be a boy" if and only if the family is of type MM.

For simplicity we took as our first example a case where the original model is uniform (Section 1.5), but the basic idea works quite generally.

EXAMPLE 4. *Loaded die.* Suppose the experiment of throwing a certain loaded die is adequately represented by the following model:

Face	1	2	3	4	5	6
Probability	.2	.1	.1	.2	.3	.1

The die is thrown and we learn that the top face shows an even number of points. This being given, what is the chance that the die shows two points?

In the original model, $P(\text{even}) = P(2) + P(4) + P(6) = .1 + .2 + .1 = .4$. This means that in a long sequence of throws an even face will occur about 40% of the time. Since the face 2 will occur in about 10% of all throws, it follows that it occurs in about $(.1) \div (.4) = \frac{1}{4}$ of those throws that result in an even face. Thus, we would want to say that the chance of the face 2 is .25, once it is given that the face is even.

Similarly, given that the face is even there is a 50% chance that it shows four points and a 25% chance that it shows six points. Faces 1, 3, and 5 are impossible on this throw. We are led to the following model for the experiment when it is known that the result is an even face:

Face	1	2	3	4	5	6
Probability	0	.25	0	.50	0	.25

We are now prepared to give the general definition of conditional probability. Suppose we have built a model for the original experiment, consisting of an event set $\mathcal{E}$ that corresponds to the list $\mathcal{R}$ of simple results of the experiment, and that a probability $P(e)$ has been assigned to each simple event e in $\mathcal{E}$. Then new information becomes available: the experiment has in fact produced one of the results on a sub-list R of the original list $\mathcal{R}$. Let E be the set of simple events that correspond to the results of R. We must construct a new model, using the same event set as before, but assigning to the simple events new probabilities that will be reasonable in the light of the new information. We shall denote by $P(e|E)$ the probability assigned by the new model to the simple event e. If e does not belong to E, then of course we shall want to put $P(e|E) = 0$.

To see what value would be reasonable if e does belong to E, imagine a sequence of n trials of the original experiment. Suppose that in this sequence the composite result R occurred $\#(R)$ times, while the simple result r corresponding to e occurred on $\#(r)$ trials. Those trials on which R did not occur are irrelevant to our present problem (since in our particular case R did occur), and by eliminating them from consideration we obtain a new and more relevant sequence consisting of $\#(R)$ trials. The frequency with which r occurred in this sequence, that is the *conditional frequency of r given R*, is

$$f(r|R) = \frac{\#(r)}{\#(R)} = \frac{\#(r)}{n} \div \frac{\#(R)}{n} = \frac{f(r)}{f(R)}$$

where $f(r)$ and $f(R)$ are frequencies in the original sequence of n trials. If n is large, we may reasonably expect $f(r)$ to be close to $P(e)$ and $f(R)$ to be close to $P(E)$, so that $f(r|R)$ should be close to $P(e)/P(E)$. Since probability is supposed to correspond to frequency, this motivates the following definition.

Definition. The *conditional probability* of a simple event e given an event E is

(1)
$$P(e|E) = P(e)/P(E) \qquad \text{if } e \text{ is in } E$$
$$P(e|E) = 0 \qquad\qquad \text{if } e \text{ is not in } E.$$

With this definition, conditional probability given E corresponds in the model to the long term frequency of occurrence of r in a sequence of experiments in which the result R has occurred; that is, to the conditional frequency of r given R.

Equation (1) defines a probability model which is known as the *conditional probability model given E*. (We shall check at the end of the section that (1) does define a probability model.)

EXAMPLE 3. *Is the other child a boy?* (*continued*). Let us rework Example 3, taking account now of the fact that boys are slightly more frequent than girls. If we use .514 as the probability of a male on each birth, and assume that the births are unrelated, it is reasonable to use the following product model as the original model:

Family type	Probability
MM	.514 × .514 = .264
MF	.514 × .486 = .250
FM	.486 × .514 = .250
FF	.486 × .486 = .236

Given that at least one of the children is a boy, what is the (conditional) probability of the other child also being a boy? Here E is the composite event corresponding to the result "at least one boy" and e the simple event corresponding to "two boys." We have

$$P(e) = P(\text{MM}) = .264$$

$$P(E) = P(\text{MM}) + P(\text{MF}) + P(\text{FM})$$

$$= .264 + .250 + .250 = .764.$$

Since e is in E, it follows that the desired probability is

$$P(e|E) = \frac{.264}{.764} = .346.$$

If the original model is realistic, this will be the long-run conditional frequency of two-boy families among all two-child families having at least one boy.

EXAMPLE 2. *Life table* (*continued*). Let us illustrate on the life table example the procedure of computing a conditional probability model. Since the values 1 and 2 of A have been ruled out by the fact that the person has reached his 20th birthday, E consists of the simple events $A = 3, 4, \ldots, 10$. From Table 1.4.1 we compute $P(E) = P(A > 2) = .022 + .032 + \ldots + .028 = .923$. (This value could also be obtained by subtracting from 1 the probabilities $P(A = 1) = .064$ and $P(A = 2) = .013$.) Therefore $P(A = 3|A > 2) = P(A = 3)/P(A > 2) = .022/.923 = .024$, and similarly for the other values. The table below compares the probability distribution of decade of death at birth with the conditional distribution at age 20.

TABLE 1. LIFE TABLE AT BIRTH AND FOR 20 YEAR OLDS

a	$P(A = a)$	$P(A = a\|A > 2)$	a	$P(A = a)$	$P(A = a\|A > 2)$
1	.064	0	6	.127	.138
2	.013	0	7	.211	.229
3	.022	.024	8	.269	.291
4	.032	.035	9	.170	.184
5	.064	.069	10	.028	.030

We still must check that (1) really defines a probability model. The quantities (1) are certainly nonnegative; it is therefore only necessary to show that the sum of the probabilities $P(e|E)$ extended over all simple events of the event set $\mathcal{E}$ is equal to 1. Since the zero probabilities of the simple events outside E do not contribute anything, it is enough to add the probabilities

(2) $$P(e|E) = \frac{P(e)}{P(E)}$$

over all simple events e in E. In doing so, we can place the fraction over the common denominator $P(E)$ and observe that the numerator, which is the sum of the probabilities $P(e)$ for all e in E, is just $P(E)$. We thus find that the sum of the terms (2) for all e in E is

$$\frac{P(E)}{P(E)} = 1,$$

as was to be proved.

PROBLEMS

1. What is the probability that the loaded die of Example 4 will show two points if we know only that the number of points showing is greater than one?

2. Let the sample space consist of five points with probabilities $P(e_1) = .1$, $P(e_2) = .15$, $P(e_3) = .2$, $P(e_4) = .2$, $P(e_5) = .35$. Let $E = \{e_1, e_3, e_4\}$. Find the conditional probability model given E, and check that it is a model.

3. Recall Problem 3.2.1. If the instructor picks up one of the tests at random and finds that the number of points on the first problem is between 21 and 30, what is the conditional probability that the number of points on the second problem will also be between 21 and 30?

4. Suppose we are observing a life span for which Table 1 4.1 is appropriate and that the individual in question has survived to his 60th birthday.
    (i) Construct the conditional probability model that is now appropriate.

(ii) What is the conditional probability that the individual will survive to the age of 80?

5. A two-child family is known to have a boy and a girl. Construct the conditional probability model, given this information, and find the probability that the boy is older than the girl if the original model is that assumed in (i) Example 3, (ii) Example 3 (continued).

6. Suppose that of two unrelated tosses with a coin whose probability of heads is p, one falls heads and the other tails. Show that the conditional probability that the first one is heads is $\frac{1}{2}$. [Hint: First construct the appropriate product model for the original experiment.]

7. Suppose a poker hand is drawn and it is observed that all five cards are red. In the conditional model, what is the probability of
(i) a hand consisting of any five specified red cards?
(ii) a heart flush?

8. Show that, if the original model is uniform, the nonzero probabilities in any conditional model will all be equal.

9. (i) Suppose that $P(e_2)/P(e_1) = \frac{1}{2}$ and that e_1, e_2 both belong to E. What can you say about $P(e_2|E)/P(e_1|E)$?
(ii) Formulate a generalization of the result found in part (i).
(iii) Use part (ii) to give an alternative solution of Problem 8.

4.2 INDEPENDENCE

In the preceding section we have seen how to modify a probability model to obtain the conditional model corresponding to a given event E. We shall now derive an important formula which expresses the probability of a composite event in the conditional model in terms of probabilities in the original model.

Let F be any composite event in $\mathcal{E}$. The probability attached to F in the conditional probability model (1.1) will be called *the conditional probability of F given E* and will be denoted by $P(F|E)$. By the general definition of the probability of a composite event (Section 1.4), $P(F|E)$ is just the sum of the conditional probabilities $P(e|E)$ for all the simple events e in F. Of course, the simple events that are in F but outside E will contribute nothing to the sum. It is therefore enough to add up the probabilities $P(e|E)$ for the simple events that are in both E and F, that is, for the simple events in $(E$ and $F)$.

When adding up the numbers $P(e|E) = P(e)/P(E)$ for all e in $(E$ and $F)$, we can place the fractions over the common denominator $P(E)$ and observe that the numerators add up to $P(E$ and $F)$. This proves the important formula

(1) $$P(F|E) = \frac{P(E \text{ and } F)}{P(E)}$$

which permits one to calculate conditional probabilities without first constructing the conditional model.

The reader may find it helpful to trace through the argument leading to (1) in the example of Figure 1.6.2a. There F consists of e_2, e_4, e_6, and e_7. In the conditional distribution given E, we have $P(e_2|E) = P(e_7|E) = 0$, while $P(e_4|E) = P(e_4)/P(E)$ and $P(e_6|E) = P(e_6)/P(E)$. Therefore $P(F|E) = 0 + 0 + P(e_4)/P(E) + P(e_6)/P(E) = [P(e_4) + P(e_6)]/P(E) = P(E \text{ and } F)/P(E)$.

EXAMPLE 1. *Poker hands.* What is the conditional probability that a poker hand is a heart flush, given that it consists only of red cards? We shall assume that the hand constitutes a sample of 5 cards drawn at random from a deck of 52, so that all $\binom{52}{5}$ possible hands are equally likely. The event E represents the result "all five cards in the hand are red" and F the result "the hand is a heart flush," so that the event (E and F) stands for the result "the hand is a heart flush." Clearly the number of simple events in E is $\binom{26}{5}$ so that

$$P(E) = \binom{26}{5} \Big/ \binom{52}{5}.$$

The number of heart flushes is $\binom{13}{5}$, and hence

$$P(E \text{ and } F) = \binom{13}{5} \Big/ \binom{52}{5}.$$

The desired probability is therefore

$$P(F|E) = P(E \text{ and } F)/P(E) = \binom{13}{5} \Big/ \binom{26}{5}.$$

Using Table A, we find this to be

$$1287/65,780 = .0196.$$

While not a large number, this is relatively much greater than the probability of a heart flush when nothing is known about the hand, which in Example 2.2.1 was found to be .000495. These calculations support the feeling expressed at the end of Example 1.1.

The conditional probability $P(F|E)$ has a frequency interpretation exactly analogous to that of $P(e|E)$ in Section 1. Let R and S be the results of the experiment represented in the event set $\mathcal{E}$ by E and F. Then in a long sequence of trials of the experiment, one has (in the notation of Section 3.2)

$$P(E) \sim f(R) \quad \text{and} \quad P(E \text{ and } F) \sim f(R \text{ and } S),$$

and hence by (1)

$$P(F|E) \sim \frac{f(R \text{ and } S)}{f(R)} = \frac{\#(R \text{ and } S)}{\#(R)}.$$

Here the right-hand side is equal to the frequency with which the result S occurs among those trials in which the result R occurred; that is, the *conditional frequency* $f(S|R)$ *of* S *given* R. The last displayed relation may therefore be rewritten as

(2) $$P(F|E) \sim f(S|R).$$

With a realistic model, a conditional probability is approximately equal to the corresponding conditional frequency.

Equation (1), on multiplication of both sides by $P(E)$, becomes

(3) $$P(E \text{ and } F) = P(E)P(F|E).$$

In this form, the equation is known as the *multiplication law*. Of course, the two forms are equivalent (except that the present form is valid even when $P(E) = 0$), but their uses are entirely different. Equation (1) is used to compute conditional probabilities from the probabilities of the original model, while the multiplication law (3) is used to compute the (unconditional) probability $P(E \text{ and } F)$ when we know $P(E)$ and the conditional probability $P(F|E)$. We shall give several illustrations of the use of (3) in the next section.

Both $P(F)$ and $P(F|E)$ are probabilities of the event F, but they are the probabilities assigned to this event by two different models, and consequently they will in general have different values. However, as we shall see below, there is an important class of cases in which

(4) $$P(F|E) = P(F).$$

When relation (4) holds, the imposition of the condition E does not change the probability of F, and we then say that F is *independent* of E.

EXAMPLE 2. *Heart face card.* Consider the experiment of drawing a card from a shuffled bridge deck, where each of the 52 cards is assigned probability $\frac{1}{52}$ of being drawn. Let E be the event corresponding to the result that the card drawn is a heart while F is the event corresponding to the draw of a face card (King, Queen, or Knave). We see that $P(E) = \frac{13}{52}$, $P(F) = \frac{12}{52} = \frac{3}{13}$, and $P(E \text{ and } F) = \frac{3}{52}$. Thus, by (1), $P(F|E) = (\frac{3}{52}) \div (\frac{13}{52}) = \frac{3}{13} = P(F)$, so that F is independent of E. This means that the frequency with which a face card is drawn among all trials is approximately the same as the conditional frequency with which a face card is drawn on those trials resulting in a heart.

It is interesting to note that, in the above example, $P(E|F) = (\frac{3}{52}) \div (\frac{3}{13}) = \frac{13}{52} = P(E)$, so that it is also true that E is independent of F. This illustrates the general phenomenon that independence is symmetric: if F is independent of E, then* E is also independent of F. In fact, it is easy to see (Problem 12) that each of the conditions $P(F|E) = P(F)$ and $P(E|F) = P(E)$ is equivalent to the symmetric condition

(5) $$P(E \text{ and } F) = P(E)P(F).$$

Definition. Two events E and F are said to be *independent* (of each other) if they satisfy condition (5).

The concept of independence finds its most important use in connection with experiments having several parts (Section 3.1). In fact, as was pointed out in Section 3.2, if such an experiment is represented by a product model, and if E and F are events relating to different factors of the model, then E and F are independent.

When applying a product model to a specific experiment, the usual approach (Section 3.1) is first to build the factor models and then to combine them by means of formula (3.1.4) into a product model. The probabilities such as $P(E)$ and $P(F)$ may then be thought of either as probabilities in the factor models α and $\mathcal{B}$ or as the equivalent probabilities in model $\alpha \times \mathcal{B}$. It is usually convenient to consider $P(E)$ and $P(F)$ as probabilities in the factor models, and then use (5) to obtain the probability $P(E \text{ and } F)$ in the product model, without the necessity of explicitly constructing the latter.

EXAMPLE 3. *Stratified sampling.* Consider a residential block having six houses on the north side and seven houses on the south side (Figure 1).

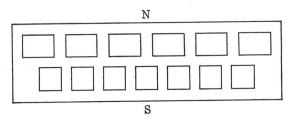

FIGURE 1.   SKETCH MAP OF BLOCK

A sample of four houses is to be drawn in a survey to check the accuracy of tax assessments. The survey leader notices that the houses on the north side are more substantial than those on the south side. If a sample of four is drawn randomly from all 13 houses, it could happen by chance that all

---

* Strictly speaking, these statements are correct only if we exclude the trivial cases $P(E) = 0$ and $P(F) = 0$, in which $P(F|E)$ and $P(E|F)$ are not defined.

four in the sample come from one side or the other. The sample could thus lead to a quite mistaken idea of the block as a whole, as discussed in Example 3.1.1.

To forestall this difficulty, it may instead be decided to draw a sample of two houses from each side. The drawing of two north-side houses may be considered as part A, and the drawing of two south-side houses as part B, of a two-part experiment. For part A, a model $\mathcal{C}$ can be built as in Section 2.1, in which the $\binom{6}{2} = 15$ possible samples of two north-side houses are regarded as equally likely. Similarly, in model $\mathcal{B}$ the $\binom{7}{2} = 21$ possible samples of two south-side houses are treated as equally likely. Finally, if the samples are drawn by separate applications of some random mechanism, it seems reasonable to suppose that the frequencies of the two parts are unrelated, and to represent the experiment as a whole by the product of the two models.

As an illustration of this product model, let us find the probability that none of the corner houses appear in the stratified sample. Let E represent the result "no corner house appears in the sample from the north side." Then $P(E) = \binom{4}{2}\Big/\binom{6}{2} = \frac{6}{15} = \frac{2}{5}.$ Similarly, if F represents "no corner house appears in the sample from the south side," $P(F) = \binom{5}{2}\Big/\binom{7}{2} = \frac{10}{21}.$ According to (5), the probability that no corner house appears in either sample is then given by

$$P(E \text{ and } F) = P(E) \cdot P(F) = \tfrac{2}{5} \cdot \tfrac{10}{21} = \tfrac{4}{21} = .190.$$

EXAMPLE 4. *Two throws of a die.* What is the probability that in two unrelated throws with a fair die we will get at least five points on each throw? Let E represent "at least five points on the first throw," and F represent "at least five points on the second throw." In the factor models, we have $P(E) = P(F) = \frac{2}{6} = \frac{1}{3}$ and $P(E \text{ and } F) = P(E) \cdot P(F) = (\frac{1}{3})(\frac{1}{3}) = \frac{1}{9}.$ This result can also be obtained directly from the uniform model of Example 1.5.3 by counting cases.

When the two sides $P(F|E)$ and $P(F)$ of (4) are not equal, the event F is said to *depend* on the event E. When this occurs, if the model is realistic the corresponding frequencies $f(S|R)$ and $f(S)$ will also be unequal. Suppose for example that $f(S|R)$ is much larger than $f(S)$; i.e., that S occurs much more frequently in those cases when R occurs, than it does in general. It is then tempting to conclude that the event R "causes" the event S to tend to occur. It has, for example, been observed that the conditional frequency of lung cancer is much higher among persons who are heavy cigarette smokers than in the population at large. Again, the conditional frequency of cavities is lower among children in communities with a high fluorine content in the water supply. It seems natural to conclude that cigarette smoking tends to cause lung cancer and that fluorine helps to prevent tooth decay. Many useful causal relations have been discovered as a result of noticing such empirical frequency relations, but it is important to realize the pitfalls of the argument. When results R and S tend to go together, it may not mean that R causes S, but rather that S causes R, or that both are causally connected with other factors while not exerting any direct influence on each other. Some examples may make this clear.

EXAMPLE 5. *Sampling without replacement.* Two marbles are drawn without replacement from a box of three marbles, one of which is red. The result "red on first draw" will occur in about one third of the trials. But its conditional frequency, given that "red on second draw" has occurred, will be zero. Yet we would not want to say that "red on second draw" exerts a causal influence on "red on first draw," since cause operates only forward in time.

EXAMPLE 6. *Insulin and diabetes.* It may be observed that the conditional frequency of diabetes is much higher among persons taking insulin than in the general population. Should one conclude that insulin causes diabetes?

EXAMPLE 7. *Income and politics.* When a college faculty was voting on a controversial issue, it was found that among the faculty members in the upper half of the income bracket a much higher proportion took the conservative side than among those in the lower half. This does not prove that higher income tends to make a person more conservative. The observations may reflect mainly the fact that as persons get older they tend toward both more conservative outlooks and higher income.

EXAMPLE 8. *Smoking and lung cancer.* As mentioned above, the incidence of lung cancer is much higher among persons who are heavy cigarette smokers than in the population at large. This fact, taken by itself, would equally well support the conclusions either that lung cancer causes smoking or that both are caused by some common constitutional or environmental factors. The mechanism causing the dependence may in part be like that of Example 7. For example, it is known that people in cities smoke more heavily than people on farms, and that the air in cities contains more carcinogens than rural air. The rural-urban difference is thus a factor that could tend to increase the dependence between smoking and cancer, and there may be other factors of a similar nature. We do not wish to imply that these considerations exonerate smoking as a cause of lung cancer, but merely want to emphasize once again that dependence does not imply a causal connection. Causal relationships can sometimes be demonstrated by means of experiments of a kind discussed in textbooks on statistics. The suspected cause must be applied in some cases and not in others, this assignment being made with the aid of a random mechanism.

PROBLEMS

1. In the product model $\alpha \times \mathfrak{B}$ specified by (3.1.1) and (3.1.4) let

$$E = \{e_2, e_3, e_4\} \quad \text{and} \quad F = \{f_1, f_3, f_5\}.$$

List the simple events of which the event $(E \text{ and } F)$ is composed, and check the validity of equation (5) for this case.

2. Suppose you attend two classes consisting of eight and ten students respectively. In the first class, two students are selected at random for recitation, and in the second class three students are selected at random, without reference to the selection in the first class.
  (i) Construct a probability model for this experiment.
  (ii) Use this model to find the probability of your not being called upon for recitation in either class.

3. In Example 3, suppose that four houses were drawn from the 13 houses on the block without stratification. What are the probabilities that
  (i) all four come from the same side of the block?
  (ii) just two come from each side of the block?

FIGURE 2.

4. Two fields contain nine and twelve plots respectively, as shown in Fig. 2. From each field, one plot is selected at random for a soil analysis.
  (i) Construct a probability model for this experiment.
  (ii) What is the probability that both selected plots are corner plots?
  (iii) What is the probability that at least one of the selected plots is a corner plot?

5. Twenty percent of the patients on which a certain heart operation is performed die during the operation. Of those that survive, ten percent die from the after-effects. What is the over-all proportion of cases dying from one or the other of these causes?

6. Let E and F be exclusive. Show that $P(F|\overline{E}) = P(F)/[1 - P(E)]$. Is this relation necessarily correct if E and F are not exclusive?

7. For two unrelated tosses with a coin, let E, F stand for

> E: heads on first toss
> F: heads on one toss and tails on the other.

Determine whether E and F are independent
  (i) if the coin is fair
  (ii) if the coin is not fair.
[Hint: See Problem 1.6.]

8. Three square fields each contain nine plots as in Figure 2a. From each, a plot is selected at random for a soil analysis, the selections being performed without reference to each other.
  (i) Construct a probability model for this experiment.
  (ii) What is the probability that all three selected plots are corner plots?

9. Solve the problem of Example 4 for two unrelated throws with a loaded die, if for each throw separately the model (1.3.1) is appropriate.

10. Find the probability of at least one six in three unrelated tosses with a fair die. [Hint: Find the probability of the complementary outcome.]

11. Five judges each are asked to compare three brands of cigarettes A, B, C. Suppose that the three brands are indistinguishable so that each of the judges without any relation to the decisions of the other judges is equally likely to rank the brands in any of the six possible orders ABC, ACB, BAC, BCA, CAB, CBA. What is the probability that all judges (i) assign the ranking ABC? (ii) rank A highest, (iii) prefer A to B?

12. (i) Use (1) to prove that the relation $P(F|E) = P(F)$ is equivalent to (5) provided $P(E)$ is not zero.
  (ii) Prove that the relation $P(E|F) = P(E)$ is equivalent to (5) provided $P(F)$ is not zero.

13. Show that if E, F are independent, then E, $\overline{F}$ are independent. [Hint: $P(E \text{ and } \overline{F}) = P(E) - P(E \text{ and } F).$]

14. Show that if E, F are independent, then $\overline{E}$, $\overline{F}$ are independent. [Hint: Use Problem 13 twice.]

4.3 TWO-STAGE EXPERIMENTS

Many interesting random experiments are performed in successive stages, with the chance results of each stage determining the conditions under which the next stage will be carried out. We shall in this section present the main ideas involved in building probability models for the simplest such experiments, those carried out in only two stages. A few illustrations will indicate the nature of the applications.

  (a) When drawing a sample of the labor force of an industry, it is frequently convenient first to draw a sample of factories, and then to visit the selected factories to draw samples of workers. The first stage is the sampling of factories, the second stage the sampling of workers within the selected factories.   This is an example of the method of *two-stage sampling*.

(b) In genetic experiments, animals may be bred to produce a first generation of offspring.   These in turn are bred to produce a second generation.   The chance inheritance of genes by the first generation determines the genetic constitutions involved in breeding the second generation (see Section 5).

(c) When designing an experiment it often happens that not enough is known about the situation to permit an efficient design, or even to decide whether a full-scale experiment is worthwhile.   In such cases it may pay to conduct a preliminary or pilot experiment whose results may be used to make this decision and to plan the main experiment if one proves necessary. This is known as a *two-stage sequential design*, the first stage consisting of the pilot study, and the second stage of the main experiment.

(d) When checking on the quality of a lot of mass-produced articles, it is frequently possible to decrease the average sample size by carrying out the inspection in two stages.   One may for example first take a small sample and accept the lot if all articles in the sample are satisfactory; otherwise a larger second sample is inspected.

All of these examples may be thought of as experiments having two parts, but it would be quite unrealistic to represent them by product models, as we did for the two-part experiments considered in Chapter 3.   In fact, the use of a product model is equivalent to the assumption that the parts are unrelated, that is, that the probabilities for the second part are not influenced by the outcome of the first part.   This assumption clearly is not appropriate in the present examples, where the results on the first stage will alter the conditions under which the second stage is carried out.

Before embarking on a general discussion of models for two-stage experiments, we shall consider a simple artificial example.

EXAMPLE 1.   *The two boxes.*   Suppose that we have two boxes, for example two drawers of a desk, of which one contains one red and one white marble, and the other three red and one green marble.   A box is chosen at random, and from it a marble is drawn at random.   What is the probability of getting a red marble?

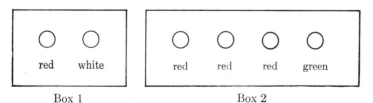

Box 1   Box 2

FIGURE 1.   THE TWO BOXES

An enthusiastic devotee of "equally likely cases" might argue as follows. There are six marbles, any one of which may be drawn; since four of them are red, the probability of getting a red marble is $\frac{4}{6} = \frac{2}{3}$. To this analysis it could be objected that one has no right to treat the six marbles as equally likely. The fact that there are fewer marbles in the first than in the second box may give those in the first box a greater chance to be chosen. We shall now present a method for obtaining an alternative model.

The approach is similar to that used in the construction of product models (Sections 3.1 and 3.2). A product model $\alpha \times \mathcal{B}$ was built up by combining two simpler models α and $\mathcal{B}$ for parts A and B of the experiment. Analogously, let us begin here by considering a model α for the first *stage* of the two-stage experiment. Suppose that the possible results of the first stage are $r_1, r_2, \ldots, r_a$. These will be represented in model α by the events $e_1, e_2, \ldots, e_a$ with probabilities $p_1, p_2, \ldots, p_a$ satisfying

(1) $$p_1 + p_2 + \ldots + p_a = 1.$$

This model will be realistic only if its probabilities are approximately equal to the frequencies they represent, that is, if

(2) $$p_1 \sim f(r_1), \quad p_2 \sim f(r_2), \quad \ldots, \quad p_a \sim f(r_a).$$

The construction of model α may be illustrated by Example 1. The first stage consists of drawing a box and it has $a = 2$ results, "first box chosen" and "second box chosen." The statement that the box is chosen at random means that the boxes would be chosen with about equal frequency, which justifies assigning the values $p_1 = \frac{1}{2}$ and $p_2 = \frac{1}{2}$.

The construction of a model for the first stage has been completely parallel to that of a model for part A of a two-part experiment, with even the same notation being used. However, the analogy between the second stage and part B is less close, since a product model was based on the assumption that the two parts are unrelated while in general the second stage will depend on the outcome of the first stage. Thus, in Example 1, if box 1 has been drawn, the marble obtained on the second stage must be either red or white, while if box 2 has been drawn, it must be either red or green. The list of results of the second stage must therefore consist of the three possibilities "red," "white," "green" if it is to cover all cases that could arise. In general, for the second stage the list of results, say s_1, $s_2, \ldots, s_b$, is a comprehensive list which covers the various second-stage experiments that may arise. These results will be represented by the events $f_1, f_2, \ldots, f_b$. (In Example 1, let f_1 represent "red," f_2 "white," and f_3 "green.")

Because of the dependence of the experimental conditions of the second stage on the result of the first stage, we have to build a separate second-stage model corresponding to each possible result of the first stage. Let us see for example how to build a model $\mathfrak{B}^{(1)}$ for the second stage when the result of the first stage is r_1. The frequencies with which the results $s_1, s_2, \ldots, s_b$ occur, among the cases in which r_1 has occurred on the first stage, are the conditional frequencies $f(s_1|r_1), f(s_2|r_1), \ldots, f(s_b|r_1)$. Let us denote the corresponding probabilities by $q_1^{(1)}, q_2^{(1)}, \ldots, q_b^{(1)}$, where of course we must have

(3) $$q_1^{(1)} + q_2^{(1)} + \ldots + q_b^{(1)} = 1.$$

The model

$$\mathfrak{B}^{(1)}: \begin{array}{cccc} f_1, & f_2, & \ldots, f_b \\ q_1^{(1)}, & q_2^{(1)}, & \ldots, & q_b^{(1)} \end{array}$$

will be a realistic model for the second stage given that the result of the first stage is r_1, provided its probabilities are approximately equal to the corresponding conditional frequencies:

(4) $$q_1^{(1)} \sim f(s_1|r_1), \quad q_2^{(1)} \sim f(s_2|r_1), \quad \ldots, \quad q_b^{(1)} \sim f(s_b|r_1).$$

Similarly, when the result of the first stage is r_2, a model $\mathfrak{B}^{(2)}$ can be built, which assigns to $f_1, f_2, \ldots, f_b$ the probabilities $q_1^{(2)}, q_2^{(2)}, \ldots, q_b^{(2)}$; and so forth up to model $\mathfrak{B}^{(a)}$ when the result of the first stage is r_a.

These models may again be illustrated by Example 1, with model $\mathfrak{B}^{(1)}$ corresponding to the cases in which box 1 is selected on the first stage, and $\mathfrak{B}^{(2)}$ to the cases in which box 2 is selected. In those trials of the experiment in which box 1 is selected, a marble is drawn at random from a box containing one red and one white marble. It is natural to expect that these marbles will occur with about equal (conditional) frequency, which justifies the assignment in model $\mathfrak{B}^{(1)}$ of

$$q_1^{(1)} = \tfrac{1}{2}, \quad q_2^{(1)} = \tfrac{1}{2}, \quad q_3^{(1)} = 0.$$

(The zero probability reflects the fact that there are no green marbles in box 1.) Similarly, appropriate probabilities for model $\mathfrak{B}^{(2)}$ are

$$q_1^{(2)} = \tfrac{3}{4}, \quad q_2^{(2)} = 0, \quad q_3^{(2)} = \tfrac{1}{4}.$$

Since the record of a two-stage experiment as a whole consists of noting the results of both stages, the simple results may conveniently be represented by the events

(5)
$$\begin{array}{cccc} e_1 \text{ and } f_1 & e_1 \text{ and } f_2 & \ldots & e_1 \text{ and } f_b \\ e_2 \text{ and } f_1 & e_2 \text{ and } f_2 & \ldots & e_2 \text{ and } f_b \\ \ldots & \ldots & & \ldots \\ e_a \text{ and } f_1 & e_a \text{ and } f_2 & \ldots & e_a \text{ and } f_b \end{array}$$

where (e_1 and f_1) represents the result "r_1 and s_1," (e_1 and f_2) represents the result "r_1 and s_2," etc. (This is the same event set that was used with the product model.) It may happen in the present case that some of the events correspond to results which are impossible (e.g. "box 1 and green"), but since our model will assign probability zero to such events, no trouble will result.

What probabilities should be assigned to the simple events of (5), for example to $(e_1$ and $f_2)$? If the model is to be realistic, $P(e_1$ and $f_2)$ must be close to $f(r_1$ and $s_2)$. This frequency, in a sequence of n trials, may be written as

$$f(r_1 \text{ and } s_2) = \frac{\#(r_1 \text{ and } s_2)}{n} = \frac{\#(r_1)}{n} \cdot \frac{\#(r_1 \text{ and } s_2)}{\#(r_1)},$$

so that

(6) $$f(r_1 \text{ and } s_2) = f(r_1)f(s_2|r_1).$$

If models α and $\mathcal{B}^{(1)}$ are realistic, we have by (2) and (4)

$$f(r_1) \sim p_1 \quad \text{and} \quad f(s_2|r_1) \sim q_2^{(1)}$$

and hence

$$f(r_1 \text{ and } s_2) \sim p_1 q_2^{(1)}.$$

This shows that $p_1 q_2^{(1)}$ will, under the assumptions made, be a realistic value for $P(e_1$ and $f_2)$. Application of similar considerations to the other cases leads to the assignment

(7)
$$
\begin{array}{llll}
P(e_1 \text{ and } f_1) = p_1 q_1^{(1)} & P(e_1 \text{ and } f_2) = p_1 q_2^{(1)} & \cdots & P(e_1 \text{ and } f_b) = p_1 q_b^{(1)} \\
P(e_2 \text{ and } f_1) = p_2 q_1^{(2)} & P(e_2 \text{ and } f_2) = p_2 q_2^{(2)} & \cdots & P(e_2 \text{ and } f_b) = p_2 q_b^{(2)} \\
\cdots & \cdots & & \cdots \\
P(e_a \text{ and } f_1) = p_a q_1^{(a)} & P(e_a \text{ and } f_2) = p_a q_2^{(a)} & \cdots & P(e_a \text{ and } f_b) = p_a q_b^{(a)}
\end{array}
$$

The model for two-stage experiments defined by (5) and (7) will be denoted by model 3.

EXAMPLE 1. *The two boxes (continued).* Let us illustrate (7) with Example 1, where e_1 and e_2 represent "box 1" and "box 2," while f_1, f_2, f_3 represent "red," "white," and "green." The probabilities are

(8)
$$P(e_1 \text{ and } f_1) = \tfrac{1}{2} \cdot \tfrac{1}{2} = \tfrac{1}{4}; \quad P(e_1 \text{ and } f_2) = \tfrac{1}{2} \cdot \tfrac{1}{2} = \tfrac{1}{4};$$
$$P(e_1 \text{ and } f_3) = \tfrac{1}{2} \cdot 0 = 0$$
$$P(e_2 \text{ and } f_1) = \tfrac{1}{2} \cdot \tfrac{3}{4} = \tfrac{3}{8}; \quad P(e_2 \text{ and } f_2) = \tfrac{1}{2} \cdot 0 = 0;$$
$$P(e_2 \text{ and } f_3) = \tfrac{1}{2} \cdot \tfrac{1}{4} = \tfrac{1}{8}.$$

Here for example the assignment of probability $\tfrac{3}{8}$ to $(e_2$ and $f_1)$ reflects our assumptions that box 2 will be chosen in about $\tfrac{1}{2}$ of the trials, and that in those cases when box 2 is chosen, a red marble will be drawn about $\tfrac{3}{4}$ of the time.

Having built the model, we can now answer the original question and find the probability that the marble drawn is red. The event corresponding to the result of getting a red marble consists of the first column of (8) and its probability is therefore $\tfrac{1}{4} + \tfrac{3}{8} = \tfrac{5}{8}$.

Two different models (the uniform model discussed at the beginning of the section and that defined by (8)) have given to the probability of getting a red marble the values $\frac{2}{3}$ and $\frac{5}{8}$. Which is right? As usual, the only sure test is experimental. The frequency with which a red marble is obtained depends on just how the boxes and marbles are chosen. Many persons approaching a desk with two drawers side by side might tend to open the one on the right. Again, if the red marbles are larger than the others, this might tend to favor their choice. But if the box, and then the marble from the box, is chosen with equal probabilities, for example by means of a table of random numbers, we would expect to get a red marble with frequency close to $\frac{5}{8}$.

EXAMPLE 2. *Sex of twins.* Consider the "experiment" of observing the sex of the first-born and second-born of a pair of human twins. We have pointed out in Example 3.2.3 that a product model is not suitable for analyzing this experiment, and shall now see how it may be represented by a two-stage model.

Twins are of two types: *identical* twins originate from a single fertilized egg and are consequently always of the same sex; *fraternal* twins originate from two separately fertilized eggs, and their sexes are unrelated. Approximately one third of all human twin pairs are identical. If we treat the type of twin as the result of the first stage of the experiment, and represent identical twins by e_1 and fraternal twins by e_2, then a reasonable model α is obtained by setting $p_1 = \frac{1}{3}$, $p_2 = \frac{2}{3}$.

We shall view the observation of the sex of first- and second-born twins as the result of the second stage. Just as in Example 1.5.2 and Problem 3.1.2, we shall represent the four possibilities by f_1: MM, f_2: MF, f_3: FM, f_4: FF, where for instance MF means "first born is male and second born is female." Observations show that the following probabilities are roughly correct:

	f_1: MM	f_2: MF	f_3: FM	f_4: FF
$\mathcal{B}^{(1)}$:	$q_1^{(1)} = \frac{1}{2}$	$q_2^{(1)} = 0$	$q_3^{(1)} = 0$	$q_4^{(1)} = \frac{1}{2}$
$\mathcal{B}^{(2)}$:	$q_1^{(2)} = \frac{1}{4}$	$q_2^{(2)} = \frac{1}{4}$	$q_3^{(2)} = \frac{1}{4}$	$q_4^{(2)} = \frac{1}{4}$

The zero values assigned to $q_2^{(1)}$ and $q_3^{(1)}$ reflect the fact mentioned above that identical twins, arising from a single fertilized egg, cannot be of mixed sex. At the time of fertilization this egg, like any other, is about equally likely to receive a male-determining or a female-determining sperm, which explains the assignments $q_1^{(1)} = \frac{1}{2}$, $q_4^{(1)} = \frac{1}{2}$. With fraternal (two-egg) twins, the two fertilizations are unrelated so that frequencies represented in the second row behave like those in ordinary two-child families.

Now let us combine models α, $\mathcal{B}^{(1)}$, and $\mathcal{B}^{(2)}$. The resulting probabilities are, in the usual rectangular array (7)

	f_1: MM	f_2: MF	f_3: FM	f_4: FF
e_1: identical	$\frac{1}{3}\cdot\frac{1}{2}=\frac{1}{6}$	$\frac{1}{3}\cdot 0=0$	$\frac{1}{3}\cdot 0=0$	$\frac{1}{3}\cdot\frac{1}{2}=\frac{1}{6}$
e_2: fraternal	$\frac{2}{3}\cdot\frac{1}{4}=\frac{1}{6}$	$\frac{2}{3}\cdot\frac{1}{4}=\frac{1}{6}$	$\frac{2}{3}\cdot\frac{1}{4}=\frac{1}{6}$	$\frac{2}{3}\cdot\frac{1}{4}=\frac{1}{6}$

From this model we see at once that the probability that both twins are male is $\frac{1}{6}+\frac{1}{6}=\frac{1}{3}$. For comparison, with ordinary two-child families the probability that both children are male is about $\frac{1}{4}$ (Problem 3.1.2).

Several other applications of two-stage models are given in the next section.

PROBLEMS

1. In Example 1, find the probability that
   (i) the only white marble is selected,
   (ii) the only green marble is selected.
Give an intuitive explanation of why these probabilities differ.

2. In Example 1, what value of p_1 would make the six marbles equally likely to be drawn?

3. In the model of Example 2, what is the probability that the twins will be of the same sex?

4. In a game of Russian Roulette, a person selects (at random) one of three guns, each containing five chambers. The number of empty chambers is four, three, and two respectively.
   (i) Construct a model for this two-stage experiment, with the result of interest at the second stage being whether the selected chamber is empty or not.
   (ii) Find the probability that the person survives this "experiment."

5. Suppose an ordered sample of size two is drawn at random without replacement from a collection of N items, say marbles numbered $1, 2, \ldots, N$.
   (i) If $e_1, e_2, \ldots, e_N$ represent the results that the first marble drawn is marble number 1, number 2, . . . , number N, what would be reasonable values for $P(e_1), P(e_2), \ldots, P(e_N)$?
   (ii) If $f_1, f_2, \ldots, f_N$ represent the results that the second marble drawn is marble number 1, number 2, . . . , number N, what would be reasonable values for $P(f_1|e_1), P(f_2|e_1), \ldots, P(f_N|e_1)$? For $P(f_1|e_2), P(f_2|e_2), \ldots, P(f_N|e_2)$? Etc.
   (iii) Using (i) and (ii), build a model for this two-stage experiment.
   (iv) Compare the model of (iii) with the uniform model built for this experiment in Sections 2.3 and 2.4.

6. A firm which has eight factories in widely different locations wishes to interview a sample of its workers. For administrative convenience it is decided to interview workers from only three of the factories. A two-stage sample is therefore taken: first three of the eight factories are selected at random; then at each of the chosen

factories, a random sample of 10% of the workers of that factory is obtained. In the model for this experiment given by (5) and (7):

(i) What results are represented by $e_1, e_2, \ldots$?

(ii) What are the possible second stages of this experiment? Is it correct to say that each possible second stage is a stratified sample?

(iii) What results are represented by $f_1, f_2, \ldots$?

7. Suppose that on each play of slot machine A there is probability $\frac{1}{2}$ of winning \$1 and probability $\frac{1}{2}$ of not winning anything, while on slot machine B there is probability $\frac{1}{10}$ of winning \$1 and probability $\frac{9}{10}$ of winning nothing. Suppose further that the probability of winning on any play is not influenced by the outcome of the preceding play. Build two-stage models for the following two experiments:

(i) A player begins with machine A; if he wins, he plays machine A a second time, otherwise he switches to machine B for his second play.

(ii) A player begins with machine B; if he wins, he plays machine B a second time, otherwise he switches to machine A for his second play.

[Hint: As simple events of the two-stage model use win-win, win-lose, lose-win, lose-lose.]

8. (i) Build a two-stage model for the experiment of selecting at random (i.e. with probability $\frac{1}{2}$ each) one of the two machines A and B of Problem 7, playing it twice if the first play wins and otherwise switching to the other machine for the second play. [Hint: Use models (i) and (ii) of the preceding problem for the two possible second stages.]

(ii) Find the probability of winning at least once in the two plays.

9. (i) Build a two-stage model for the experiment of selecting at random one of the slot machines of Problem 7 and playing it twice.

(ii) Find the probability of winning at least once in the two plays.

(iii) Which of the two methods of playing, described in Problems 8(i) and 9(i), do you prefer, and why?

[Hint: Note that a binomial trials model is appropriate for the second stage of 9(i).]

4.4 PROPERTIES OF TWO-STAGE MODELS; BAYES' LAW

We shall now derive certain properties of the model $\mathfrak{I}$ defined by (5) and (7) of the preceding section. As was the case with the product model $\mathfrak{A} \times \mathfrak{B}$, the symbols $e_1, e_2, \ldots, f_1, f_2, \ldots$ are being used in more than one sense. In model $\mathfrak{A}$, e_1 denotes the simple event which corresponds to the result r_1 of the first stage; in model $\mathfrak{I}$, e_1 denotes the composite event consisting of the first row of (3.5), but still represents r_1. Since e_1 represents the same experimental result in the two models, it should be assigned the same probability in both models, and this has in fact been done; by (3.7), the sum of the probabilities in the top row of (3.5) is

$$(1) \quad P(e_1) = p_1 q_1^{(1)} + p_1 q_2^{(1)} + \ldots + p_1 q_b^{(1)} = p_1(q_1^{(1)} + q_2^{(1)} + \ldots + q_b^{(1)})$$
$$= p_1 \cdot 1 = p_1$$

which is just the probability of e_1 in model $\mathfrak{A}$.

The same argument applies to $e_2, \ldots, e_a$. As an immediate consequence of this fact we see that (3.7) is a legitimate model. The sum of all of the probabilities of (3.7) is the sum of the row-sums, which by the above result and (3.1) is $p_1 + p_2 + \ldots + p_a = 1$.

In building model 3 we introduced the q's to represent certain conditional frequencies, for example $q_2^{(1)}$ to represent $f(s_2|r_1)$. Since in model 3 the result r_1 is represented by e_1 and the result s_2 by f_2, one might hope that $q_2^{(1)}$ would equal $P(f_2|e_1)$. This is in fact the case, as may be seen by combining (2.1), (3.7), and (1):

$$P(f_2|e_1) = P(e_1 \text{ and } f_2)/P(e_1) = (p_1 q_2^{(1)})/p_1 = q_2^{(1)}.$$

Just as was the case with the e's, the f's also denote more than one event. Thus f_2 represents the result s_2 not only in model 3, where it is the composite event consisting of the second column of (3.5), but also in models $\mathfrak{B}^{(1)}, \ldots, \mathfrak{B}^{(a)}$, in each of which it is a simple event. However, while e_1 has the same probability in both models $\mathfrak{A}$ and 3, the probability of f_2 will be different in the different models, reflecting the dependence of the second stage on the outcome of the first. Thus, in model $\mathfrak{B}^{(1)}$ the probability assigned to f_2 was $q_2^{(1)}$, in model $\mathfrak{B}^{(2)}$ it was $q_2^{(2)}$, etc. What is the probability of f_2 in model 3? Since in model 3 the event f_2 consists of the second column of (3.5), we have

$$\begin{aligned}
(2) \quad P(f_2) &= p_1 q_2^{(1)} + p_2 q_2^{(2)} + \ldots + p_a q_2^{(a)} \\
&= P(e_1)P(f_2|e_1) + P(e_2)P(f_2|e_2) + \ldots + P(e_a)P(f_2|e_a).
\end{aligned}$$

The probability assigned to f_2 in model 3 is thus a "weighted average" of the values assigned in model $\mathfrak{B}^{(1)}, \ldots, \mathfrak{B}^{(a)}$, the weights being $p_1, \ldots, p_a$. Similar formulas hold for $f_1, f_3, \ldots, f_b$. To illustrate this formula, recall Example 3.1. The conditional probability of a white marble is $q_2^{(1)} = \frac{1}{2}$ if box 1 has been drawn, and is $q_2^{(2)} = 0$ if box 2 has been drawn. The overall probability of a white marble is therefore by (2)

$$P(f_2) = \tfrac{1}{2} \cdot \tfrac{1}{2} + \tfrac{1}{2} \cdot 0 = \tfrac{1}{4}.$$

There are many interesting and important two-stage experiments in which one cannot observe the result of the first stage but only that of the second stage. In such cases, the second-stage result may provide indirect information about the unobserved first stage, and in fact it is frequently the purpose of the second stage to provide this indirect information.

EXAMPLE 1. *Diagnostic tests.* For many diseases, diagnostic tests have been developed that are helpful in detecting the presence of the disease. There is, for example, a skin test for tuberculosis, a blood test for syphilis, a cytological test for cancer, etc. Unfortunately such tests are never perfect. A test may on occasion give a positive reaction, i.e., indicate that the disease is present, even when it is not; such a reaction is called a *false positive.* Similarly the test may result in a *false negative*, by showing a negative reaction when applied to an individual who is in fact suffering from the disease.

The application of a diagnostic test may be viewed as a two-stage experiment. The selection of the individual who receives the test constitutes the first stage; this individual may be either "sick" or "healthy," i.e., he may either have or not have the disease in question. The application of the test to the individual constitutes the second stage, the result of which is either a positive or a negative reaction.

In the routine application of a diagnostic test, the result of the first stage ordinarily is not observed. To determine whether or not the disease is present may require an extensive and expensive period of careful clinical observation; it may in some cases not become definitely known until much later when an autopsy is performed. However, the result of the second stage, a positive or negative reaction on the test, is directly observed. The purpose of the second stage is in fact to provide (indirect) information about the individual's health.

EXAMPLE 2. *College admission.* Not all of the applicants for admission to a college would, if admitted, be able to do successful work. We may accordingly classify the applicants as "able" or "unable" on this basis. We shall regard this classification as the first stage of an experiment, although, of course, when an applicant presents himself, the registrar cannot observe into which category he falls. In order to decide whether to admit the applicant, the registrar gives him an entrance examination which he may either pass or fail. This result constitutes the observable second stage. The purpose of the examination is in fact to provide indirect evidence about the ability of the student to do successful work.

Suppose that (3.5) and (3.7) provide a satisfactory model for a certain two-stage experiment, for which the first-stage results, represented by $e_1, e_2, \ldots$, are of particular interest but cannot be directly observed. Prior to the experiment these events have the probabilities $P(e_1) = p_1$, $P(e_2) = p_2, \ldots$. We shall call these the *prior* probabilities of $e_1, e_2, \ldots$. Now the experiment is performed, and it is seen that the result represented by f_2 has occurred. Once this partial information is in hand, the principles of Section 1 show that the relevant probabilities for $e_1, e_2, \ldots$ are now the *conditional* probabilities given f_2: $P(e_1|f_2), P(e_2|f_2), \ldots$. We shall call these the *posterior* probabilities of $e_1, e_2, \ldots$ since they are relevant *after* the experiment. The posterior probabilities can be computed from formula (2.1) for conditional probabilities. Thus we see, for example, from (3.7) that

$$P(e_1|f_2) = P(e_1 \text{ and } f_2)/P(f_2) = P(e_1)P(f_2|e_1)/P(f_2)$$

and hence from (2) that

(3) $$P(e_1|f_2) = \frac{P(e_1)P(f_2|e_1)}{P(e_1)P(f_2|e_1) + P(e_2)P(f_2|e_2) + \cdots + P(e_a)P(f_2|e_a)}$$

Similar formulas hold in the other cases. This formula, which expresses a posterior probability in terms of prior and conditional probabilities, is known as *Bayes' law*.

EXAMPLE 3. *The two boxes.* Recall Example 3.1, but suppose now that we are permitted to observe not which box was chosen but only the color of the selected marble. Prior to this observation, each box has probability $\frac{1}{2}$, or $P(e_1) = P(e_2) = \frac{1}{2}$. Suppose that the experiment is performed and that the selected marble is red. This result is represented in the model by f_1. Since $P(f_1|e_1) = \frac{1}{2}$, and $P(f_1|e_2) = \frac{3}{4}$, application of Bayes' law gives

$$P(e_1|f_1) = \frac{P(e_1)P(f_1|e_1)}{P(e_1)P(f_1|e_1) + P(e_2)P(f_1|e_2)} = \frac{\frac{1}{2}\cdot\frac{1}{2}}{\frac{1}{2}\cdot\frac{1}{2} + \frac{1}{2}\cdot\frac{3}{4}} = \frac{2}{5}$$

$$P(e_2|f_1) = \frac{P(e_2)P(f_1|e_2)}{P(e_1)P(f_1|e_1) + P(e_2)P(f_1|e_2)} = \frac{\frac{1}{2}\cdot\frac{3}{4}}{\frac{1}{2}\cdot\frac{1}{2} + \frac{1}{2}\cdot\frac{3}{4}} = \frac{3}{5}.$$

These are the posterior probabilities of the two boxes, after it is known that a red marble was obtained. Before the experiment the two boxes are equally likely, but after observing a red marble the second box is more likely than the first. The reason for this is that the probability of a red marble is higher when drawing from the second box than from the first.

EXAMPLE 1. *Diagnostic tests (continued).* The authorities of a college are considering giving a diagnostic test to the entire student body in order to identify those students who have a certain infectious disease. It is known that the test gives some false positive reactions, and the plan calls for subjecting all students with positive reactions to an expensive clinical examination to determine whether they do in fact have the disease. The infirmary wants to know what fraction of the students will have to be examined clinically, i.e. what fraction will give a positive reaction. By (2) we have

(4) $P(\text{positive})$
$$= P(\text{sick})P(\text{positive}|\text{sick}) + P(\text{healthy})P(\text{positive}|\text{healthy}).$$

This formula will be useful only if numerical values can be supplied for the terms on the right. Suppose that previous studies of the test indicate that it gives a positive reaction to about 80% of the persons having the disease, and to about 10% of the persons who do not, so that it is reasonable to assume $P(\text{positive}|\text{sick}) = .8$ and $P(\text{positive}|\text{healthy}) = .1$. Suppose further that general experience with the disease suggests that its incidence among college students is about 1%, so that one may put $P(\text{sick}) = .01$.

With these values, (4) gives $P(\text{positive}) = .01 \times .8 + .99 \times .1 = .008 +$ .099 $= .107$. Thus, it may be anticipated that about 11% of the students will have to be examined, and that as a result of the test about 80% of the students having the disease will be identified.

From the point of view of a student who takes the diagnostic test and gets a positive reaction, the interesting question (before he undergoes the clinical examination) is: "How likely am I to have the disease?" The relevant probability is provided by Bayes' law:

$$P(\text{sick}|\text{positive}) = P(\text{sick})P(\text{positive}|\text{sick})/P(\text{positive})$$
$$= (.01 \times .8)/.107 = .075.$$

Consider now the frequency interpretation of this probability. It shows that about 92% of the students who have a positive reaction and must therefore undergo the clinical examination, are in fact healthy. The reason for this somewhat startling conclusion is that the disease is quite rare (incidence of 1%), so that even with a rather low rate of false positives (10%), the bulk of the positive reactions come from the healthy group. This illustrates the general fact that, when diagnostic tests for rare diseases are applied in mass screening surveys, the majority of the positive reactors are healthy. Nevertheless such surveys may be useful, since they permit the expensive examination to be restricted to a small fraction of the whole population.

PROBLEMS

1. Of two boxes, one contains one red and one white marble, the other two red and three white marbles. A box is selected at random and a marble is drawn at random from the selected box. Use (2) to find the probability that the marble is red.

2. Using the model for ordered sampling of Problem 3.5 and (2)
   (i) find the probabilities $P(f_1), P(f_2), \ldots, P(f_N)$;
   (ii) compare $P(f_2)$ with $P(f_2|e_1)$ by giving the frequency interpretation of each.

3. In any model (not necessarily of a two-stage experiment) suppose that the event set ε is broken down into the exclusive event sets $E_1, E_2, \ldots$, so that $\varepsilon = (E_1 \text{ or } E_2 \text{ or } \ldots)$. Prove that for any event F, the probability of F can be computed by the following "breakdown law,"

(5) $$P(F) = P(E_1)P(F|E_1) + P(E_2)P(F|E_2) + \ldots.$$

[Hint: Apply first the addition law and then the multiplication law to the right side of (1.6.1).]

4. A box contains three red and seven white marbles. A marble is drawn at random and in its place a marble of the other color is put in the box. The marbles are stirred and another one is drawn at random. Find the probability that it is red. [Hint: Apply (5), with E_1, E_2 representing the two possible colors of the first marble drawn.]

5. A box contains three pennies, of which two are fair and the third is two-headed.

　(i) A penny is selected at random and tossed.　What is the probability that it will fall heads?

　(ii) If the selected penny is tossed twice, what is the probability that it gives heads both times?

[Hint: Use (5) with E_1, E_2 representing the selection of a fair penny or the two-headed penny respectively.　In (ii), assume that, if a fair penny has been selected, the two tosses with this penny are unrelated.]

6. A box contains six pennies, which may be fair, two-headed, or two-tailed.　A penny is selected at random and is tossed twice.　How many pennies should there be of each of the three types so that the experiment simulates that of Example 3.2?

7. Suppose that the probability is p that the weather (sunshine or rain) is the same on any given day as it was on the preceding day.　It is raining today.　What is the probability that it will rain the day after tomorrow?　[Hint: Use (5), with E_1 and E_2 representing the possible states of the weather tomorrow.]

8. (i) Under the assumptions of Example 1 (continued), find the probability of an incorrect diagnosis.

　(ii) Compare the probability obtained in (i) with the probability of an incorrect diagnosis for the "diagnostic procedure" of declaring every student healthy without performing a test.

9. A lot of 25 items is inspected by the following two-stage sampling plan.　A first sample of five items is drawn.　If one or more is bad, the lot is rejected; if all are good, a second sample of ten items is drawn (from the 20 items remaining). The lot is rejected if any of the items in the second sample is bad, and is accepted if all are good.　Find the probability of accepting a lot containing two bad items. [Hint: Use (5), with E_1, E_2 representing the possibilities that the first sample does or does not contain at least one bad item.]

10. Under the assumptions of Problem 3, prove the following generalization of Bayes' law:

$$P(E_1|F) = \frac{P(E_1)P(F|E_1)}{P(F)} = \frac{P(E_1)P(F|E_1)}{P(E_1)P(F|E_1) + P(E_2)P(F|E_2) + \ldots}.$$

Use (6) to find

　(i) in Problem 1 the probability $P(\text{box } 1|\text{red})$.

　(ii) in Problem 5(i) the probability that the two-headed penny was selected given that the penny fell heads.

　(iii) in Problem 5(ii) the probability that the two-headed penny was selected that the penny fell heads both times.

　　　　ple 1 (continued), find the conditional probability $P(\text{sick}|\text{negative})$.

4.5　APPLICATIONS OF PROBABILITY TO GENETICS

That the inheritance of certain traits could be regarded as a random experiment was first pointed out by Mendel* in 1866, on the basis of his

* Gregor Mendel, 1822–1884.

studies of the culinary pea.   To take a somewhat more explicative example than any of Mendel's, suppose that a certain plant may have red (R), pink (P), or white (W) flowers.   It is found that the seeds obtained from crossing two red-flowered plants will always produce red-flowered plants: let us represent this fact schematically by the formula R × R → R. Similarly, we find W × W → W and R × W → P.   But the other crosses will give variable results.   From R × P we may obtain either R or P, and the record of the successive results will look like the record of a sequence of penny tosses, the red- and pink-flowering plants occurring in about equal frequency in a large experiment.   Similarly W × P produces W and P with about equal frequency.   Finally the cross P × P will give all three types, P about half the time and R and W each about one quarter of the time.

To explain such observations Mendel postulated that there were certain entities, now called *genes*, responsible for flower color and passed on from the plants to their progeny.   The present example involves two types of genes, which we may denote by A and a.   Each plant has two genes so that there are three kinds of plants, or genotypes: AA, Aa, and aa.   A plant (AA), both of whose genes are of type A, will have red flowers.   A plant (aa), both of whose genes are of type a, will have white flowers.   Finally, a plant (Aa) with one gene of each type will have pink flowers.

Each offspring obtains one gene from each parent to make up its own pair.   This explains why R × R → R, since when we cross an AA plant with another AA plant, the offspring must also be AA.   Similarly (aa) × (aa) → (aa), and (AA) × (aa) → (Aa).   The varying results are now also explained: in the (AA) × (Aa) cross, the offspring is sure to get A from the first parent, but may receive either A or a from the other, and thus may be either AA or Aa.   Similarly the (Aa) × (Aa) cross may produce each of the three types.

To explain the stable frequencies, we now introduce probability assumptions into the model.   We suppose

(i)   from an (Aa) parent, an offspring has probability $\frac{1}{2}$ of receiving each of the genes A and a;

(ii)   the genes obtained by an individual from his two parents are unrelated.

Breeding experiments also justify another assumption of unrelatedness:

(iii)   the genes passed on by a parent to different offspring are unrelated.

With these simple assumptions, all the Mendelian frequencies are explained.   Thus in an (Aa) × (Aa) cross, the probability is $\frac{1}{4}$ that the offspring will be (AA), since there is probability $\frac{1}{2}$ of obtaining the A gene from each parent, and by assumption (ii) these probabilities are to be multiplied.   The table below shows the nine possible crosses, and the probabilities of each of the three possible offspring in each case.

TABLE 1. PROBABILITIES OF GENOTYPES

Father \ Mother	AA		Aa		aa	
AA	AA	1	AA	$\frac{1}{2}$	AA	0
	Aa	0	Aa	$\frac{1}{2}$	Aa	1
	aa	0	aa	0	aa	0
Aa	AA	$\frac{1}{2}$	AA	$\frac{1}{4}$	AA	0
	Aa	$\frac{1}{2}$	Aa	$\frac{1}{2}$	Aa	$\frac{1}{2}$
	aa	0	aa	$\frac{1}{4}$	aa	$\frac{1}{2}$
aa	AA	0	AA	0	AA	0
	Aa	1	Aa	$\frac{1}{2}$	Aa	0
	aa	0	aa	$\frac{1}{2}$	aa	1

The Mendelian theory is one of the most satisfying in all of science. It is simple, elegant, and far-reaching. It is now known that mechanisms of this sort occur throughout the plant and animal kingdoms. Things are not always quite as simple as we have here suggested. Many traits depend on more than two types of genes—for example, the A-B-O blood groups in man seem to involve three types, disregarding subtypes. Many traits are determined by more than one pair of genes (hair color, for example). And the development of an individual depends not only on his genetic inheritance, but also on his environment. But there are many traits in man that can be understood in terms of the simple model we have presented above.

Among the properties inherited according to the simple mechanism described above are a number of diseases or crippling defects which appear in childhood and lead to the death of an affected individual before maturity. We shall assume, as is frequently the case, that all AA- and Aa-individuals are healthy, showing no signs of the defect, but that all aa-individuals are affected. Because of its death-bringing qualities, the gene a in such cases is called *lethal*. The lethal gene is harmless in a single dose (Aa) becoming effective only in a double dose (aa). An individual of the (Aa) type may be called a *carrier* of the lethal gene, which is harmless to him but which he may pass on to his descendants. It follows from the assumptions made that affected individuals can result only from marriages of two Aa individuals. Thus there is strong reason for a carrier to marry only an AA individual, as only this will insure that all his children will escape the lethal combination aa.

Unfortunately it is usually the case that AA- and Aa-individuals are not distinguishable: when A is present in even a single dose, it determines the physical appearance of the individual. The gene A is then said to be dominant over the gene a. In this case, the Aa individual will not know that he is a carrier of the lethal gene since a healthy individual may be either AA or Aa. Can we attach probabilities to these two possibilities?

Let us suppose that the fraction of healthy adults in the population who carry the lethal gene is the same for males and females, and let us denote this fraction by λ. (This supposition would not be realistic if the lethal gene were "sex-linked.") We shall indicate in the next section how the value of λ may be estimated, and will now only say that typically λ is small. If an adult male or female individual I is then selected either at random from the population, or in such a way that the factors leading to his selection are unrelated to his genetic status, an appropriate model for the genotype of I is

(1)

genotype of I	AA	Aa
probability	$1 - \lambda$	λ

Suppose now however that the person in question comes to our attention because he is calling on a genetic counselor for advice. The reason for his seeking advice is frequently that something is known about his genetic status, and such information may change the probability dramatically. For example, if the individual has an affected child, it becomes certain that both he and his spouse are Aa—the probability that he is a carrier rises from λ to 1. If a person has an affected relative, such as a brother, uncle, or cousin, it follows that the lethal gene runs in the family, and the probability of his being a carrier also rises. We shall now compute this probability for two such cases.

EXAMPLE 1. *Affected sib.* Suppose that an adult individual I had an affected brother or sister. This implies that both of I's parents are carriers, and hence that the appropriate model for the genotype of I *at birth* is given by the central block of Table 1:

(2)

genotype of I	AA	Aa	aa
probability at birth	$\frac{1}{4}$	$\frac{1}{2}$	$\frac{1}{4}$

However, since I has survived to adulthood, he cannot be aa, and the appropriate conditional model, given this information, is by (1.1)

(3)

genotype of I	AA	Aa
probability in adulthood	$\frac{1}{3}$	$\frac{2}{3}$

where in writing (3) we have for simplicity omitted the genotype aa whose probability is zero.

EXAMPLE 2. *Affected uncle.* As a second example, suppose that an adult individual I had an uncle or aunt who was affected, say his father's brother. This is a considerably more complicated problem than that treated in Example 1. Its analysis requires a two-stage model: the first stage pertains to the genotypes of I's parents, and the second stage to those of I himself. Since I's father F had an affected sib, the appropriate model for F's genotype is, by Example 1,

(4)

genotype of F	AA	Aa
probab lity	$\frac{1}{3}$	$\frac{2}{3}$

Since I's mother M is not known to have any affected relatives, we may use model (1) for her genotype

(5)

genotype of M	AA	Aa
probability	$1 - \lambda$	λ

If the genotypes of F and M are assumed to be unrelated, the product of models (4) and (5) may serve as model α for the first stage:

(6)

Event	e_1 (F is AA, M is AA)	e_2 (F is Aa, M is AA)	e_3 (F is AA, M is Aa)	e_4 (F is Aa, M is Aa)
Probability	$\frac{1}{3}(1 - \lambda)$	$\frac{2}{3}(1 - \lambda)$	$\frac{1}{3}\lambda$	$\frac{2}{3}\lambda$

The second stage consists of I's "choice" of genes from his two parents. Corresponding to each possible result of the first stage, the conditional model for the second stage is the appropriate block of Table 1. The probabilities of the four conditional models $\mathcal{B}^{(1)}, \ldots, \mathcal{B}^{(4)}$ corresponding to $e_1, \ldots, e_4$ are shown in the following array.

(7)

	f_1 (I is AA)	f_2 (I is Aa)	f_3 (I is aa)
$\mathcal{B}^{(1)}$	1	0	0
$\mathcal{B}^{(2)}$	$\frac{1}{2}$	$\frac{1}{2}$	0
$\mathcal{B}^{(3)}$	$\frac{1}{2}$	$\frac{1}{2}$	0
$\mathcal{B}^{(4)}$	$\frac{1}{4}$	$\frac{1}{2}$	$\frac{1}{4}$

Combining (6) and (7) with the aid of (3.7) gives for the 12 events of the two-stage model the following probabilities, where for example $P(e_2 \text{ and } f_1)$ = $P(e_2)P(f_1|e_2) = \frac{2}{3}(1 - \lambda) \cdot \frac{1}{2} = \frac{1}{3}(1 - \lambda)$.

	f_1	f_2	f_3
e_1	$\frac{1}{3}(1-\lambda)$	0	0
e_2	$\frac{1}{3}(1-\lambda)$	$\frac{1}{3}(1-\lambda)$	0
e_3	$\frac{1}{6}\lambda$	$\frac{1}{6}\lambda$	0
e_4	$\frac{1}{6}\lambda$	$\frac{1}{3}\lambda$	$\frac{1}{6}\lambda$

(8)

Summing the columns of (8) we obtain by (4.2) the probabilities for I's genotype at birth:

$$P(f_1) = \tfrac{2}{3} - \tfrac{1}{3}\lambda, \qquad P(f_2) = \tfrac{1}{3} + \tfrac{1}{6}\lambda, \qquad P(f_3) = \tfrac{1}{6}\lambda.$$

But since I has reached adulthood, we know that he cannot be aa, and therefore by (2.1) his probability of being a carrier is the conditional probability

$$P(I \text{ is Aa}|I \text{ is not aa}) = \frac{\tfrac{1}{3} + \tfrac{1}{6}\lambda}{1 - \tfrac{1}{6}\lambda}.$$

As remarked above, λ is usually small, so that to a first approximation one may neglect $\tfrac{1}{6}\lambda$ and say that this probability is approximately $\tfrac{1}{3}$. Roughly speaking, it is half as dangerous to have an affected uncle or aunt as to have an affected brother or sister.

A simple intuitive argument leads to this same approximate result. There is probability $\tfrac{2}{3}$ that F carries the gene a, and if he does, I has half a chance of getting it. Therefore I has probability $\tfrac{1}{3}$ of inheriting the gene a from his father. Compared with this, the chance of getting gene a from his mother is negligible.

Similar calculations can be made for other affected relatives. We summarize in Table 2 the approximate probabilities (assuming λ to be small) that a healthy adult is a carrier given that certain relatives are affected.

TABLE 2. RISK OF BEING A CARRIER

Affected relative	Approximate probability
Child	1
Brother or sister	$\tfrac{2}{3}$
Uncle or aunt	$\tfrac{1}{3}$
First cousin	$\tfrac{1}{4}$
Great uncle or aunt	$\tfrac{1}{6}$

The probabilities in this table become very important when two individuals, both of whom have a family history of the same genetic disease, are contemplating marriage. For example, if both individuals have an affected brother or sister, each has two chances in three of being a carrier. It is reasonable to treat these results as unrelated; and the probability that both are carriers is therefore $\frac{2}{3} \cdot \frac{2}{3} = \frac{4}{9}$. Any child they might have would thus have probability $\frac{4}{9} \cdot \frac{1}{4} = \frac{1}{9}$ of being affected. This probability might be large enough to discourage the marriage of such persons.

PROBLEMS

1. Two carriers marry and have n children. If the number of affected among these is Z, what is the distribution of Z?

2. An individual F is mated with an individual M known to be a carrier. They have n children all of which are healthy. How unlikely is this event if F is a carrier?

3. An individual F is randomly selected from the adult population (whose proportion of carriers is λ) and mated with an individual M known to be a carrier. What is the probability that F is a carrier if it is given that
   (i) they have a child C who is healthy;
   (ii) they have two children, both of whom are healthy;
   (iii) they have n children, all of whom are healthy?
[Hint: Use Bayes' law.]

4. Verify the entries of (8).

5. A man F is known to be the carrier of the lethal gene a. His wife M is randomly chosen from a population of which a proportion λ are carriers. How does the probability that their child C is a carrier depend on λ? Explain.

6. An adult woman (S) whose brother (B) has an affected child (and is therefore a carrier) wishes to know the chance that she is a carrier.
   (i) Find $P(B = \text{Aa and } S = \text{Aa})$.
   (ii) Find $P(B = \text{Aa and } S = \text{AA})$.
   (iii) Find $P(S = \text{Aa}|B = \text{Aa})$.
[Hints: (i) Use the break-down law (4.5) with

$$E: (B = \text{Aa and } S = \text{Aa}), \qquad F_1: (F = \text{AA and } M = \text{Aa}),$$
$$F_2: (F = \text{Aa and } M = \text{AA}), \qquad F_3: (F = \text{Aa and } M = \text{Aa}).$$

(iii) Use (i).]

7. (i) Show that if λ is sufficiently small that terms in λ^2 may be neglected, the probability in Problem 6(iii) is approximately equal to $\frac{1}{2}$.
   (ii) Use part (i) to explain the entry $\frac{1}{4}$ in Table 2.

4.6 MARRIAGE OF RELATIVES

In most human societies there is a prohibition against marriages of close relatives. In this connection it is interesting to observe that the probability of affected children (in the sense of the preceding section) is typically much larger in such marriages than in marriages of unrelated persons. For simplicity, consider the case of brother-sister marriages, which were actually favored in the royal families of ancient Egypt. What is the probability that a brother B and sister S are both carriers of the lethal gene a, so that their marriage would be genetically dangerous, assuming that their parents are unrelated healthy persons? Again a two-stage model is required. For the first stage, we assume that the father F and mother M each has genotype given by model (5.1), and since they are unrelated (in both senses!), the product model is appropriate for the genotypes of the parents:

(1)

event	e_1 (F is AA, M is AA)	e_2 (F is Aa, M is AA)	e_3 (F is AA, M is Aa)	e_4 (F is Aa, M is Aa)
probability	$(1 - \lambda)^2$	$(1 - \lambda)\lambda$	$\lambda(1 - \lambda)$	λ^2

Consider now the second stage, pertaining to the genotypes of B and S. For each result of the first stage (i.e., for each combination of parental genotypes), the genotypes at birth of both children are governed by the appropriate block of Table 5.1. By assumption (iii) of the preceding section, the model for the genotypes of B and S is given by the product of this block with itself. It will be enough to distinguish the following three events on the second stage.

f_1: neither B nor S is affected, and at most one is a carrier (in which case there is no genetic counterindication to their marriage);

f_2: both B and S are carriers;

f_3: at least one of B and S is affected.

To compute for example $P(f_2|e_2)$, we note that when F is Aa and M is AA, then B and S each has probability $\frac{1}{2}$ of being a carrier, so that the conditional probability of both being carriers is $\frac{1}{2} \cdot \frac{1}{2} = \frac{1}{4}$. In this way the following four conditional models are obtained.

(2)

	f_1	f_2	f_3
$\mathcal{B}^{(1)}$	1	0	0
$\mathcal{B}^{(2)}$	$\frac{3}{4}$	$\frac{1}{4}$	0
$\mathcal{B}^{(3)}$	$\frac{3}{4}$	$\frac{1}{4}$	0
$\mathcal{B}^{(4)}$	$\frac{5}{16}$	$\frac{4}{16}$	$\frac{7}{16}$

By summing the columns we find that at birth the genotypes of B and S have probabilities

$$P(f_1) = (1 - \lambda)^2 + \tfrac{3}{2}\lambda(1 - \lambda) + \tfrac{5}{16}\lambda^2$$
$$P(f_2) = \qquad\qquad \tfrac{1}{2}\lambda(1 - \lambda) + \tfrac{4}{16}\lambda^2$$
$$P(f_3) = \qquad\qquad\qquad\qquad\qquad \tfrac{7}{16}\lambda^2.$$

However, once the children are grown, f_3 is excluded and the relevant probability of both being carriers is the conditional probability

$$(3) \qquad\qquad P(f_2 | \text{not } f_3) = \frac{\tfrac{1}{2}\lambda - \tfrac{1}{4}\lambda^2}{1 - \tfrac{7}{16}\lambda^2}.$$

Since λ is small, λ^2 will be very small and negligible in comparison with λ, so that an approximate value is

$$(4) \qquad\qquad P(f_2 | \text{not } f_3) \sim \tfrac{1}{2}\lambda.$$

For example, if $\lambda = .01$, the exact value (3) is .00498 while the approximate value (4) is .005.

For comparison with this value, let us see what is the probability that a healthy man I and a healthy woman J, who are not related to each other, are both carriers. Since for both males and females the fraction of healthy adults who are carriers is λ, we may use model (5.1) for both I and J. If the genotypes of I and J are assumed to be unrelated, these models may be multiplied together. In the resulting product model,

$$(5) \qquad\qquad P(I \text{ and } J \text{ are both carriers}) = \lambda^2.$$

When λ is small, both of the probabilities (4) and (5) will be small, but (4) will be *relatively* very much greater than (5). For example, if $\lambda = .01$, then $\tfrac{1}{2}\lambda = .005$ and $\lambda^2 = .0001$, so that (4) is 50 times as large as (5).

This result may seem surprising at first since we have not supposed that the family of B and S has any history of the disease. The mere fact that they are sibs increases by a factor of 50 the risk that both are carriers, as compared with the risk that both of the unrelated individuals I and J are carriers. The explanation rests on the fact that B and S draw their genes from the same source (F and M), while I and J draw from different sources. F and M are no more likely to be carriers than are I and J, but if one of them is a carrier (the probability of which is about 2λ), there is a substantial chance ($\tfrac{1}{4}$) that *both* B and S will draw the lethal gene.

Calculations similar to those leading to (4) can be made for marriages among other close relatives. Some results of this kind are shown in Table 1. The approximate probability of two relatives both being carriers is seen to be proportional to λ, with the factor of proportionality decreasing as the relationship becomes more distant. The value of this factor can in fact be used to define the closeness of the relationship.

TABLE 1

If I and J are	the approximate probability that both I and J are carriers is
Unrelated	λ^2
Brother and sister	$\frac{1}{2}\lambda$
Father and daughter	$\frac{1}{2}\lambda$
Half brother and half sister	$\frac{1}{4}\lambda$
Uncle and niece	$\frac{1}{4}\lambda$
First cousins	$\frac{1}{8}\lambda$

The fact that brother-sister marriages are such bad genetic risks is thought by some anthropologists to explain the taboo against such marriages that has existed in most human societies. If in a primitive society brother-sister marriages were common, it would soon be observed that diseased children were primarily to be found among their offspring, and the conclusion might be drawn that such marriages were not favored by the gods.

The conclusion that brother-sister marriages are relatively bad genetic risks rests on the assumption that λ is small. For sufficiently large values of λ, the probability (3) actually will be smaller than the probability (5). For example, in some regions of West Africa, the gene responsible for sickle-cell anemia is carried by a considerable proportion of the adult population. If this proportion were for example 50%, a brother-sister marriage would be a slightly better genetic risk than the marriage of unrelated persons (Problem 2).

Let us consider next how one may determine the value of λ for a particular lethal gene. Since carriers Aa do not in general differ in appearance from AA individuals, one cannot conduct a census to determine the frequency λ of carriers in the adult population. However, by (5) we may expect the proportion of couples Aa $\times$ Aa to be λ^2. From Table 5.1, about $\frac{1}{4}$ of the children of such couples will be affected, and no other children can be. This suggests that the frequency of affected children in the population will be about $\frac{1}{4}\lambda^2$. If for example it is observed that one child in 40,000 is affected, we may estimate that

$$(6) \qquad \frac{\lambda^2}{4} = \frac{1}{40,000} \quad \text{or} \quad \lambda = .01.$$

This approach is based on several assumptions that may not be satisfied in practice. When a child is found to be affected, and the parents thus learn that they are both carriers, they may well decide to have no further children. This could result in smaller families among such couples than in the population at large, and hence to a fraction of affected children lower than $\lambda^2/4$, so that the estimate (6) for λ would be too small. This difficulty could be overcome by restricting the frequency count of affected children to first-born children.

Another assumption which may not be satisfied is that leading to (5). The use of a product is valid only if there is no relation between the genotypes of I and J. At first this seems reasonable, since it was assumed that the possession of a single a gene does not affect appearance. To see that the assumption of (statistical) unrelatedness may nevertheless not be at all realistic, consider once more the case of sickle-cell anemia. In the population of the United States, the gene a for this disease is carried much more frequently by Negroes than by persons of other races. Since people tend to marry others of the same race, equation (5) is grossly wrong in this case. This is an example of indirect dependence (Section 2); the genotypes of husband and wife become dependent through the indirect effect of the factor of race.

PROBLEMS

1. Verify the entries of (2).

2. Verify that (5) is bigger than (3) when $\lambda = \frac{1}{2}$.

3. A man F is known to be a carrier; the genotype of his wife M is given by model (5.1).
  (i) What are the probabilities of the genotypes of their daughter D at birth?
  (ii) What is the conditional probability of D being a carrier given that she is healthy?

4. (i) Suppose that the genotypes of a man F and his wife M are unrelated and both given by model (5.1). Show that the probability of both F and his healthy daughter D being carriers is $(\lambda/2) \div (1 - \lambda/4)$.
  (ii) Use (i) to verify an entry in Table 1.
  (iii) Use (i) to find for what values of λ father-daughter marriages are genetically safer than the marriages of unrelated persons.
[Hint: (i) Use Problem 3(ii).]

4.7 PERSONAL PROBABILITY

So far we have been regarding the probability of a result in a random experiment as the mathematical abstraction of the frequency with which the result would occur in a long sequence of similar and unrelated experiments. In addition to this interpretation of probability as frequency, there is a quite different interpretation according to which the probability of a statement represents a certain numerical measure of a person's degree of belief in the statement. We shall in this section discuss this alternative "personal" or "subjective" view of probability and illustrate its use in several problems.

The use of the word probability in everyday speech often has a personal aspect. If an astronomer says "there is probably vegetable life on Mars," or if a sports enthusiast says "the chances are two out of five that the home team will win tomorrow's game," or if a juror thinks "it is unlikely that the witness told the truth," they are not thinking of a frequency interpretation, but are giving a personal assessment of the situation based on a subjective evaluation of the evidence.

How can one arrive at the numerical value of one's personal probability for a given statement? In principle this can always be done by asking whether or not one would accept a bet offered at various odds. Suppose that two horses H and L are to run a race, and you wish to discover your personal probability that horse H will win. If you would be willing to take either side of an even money bet that H will win, this can be interpreted as meaning that you think horse H has half a chance to win, so that for you, $P(\text{H will win}) = \frac{1}{2}$. Now consider another spectator who thinks that H is more likely to win than L. Suppose he would be indifferent between the alternatives

(i) getting $2 if H wins,
(ii) getting $3 if L wins.

If we interpret probability as long-run frequency, his average gain in the two cases would be about

(i') $2 \cdot P(\text{H will win})$,
(ii') $3 \cdot P(\text{L will win})$.

His indifference may be interpreted as meaning that, for him, (i') and (ii') are equal. Since

$$P(\text{H will win}) + P(\text{L will win}) = 1,$$

it follows that *for him*

$$P(\text{H will win}) = \tfrac{3}{5}, \quad P(\text{L will win}) = \tfrac{2}{5}.$$

By such considerations it is theoretically possible for any person to work out his personal probabilities for any set of possible results. In practice, many people find it very difficult to make the required assessment, especially when the set of results is large.

From the mathematical point of view, the model just developed is indistinguishable from the probability models we have been using: as before, there is an event set, and to each event is assigned a nonnegative probability in such a way that the probabilities add up to 1. Although the conceptual interpretations of personal and frequency probability differ, the formal calculus is the same. The addition law, the multiplication law, Bayes' law, etc. are used in the same way regardless of the meaning attached to the probabilities.

One important aspect of personal probability is that it is a function of the person involved: for two different people, the probabilities of a given statement may be markedly different, reflecting the different information, experience, attitudes, or even prejudices, on which they base their beliefs. To the frequentist, on the other hand, the probability of a result depends on the conditions of the experiments, but at least ideally ought not to differ according to personal knowledge and attitudes.

In contrast with the subjective approach, the frequency interpretation is sometimes called "objective." This term is somewhat misleading, since in reality both approaches involve subjective elements. The frequentist exercises judgement in deciding what assumptions to make in building his probability model, so the choice of model will inevitably involve subjective evaluations. The subjectivist, on the other hand, will presumably consider any relevant frequency experience in formulating his personal probability.

One of the most important differences is that the subjectivist is willing to apply probability ideas to a wider class of problems than is the frequentist. Suppose you meet a stranger in a bar, who offers to toss a coin to decide who pays for the drinks. He will pay if the coin falls tails, you will pay if it falls heads. The thought crosses your mind that the coin may be two-headed, but you are too delicate to ask to examine it. What is the probability that the coin is two-headed? The frequentist may hesitate to answer this question, he may even say that the question is meaningless, while the subjectivist need in principle only ask himself which way he would bet at various odds to arrive at his personal probability for the coin to be two-headed.

An interesting class of problems arises when a subjective probability has to be modified in the light of fresh evidence to which a frequency interpretation can be given. Suppose for example you accept the stranger's offer, he tosses, and the coin falls heads. This experimental result will reinforce to some extent your prior suspicions that the coin is two-headed. (If the coin had fallen tails, your suspicions would by now have disappeared.) Let us see by how much the suspicion should be increased by the result "heads," using a subjective approach.

Suppose that, before the coin was tossed, your personal probability for the hypothesis "coin is two-headed" was equal to π, so that your personal probability for "coin is fair" was $1 - \pi$. (We assume for simplicity that there are only these two possibilities.) If the coin is fair, everyone would agree that the probability of "heads" is $\frac{1}{2}$. By Bayes' law,

$$P(\text{Coin is two-headed}|\text{Heads}) = \frac{\pi \cdot 1}{\pi \cdot 1 + (1 - \pi) \cdot \frac{1}{2}} = \frac{2\pi}{1 + \pi}.$$

For example, if originally you thought there was a ten percent chance that the coin is two-headed, after the coin fell heads you should have increased the chance to $2(.1)/(1 + .1) = .182$. The following table shows how the probability of two heads after the toss (the *posterior* probability) depends on the probability of two heads before the toss (the *prior* probability):

Prior	0	.01	.1	.5	.9	.99	1
Posterior	0	.0198	.182	.667	.947	.9950	1

Notice that if you are certain before the experiment that the coin is two-headed ($\pi = 1$) or that the coin is fair ($\pi = 0$), then the experiment will not change your probability. It is generally true that if the prior probability for any statement is 1, the same is true of the posterior probability (Problem 3). If a person's mind is made up, he will not be confused by the facts!

We conclude with two examples of greater applicational interest.

EXAMPLE *1*. *Disputed authorship.* There are a number of literary works whose authorship is in dispute; for example, certain of the Federalist Papers are assumed to have been written either by Madison or by Hamilton. Efforts have been made to resolve the doubt by frequency counts of stylistic elements in the disputed papers and in known works of the two men.

To simplify the example drastically, suppose that a work whose author is known to be either M or H contains a certain peculiar stylistic construction. Author M is fonder of this construction than is author H. In fact, this construction may be found in 60% of the similar works known to be by M, but in only 10% of those by H. Intuitively, its occurrence in the disputed work tends to support the claims of M, but how strongly?

Suppose a historian, before the stylistic analysis, attaches personal probability .3 to the statement "Author is M" and .7 to "Author is H." After the stylistic analysis, his posterior probability for "Author is M" will according to Bayes' law be given by

$$P(\text{Author is M}|\text{Stylistic analysis}) = \frac{.3 \times .6}{.3 \times .6 + .7 \times .1} = \frac{.18}{.25} = .72.$$

This calculation could not of course be defended if the prior assessment that $P(\text{Author is M}) = .3$ had been based on a consideration of style, for in that case the stylistic analysis would not constitute entirely new evidence. In practice it might be difficult for the historian to know the extent to which his prior ideas were influenced by the style of the work.

EXAMPLE *2*. *Probability of guilt.* Another interesting use of personal probability is in criminology, where one wishes to know how likely it is that a man accused of committing a crime is in fact guilty. Suppose it is known that the criminal has a certain property A (he may, for example, be known to be left handed and to belong to a certain blood group). If the accused is guilty, he is certain to possess property A. However, even if he is innocent he may possess property A. If the fraction of persons with property A in the population is p, one might assign to $P(A|\text{innocent})$ the value p. Suppose that the accused is found to possess property A. If for a police official the personal prior probability before this observation was π that the accused is guilty, his posterior probability is by Bayes' law

$$\frac{\pi \cdot 1}{\pi \cdot 1 + (1 - \pi) \cdot p}.$$

The following table shows how this quantity depends on p and π.

	π 0	.1	.3	.5	.7	.9	1
p							
.1	0	.53	.81	.91	.96	.99	1
.3	0	.27	.59	.77	.89	.97	1
.5	0	.18	.46	.67	.81	.94	1
.7	0	.14	.38	.59	.77	.93	1
.9	0	.11	.32	.53	.72	.91	1

(1)

We wish to emphasize that the calculation above could be defended only if the information about property A was not involved in bringing the original accusation. In building the model, we assigned to $P(A|\text{innocent})$ the frequency p with which property A occurs in the population. This assignment would certainly not be reasonable if for example the police had merely looked around for the nearest person with property A and then accused him of the crime.

One must also be careful to see that the value of p is drawn from relevant experience. A blood group or type of hair may for example be rare in the population as a whole, but perhaps be common in the village in which the crime was committed. As with all cases of applying mathematical arguments to real situations, great caution is needed to avoid serious fallacies.

PROBLEMS

1. Consider the problem of drinking with the stranger in the bar, under the assumptions made in the text.

    (i) Suppose he tosses the coin twice and gets "heads" each time. What is your posterior probability that the coin is two-headed (a) for arbitrary π, (b) for $\pi = .1$?

    (ii) What, for arbitrary π, is this posterior probability if he tosses the coin n times and gets "heads" every time?

    (iii) What happens to the posterior probability of (ii) when n is very large (a) for $\pi < 1$, (b) for $\pi = 1$?

2. Verify the entry in (1) for $\pi = .7$, $p = .3$.

3. Suppose that the prior probability for a statement S is 1, and that an event A is observed which is possible according to S.   Use Bayes' law to find $P(S|A)$.

4. Let the prior probability of a statement S be π.   The ratio $\pi/(1 - \pi)$ is called the *prior* odds ratio for S.   An event A is observed.   How is the *posterior* odds ratio $P(S|A)/[1 - P(S|A)]$ related to the prior odds ratio?

5. A detective, informed that a criminal had red hair, accused the nearest red-haired person.   What would be a reasonable value to assign to P(accused has red hair|accused is innocent)?

CHAPTER 5

RANDOM VARIABLES

5.1 DEFINITIONS

When a random experiment is performed, we are often not interested in all the details of the result, but only in the value of some numerical quantity determined by the result. For example, when deciding on the quality of a lot of mass-produced items by inspecting a random sample, we are interested only in the total number of defective items in the sample—which particular sampled items are good, and which are bad, is of no concern to us. Again, the dice player may be interested not in the number of points showing on each die separately but only in the total points showing on the two dice together. It is natural to refer to a quantity whose value is determined by the result of a random experiment as a *random quantity*.

EXAMPLE *1*. *Number of boys in a two-child family.* If two-child families are classified according to the sex of the first and second child, four simple results are possible as listed in the first column of the tableau. Suppose we are interested in the random quantity "number of boys." The value of this quantity for each simple result is shown in the second column.

Simple result	Number of boys
first child male, second child male	2
first child male, second child female	1
first child female, second child male	1
first child female, second child female	0

EXAMPLE *2*. *Number of matchings.* A magazine prints a row of three pictures of movie stars, say Alice, Barbara, and Charlotte. Also given are baby pictures of the three stars, and the reader is invited to match them. He may put the baby pictures in 3! = 6 different orders shown in column one of the tableau. The quantity of interest is the "number of matchings." The value of this quantity corresponding to each simple result is shown in the second column.

Simple result	Number of matchings
Alice, Barbara, Charlotte	3
Alice, Charlotte, Barbara	1
Barbara, Alice, Charlotte	1
Barbara, Charlotte, Alice	0
Charlotte, Alice, Barbara	0
Charlotte, Barbara, Alice	1

A random quantity is represented in the model by a *random variable*. Just as a random quantity attaches a value to each simple result of a random experiment, the corresponding random variable attaches a value to each simple event. (In the language of mathematics, a random variable is thus a *function* of the simple event.) We shall consistently use capital letters to denote random variables.

EXAMPLE 1. *Number of boys in a two-child family (continued)*. Let us represent the random quantity "number of boys" by the random variable B. In the notation of Example 1.5.2, the tableau of Example 1 becomes

Simple event	Value of B
MM	2
MF	1
FM	1
FF	0

EXAMPLE 2. *Number of matchings (continued)*. Let us represent the random quantity "number of matchings" by the random variable M. If we use ABC to represent the arrangement "Alice, Barbara, Charlotte," etc., the tableau of Example 2 becomes

Simple event	Value of M
ABC	3
ACB	1
BAC	1
BCA	0
CAB	0
CBA	1

For general discussion, suppose that a random experiment has simple results $r_1, r_2, \ldots$, and that the corresponding values of a random quantity

q are $q(r_1)$, $q(r_2)$, ... It is not necessary for the numbers $q(r_1)$, $q(r_2)$, . . . all to be distinct, as both examples show. The set of distinct values of q is known as its *value set.* Thus, in Example 1 the value set of "number of boys" is $\{0, 1, 2\}$, while in Example 2 the value set of "number of matchings" is $\{0, 1, 3\}$. As other examples, the value set of the total number of points showing when two dice are thrown is $\{2, 3, . . . , 12\}$; when a random sample of size 25 is drawn from a lot consisting of 20 good and 30 defective items, the value set of the number of defective items in the sample is $\{5, 6, . . . , 25\}$.

Suppose that the random quantity q, which attaches value $q(r_1)$ to the simple result r_1, etc., is represented in the model by the random variable Z, which attaches the value $Z(e_1)$ to the simple event e_1, etc.

Random experiment		Model	
Simple result	Value of q	Simple event	Value of Z
r_1	$q(r_1)$	e_1	$Z(e_1)$
r_2	$q(r_2)$	e_2	$Z(e_2)$
.	.	.	.
.	.	.	.
.	.	.	.

The reader will notice that, in both examples, the second columns of the two tableaus are identical. This will be the case quite generally if the random variable Z is to represent the random quantity q. That is, if e_1 corresponds to r_1, etc., we must have

(1) $$Z(e_1) = q(r_1), \quad Z(e_2) = q(r_2), ...$$

Thus, the value set of Z will always coincide with that of q.

As we have pointed out, the numbers $q(r_1)$, $q(r_2)$, . . . need not be distinct. Therefore, the occurrence of a particular value of the random quantity q may be a composite result. Thus, in Example 1, the result "number of boys is one" is composed of the two simple results "first child male, second child female" and "first child female, second child male." This composite result is represented in the model by the composite event $\{MF, FM\}$, consisting of the two simple events for which B takes on the value 1. It is therefore natural to denote this composite event by the formula $B = 1$, as we have in fact already done in Example 1.5.2. Similarly, in Example 2, $M = 1$ denotes the composite event $\{ACB, BAC, CBA\}$ which represents the composite result "number of matchings is one." In general, if z is one of the possible values of a random variable Z, we shall denote by $Z = z$ the event consisting of all simple events e for which $Z(e) = z$. The event $Z = z$ represents in the model the result (which may be simple or composite) that the random quantity q takes on the value z.

Consider now the probability of the event $Z = z$, corresponding to the frequency with which the random quantity takes on the value z. It follows from Section 1.4 and the definition of the event $Z = z$ that $P(Z = z)$ is the sum of the probabilities of all those simple events e for which $Z(e) = z$. Therefore the value of $P(Z = z)$ will depend on the probabilities that are assigned to the simple events of the model. Thus, use in Example 1 of the probabilities

(2) $\qquad P(\text{MM}) = \tfrac{1}{4}, \quad P(\text{MF}) = \tfrac{1}{4}, \quad P(\text{FM}) = \tfrac{1}{4}, \quad P(\text{FF}) = \tfrac{1}{4}$

gives

$$P(B = 0) = \tfrac{1}{4}, \quad P(B = 1) = \tfrac{1}{4} + \tfrac{1}{4} = \tfrac{1}{2}, \quad P(B = 2) = \tfrac{1}{4}.$$

On the other hand, the product model suggested in Example 3.3.2 assigns to the simple events the probabilities

(3) $\qquad P(\text{MM}) = (.514)^2 = .264, \ P(\text{MF}) = P(\text{FM}) = .514 \times .486 = .250,$

$$P(\text{FF}) = (.486)^2 = .236,$$

and hence gives (as was already computed in Example 4.1.3),

$$P(B = 0) = .264, \ P(B = 1) = .250 + .250 = .500, \ P(B = 2) = .236.$$

PROBLEMS

1. What is the value set of the sum of points on (i) three dice, (ii) n dice?

2. When a random sample of size 10 is drawn from a lot containing 20 good and 8 defective items, what is the value set of the number of defective items in the sample?

3. For the random variable T of Example 1.5.3, list the simple events (1.5.2) making up each of the events $T = 2, T = 3, T = 4, \ldots, T = 12$.

4. In the model of Example 2.1.1, suppose that the marbles numbered 1, 2, 3 represent the Liberals, while 4, 5, 6, 7 represent the Conservatives. If D represents the number of Conservatives included in the delegation,
    (i) list the simple events from (2.1.1) making up the event $D = 1$;
    (ii) what value does D assign to the simple event (346)?

5. Under the assumptions of Problem 1.5.6,
    (i) find the value set of the random quantity "number of boys in the family";
    (ii) if this random quantity is represented in the model by B, what value does B assign to the simple event FMF?
    (iii) list the simple events making up the event $B > 0$;
    (iv) find the probability $P(B > 0)$.
[Hint: (iii) The event $B > 0$ is the union of the events $B = 1$, $B = 2$, and $B = 3$.]

6. If two digits are produced by the random digit generator of Problem 1.5.8, and if Z represents the product of the two digits,
    (i) list the simple events making up the event $Z = 12$;

(ii) find the probability of the event $Z = 12$;

(iii) list the simple events making up the event $Z < 5$;

(iv) find the probability of the event $Z < 5$.

7. Under the assumptions of Problem 1.5.9, let Z represent the number of correct answers.

(i) List the simple events making up the event $Z = 2$.

(ii) Find the probability $P(Z = 2)$.

(iii) Find the probability $P(Z \leq 1)$.

[Hint: (iii) "$Z \leq 1$" is read "Z is less than or equal to 1" and is the union of the events $(Z = 0)$ and $(Z = 1)$.]

8. For the total number T of points showing in two throws with a die, find the probability of the event $T = 4$ if the two throws are unrelated and

(i) the die is loaded and its probabilities are specified by (1.3.1);

(ii) the die is fair.

9. Let T represent the sum of the number of points on three unrelated throws with a fair die.

(i) If the simple events are labeled as in Problem 1.5.11, list the simple events making up the event $T = 5$.

(ii) Find the probability $P(T = 5)$.

5.2 DISTRIBUTION OF A RANDOM VARIABLE

The most important aspects of a random variable are its value set and the probabilities of it taking on its various possible values. As an illustration, consider the random variable T which represents the sum of the number of points showing on two dice. With the model of Example 1.5.3, the possible values t of T and their probabilities are given by

(1)

t	2	3	4	5	6	7	8	9	10	11	12
$P(T = t)$	$\frac{1}{36}$	$\frac{2}{36}$	$\frac{3}{36}$	$\frac{4}{36}$	$\frac{5}{36}$	$\frac{6}{36}$	$\frac{5}{36}$	$\frac{4}{36}$	$\frac{3}{36}$	$\frac{2}{36}$	$\frac{1}{36}$

(Problem 1.5.4).

A table like (1) which associates with each possible value z of a random variable Z the probability $P(Z = z)$ that the value z will occur, is known as the *distribution* of the random variable. (The distribution assigns a real number to each element in the value set and is therefore a function defined over the value set.) Since a random variable always assumes just one of its possible values, these values represent exclusive events that between them exhaust all the possibilities. It follows that the sum of the numbers $P(Z = z)$ over all values of z in its value set must be equal to 1. This fact provides a useful check when we are computing a distribution; for example, the probabilities displayed in the second row of (1) are seen to add up to 1.

EXAMPLE 1. *The delegation.* A very important class of problems, which we shall examine at length in Section 6.2, arises in the theory of sampling. In Example 2.1.1, we considered the drawing of a sample of three as a delegation from a seven-man council consisting of four Conservatives and three Liberals. The number of Conservatives in the delegation is a quantity whose value is determined by the result of the random selection of the sample. Therefore it is a random quantity, and we shall represent it in the model by the random variable D. The computation of Example 2.1.1 shows that $P(D = 3) = \frac{4}{35}$; we shall now obtain the complete distribution of D.

To facilitate the discussion, let us suppose that the Liberal members of the council are numbered 1, 2, 3 while the Conservative members are numbered 4, 5, 6, 7. The 35 possible samples are shown below, grouped according to the value of D.

$$
\begin{array}{lllllll}
D = 0: & 123 \\
D = 1: & 124 & 125 & 126 & 127 \\
       & 134 & 135 & 136 & 137 \\
       & 234 & 235 & 236 & 237 \\
D = 2: & 145 & 146 & 147 & 156 & 157 & 167 \\
       & 245 & 246 & 247 & 256 & 257 & 267 \\
       & 345 & 346 & 347 & 356 & 357 & 367 \\
D = 3: & 456 & 457 & 467 & 567
\end{array}
$$

If we regard the $\binom{7}{3} = 35$ samples as equally likely, the probability $P(D = d)$ that D takes on any specified value d can be found simply by counting the number of samples for which D has the value d, and dividing by 35. In this way, we find the following distribution for D, of which the last term agrees with the value found earlier.

d	0	1	2	3
$P(D = d)$	$\frac{1}{35}$	$\frac{12}{35}$	$\frac{18}{35}$	$\frac{4}{35}$

Notice that the probabilities add up to 1.

EXAMPLE 2. *Indicator.* A very simple but frequently useful kind of random variable is one whose value set is $\{0, 1\}$; such a random variable is called an *indicator*. Let I be an indicator random variable, and let E be the set of simple events for which I takes on the value 1. Then $\overline{E}$ must be the set of simple events for which I takes on its other possible value, 0. Thus $I = 1$ if and only if the event E occurs, and we say that I "indicates" the occurrence of E. For instance, suppose that $I = 1$ if and only if $D = 3$ in the previous example; then I indicates a delegation made up entirely of Conservative members. If the probability that $I = 1$ is p, then the distribution of I is

i	0	1
$P(I = i)$	$1 - p$	p

It is important to notice that quite different random variables may have the same distribution. This point is illustrated in Problems 8 and 9.

It is often instructive to present a distribution in a graphical form. Since $P(Z = z)$ takes on numerical values corresponding to the possible values z, we can do this by plotting the points $(z, P(Z = z))$ on graph paper. Another, slightly different, method that will have advantages for us later is illustrated for distribution (1) in Figure 1. Instead of plotting the point $(z, P(Z = z))$, one may draw a rectangle whose base is centered at z and whose area is equal to $P(Z = z)$. This graphical representation of a distribution is called a *histogram*. (Each bar of the histogram in Figure 1 has unit width, since the values of the random variable are consecutive integers, and height equal to the probability of the value to which it corresponds.)

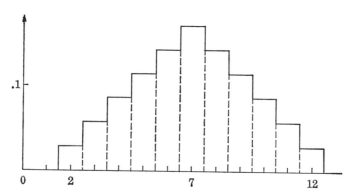

FIGURE 1.   HISTOGRAM FOR POINTS ON TWO DICE

When dealing with experiments composed of several parts, one is frequently concerned with random quantities each of which relates to a different part. (Thus, in two throws of a die, one may be interested in the number of points on the first and the number of points on the second throw.) Let these be represented in the model by the random variables Z and W, and let E denote the event that Z takes on some particular value z, and F that W takes on some particular value w. Then, if a product model is being used, the probability that $Z = z$ and $W = w$ is the probability of the event $(E$ and $F)$, which by (3.2.13) equals $P(E)P(F)$.

This argument shows quite generally that if Z and W correspond to different factors of a product model, we have

(2) $P(Z = z \text{ and } W = w) = P(Z = z)P(W = w)$ for all z, w.

Corresponding to the terminology for independent events mentioned in Section 3.2, it is customary to refer to random variables Z and W for which (2) holds as "independent."

Definition. Two random variables Z and W defined on any probability model are said to be *independent* if they satisfy (2).

In this terminology we have proved above that two random variables defined on different factors of a product model are independent. In fact, random variables defined on different factors will be the only independent random variables that we shall have occasion to discuss.

These remarks easily generalize to experiments with more than two parts. If the random variables $Z_1, Z_2, Z_3, \ldots$ represent random quantities relating to different parts and a product model is being used, then formula (3.2.14) shows that for any possible values $z_1, z_2, z_3, \ldots$ we have

$$(3) \qquad \begin{aligned} P(Z_1 = z_1 \text{ and } Z_2 = z_2 \text{ and } Z_3 &= z_3 \text{ and } \ldots) \\ &= P(Z_1 = z_1)P(Z_2 = z_2)P(Z_3 = z_3) \cdots . \end{aligned}$$

Again extending the terminology for independent events, random variables $Z_1, Z_2, Z_3, \ldots$ defined over any probability model are said to be *independent* if they satisfy (3) for all $z_1, z_2, z_3, \ldots$. Thus in particular, random variables defined over different factors of a product model are independent.

PROBLEMS

1. Under the assumptions of Problem 1.5.6, find the distribution of the number B of boys in the family.

2. Under the assumptions of Problem 1.5.9, find the distribution of the number of correct answers.

3. Find the distribution of the sum of points on two throws with the loaded die whose probabilities are specified by formula (1.3.1).

4. Draw a histogram for the distribution of (i) the random variable D of Example 1; (ii) the random variable A of Example 1.4.1; (iii) the random variable B of Problem 1.7.5; (iv) the random variable S of Problem 1.7.7.

5. In two throws with the die of Problem 3, what is the probability that the number of points in both throws is even?

6. From a half-dozen eggs, of which two are rotten, two are selected at random. If D denotes the number of rotten eggs in the sample, (i) find $P(D = 0)$ and $P(D = 2)$; (ii) using the fact that the sum of the probabilities of all values is 1, find $P(D = 1)$.

7. From the city council of Example 1, a delegation of three is selected at random in April; in September it is necessary to send to Washington another delegation, of two members, and it is decided again to select it at random from the full council.

What is the probability that both delegations consist entirely of Liberals?   [Hint: Build a product model.]

8. In three tosses with a fair coin, let Z be the number of tails and W the number of heads.
   (i) Show that Z and W have the same distribution.
   (ii) Show that Z and W are different random variables.
[Hint: (i) Find the distribution of Z and that of W.   (ii) Find a simple event e for which $Z(e)$ and $W(e)$ are not equal.]

9. If a model and two random variables Z and W are given by the following table

e	e_1	e_2	e_3	e_4	e_5
$P(e)$	$\frac{1}{8}$	$\frac{1}{8}$	$\frac{1}{8}$	$\frac{1}{4}$	$\frac{3}{8}$
$Z(e)$	3	6	6	3	8
$W(e)$	8	8	8	6	3

determine whether Z and W have the same distribution.

5.3 EXPECTATION

Like many of the ideas of probability, the notion of expectation arose in the study of gambling games, and was later found to have broader applications.   As the motivating example, let us suppose that a gambler is to pay a casino a fixed price for the privilege of playing a chance game that may pay him varying amounts.   If one disregards the casino's need to meet its overhead and make a profit, it would generally be agreed that a "fair" price for the game would be the amount the gambler might expect, on the average, to win.   An example will illustrate the point.

EXAMPLE 1.   *Throwing a die.*   Suppose the gambler throws a fair die, after which the casino pays him as many dollars as there are points on the upper face.   If he plays many times, the gambler may expect to win one dollar about $\frac{1}{6}$ of the time, two dollars $\frac{1}{6}$ of the time, and so forth.   Thus his average winning per game would be about

$$\tfrac{1}{6}\cdot 1 + \tfrac{1}{6}\cdot 2 + \ldots + \tfrac{1}{6}\cdot 6 = \tfrac{1}{6}(1 + 2 + \ldots + 6) = \tfrac{21}{6} = \tfrac{7}{2}$$

dollars.   This sum might be taken as a fair price to pay for the privilege of playing the game; a gambler paying this price would, in a long sequence of games, probably have an average winning per game near zero.

Study of the example will suggest how one may calculate for any random quantity the value which it may be expected to have on the average.   So that we may refer to them easily, let us number the simple results, denoting them by r_1, r_2, $\ldots$, and denote the corresponding simple events by e_1, e_2, $\ldots$.   In a sequence of n trials of the experiment, let $\#(r_1)$, $\#(r_2)$, $\ldots$

denote the numbers of occurrences of the results r_1, r_2, ... Consider a random quantity that is represented in the model by the random variable Z. We shall now compute the sum of the n values taken on by the random quantity in these n trials. Whenever r_1 occurs, the value of the random quantity is $Z(e_1)$, so that the $\#(r_1)$ occurrences of r_1 contribute $Z(e_1)\#(r_1)$ to the sum. Similarly, the $\#(r_2)$ occurrences of r_2 contribute $Z(e_2)\#(r_2)$, and so on. Therefore the sum of all n values is

$$Z(e_1)\#(r_1) + Z(e_2)\#(r_2) + \ldots .$$

Dividing this total by n we see that the average of the observed values of the random quantity is

$$Z(e_1)f(r_1) + Z(e_2)f(r_2) + \ldots .$$

Our basic idea of probability as representing long-run frequency suggests that when n is large, the frequencies $f(r_1)$, $f(r_2)$, . . . should be close to the probabilities $P(e_1)$, $P(e_2)$, . . . , so that the average of a great many observed values should be close to $Z(e_1)P(e_1) + Z(e_2)P(e_2) + \ldots .$ This is what we would expect the random quantity to be on the average. It is called the *expected value* of Z, or the *expectation* of Z, and is denoted by $E(Z)$.

Definition. The expected value of the random variable Z is

(1) $$E(Z) = Z(e_1)P(e_1) + Z(e_2)P(e_2) + \ldots .$$

The expectation of Z in the model represents the long-run average value of the random quantity which Z represents, just as probability represents long-run frequency.

EXAMPLE 1. *Throwing a die (continued).* Let us apply the definition to our motivating example. If X represents the number of points showing when a fair die is thrown, and we use the model of Example 1.3.1 which assigns probability $\frac{1}{6}$ to each of the six simple events, then $E(X)$ is seen to have the value $\frac{7}{2}$ calculated above.

Just as it is important to make a conceptual distinction between a *result*, which is something that may happen when a random experiment is performed, and the *event* that represents this result in the mathematical model for the experiment, it is important to distinguish between a *random quantity* and the *random variable* that represents this quantity in the model. However, in discussing specific applications it is often convenient to be somewhat careless, and to employ the same terms and notations for both. Thus, we may say that X "is" the number of points showing rather than that X "represents in the model" the number of points showing, or to speak of the "expected number of points" when in reality we mean the "expected value of the random variable representing the number of points." This short-cut usage is customary, and is exactly parallel to that discussed for results and events in Section 1.4.

EXAMPLE 2. *The delegation.* What is the expected value of D, the random variable representing the number of Conservatives in the delegation of Example 2.1? The possible values of D are 0, 1, 2, 3 with probabilities $\frac{1}{35}, \frac{12}{35}, \frac{18}{35}, \frac{4}{35}$ respectively. Therefore

$$E(D) = 0 \cdot \frac{1}{35} + 1 \cdot \frac{12}{35} + 2 \cdot \frac{18}{35} + 3 \cdot \frac{4}{35} = \frac{12}{7} = 1.71.$$

EXAMPLE 3. *Bridge bonus.* In the game of bridge, a rubber is won by the team that first wins two games. If the team wins a rubber by the score of two games to none (2–0), it gets a bonus of 700 points. If it wins the rubber 2–1, its bonus is 500 points. It sometimes happens that a rubber is interrupted when the score stands 1–0. What would be a fair bonus to give to the leading team in that case?

Let us suppose that each team has probability $\frac{1}{2}$ of winning each game, and that the games are unrelated, so that the binomial trials model with $p = \frac{1}{2}$ may be used. If the rubber had been continued, there would have been three possible outcomes, shown in the first two columns below. The third column lists the bonus won by the leading team in each case, while the last column gives the probabilities of the various possible outcomes.

Leading team on		Bonus	Probability
2nd game	3rd game		
Wins	—	700	$\frac{1}{2}$
Loses	Wins	500	$\frac{1}{4}$
Loses	Loses	−500	$\frac{1}{4}$

The expected bonus is

$$700 \cdot \tfrac{1}{2} + 500 \cdot \tfrac{1}{4} - 500 \cdot \tfrac{1}{4} = 350.$$

Actually, the rules of bridge provide a bonus of only 300 points. This may reflect the fact that the leading team (called "vulnerable") is placed at a disadvantage by the rules, so that its chance of winning the next game is somewhat less than $\frac{1}{2}$, and the binomial trials model is not appropriate.

EXAMPLE 4. *Gambling systems.* A gambler who has 7 dollars plays the following system. At the first toss of a coin, he bets 1 dollar on heads, and quits if he wins. If he loses, he bets 2 dollars on heads at the second toss, and quits if he wins. If he loses again, he bets his final 4 dollars on heads at the third toss. His system gives him probability $\frac{7}{8}$ of winning a dollar but what is the expected value of his final gain G? We distinguish four simple events, with the corresponding gains g and probabilities that $G = g$ as shown.

Event	H	TH	TTH	TTT
g	1	1	1	-7
$P(G = g)$	$\frac{1}{2}$	$\frac{1}{4}$	$\frac{1}{8}$	$\frac{1}{8}$

The expected gain is then

$$E(G) = 1 \cdot \tfrac{1}{2} + 1 \cdot \tfrac{1}{4} + 1 \cdot \tfrac{1}{8} - 7 \cdot \tfrac{1}{8} = 0.$$

Thus the gambler will on the average come out even: the game is "fair." Although he has a good chance to win a small amount, this is counterbalanced by the large loss he sustains if he loses. (It is a general fact, not recognized by many advocates of gambling systems, that in a fair game no system can give a positive expected gain.)

EXAMPLE 5. *Lottery.* The following model provides the basis for the topic of "sampling by variables" which plays an important role in the theory of statistics. Suppose that the amount of the prize in a lottery is to be determined by drawing a ticket from a box. The box contains N tickets, on each of which is written an amount. Let v_1 be the amount written on the first ticket, v_2 the amount on the second ticket, and so forth up to v_N. The tickets are thoroughly mixed and one is drawn at random. The prize is then equal to the amount written on the ticket that is drawn. (Most actual lotteries are of course conducted in a somewhat different way, but "lottery" will be a convenient label for the model described above.)

We shall assume that each ticket has the same probability $1/N$ of being drawn. Since the amount of the prize is determined by the result of the random draw, it is a random quantity; the random variable representing it in the model will be denoted by Y. The expected value of Y by formula (1) is

$$E(Y) = v_1 \cdot \frac{1}{N} + v_2 \cdot \frac{1}{N} + \ldots + v_N \cdot \frac{1}{N} = \frac{1}{N}(v_1 + v_2 + \ldots + v_N),$$

which is the arithmetic mean of the amounts written on the N tickets. We shall denote such an arithmetic mean by placing a bar over the symbol that denotes the values being averaged:

$$\bar{v} = \frac{v_1 + v_2 + \ldots + v_N}{N} \qquad \text{(read "v bar").}$$

The formula

(2) $$E(Y) = \bar{v}$$

asserts that the expected value of the prize is the arithmetic mean of the amounts shown on the tickets. As a numerical illustration suppose there are $N = 10$ tickets, showing amounts

$$v_1 = 5, \quad v_2 = v_3 = v_4 = 2, \quad v_5 = v_6 = \ldots = v_{10} = 0.$$

The expectation of Y is then

$$\bar{v} = (5 + 2 + 2 + 2 + 0 + \ldots + 0)/10 = 1.1.$$

If the amounts are in dollars, $1.10 would be a fair price to pay for playing the lottery.

PROBLEMS

1. Throw a die 100 times, recording the numbers shown. Compare the average of these numbers with the expected value $\frac{7}{2}$ found in Example 1.

2. Find the expected number B of boys in a 3-child family under the assumptions of Problem 1.5.6.

3. If X is the number of points on the loaded die whose distribution is given by (1.3.1), determine (i) $E(X)$, (ii) $E(X^2)$.

4. What is $E(Y)$ if Y is the number of red lights encountered on his way to work by the person of Problem 1.4.7?

5. Find the expected number of correct answers under the assumptions of Problem 1.5.9.

6. In Example 3, for what value of the probability that the vulnerable team will win, is the 300 point bonus fair? [Hint: Find the expected value of the bonus when the probability is p.]

7. A lottery of the type of Example 5 has first prize of $1000, second prize $500, and five $100 prizes. Would you want to pay $1 for a ticket if there were (i) 1000 tickets, (ii) 3000 tickets?

8. Study Example 4, and devise a system whereby a gambler with 31 dollars can arrange to win a dollar with probability $\frac{31}{32}$. With this system, what is his expected gain?

9. If Z denotes the number of plays the gambler of Example 4 will make before quitting, find $E(Z)$.

10. Give the value set and distribution of the random variable Y in the numerical illustration of Example 5.

5.4 PROPERTIES OF EXPECTATION

Formula (1) of the preceding section

$$(1) \qquad E(Z) = Z(e_1)P(e_1) + Z(e_2)P(e_2) + \ldots$$

may be put into an alternative form which is often simpler to use. To introduce the idea of the simplification, let us recall Example 3.5. In that example, as so often happens, the random variable takes on the same value for two or more simple events. Thus, Y has the value 2 for three different tickets, which together contribute to $E(Y)$ the amount

$$2 \cdot \tfrac{1}{10} + 2 \cdot \tfrac{1}{10} + 2 \cdot \tfrac{1}{10} = 2 \cdot \tfrac{3}{10} = 2 \cdot P(Y = 2).$$

The single ticket with $Y = 5$ contributes $5 \cdot P(Y = 5)$ to the value of $E(Y)$ and the six tickets labeled 0 contribute nothing. Thus

$$E(Y) = 5 \cdot P(Y = 5) + 2 \cdot P(Y = 2) + 0 \cdot P(Y = 0)$$
$$= 5 \cdot \tfrac{1}{10} + 2 \cdot \tfrac{3}{10} + 0 \cdot \tfrac{6}{10} = 1.1.$$

The example suggests how formula (1) may be simplified in general. Consider first all of the simple events for which Z takes on the value z_1; let the set of these be E_1, so that $P(E_1) = P(Z = z_1)$. In the corresponding terms of (1), the first factor is always z_1. Their total contribution to (1) is therefore z_1 multiplied by the sum of the probabilities of the simple events in E_1, that is, $z_1 P(E_1)$. In just the same way, let E_2 denote the set of simple events for which Z takes on the value z_2. The contribution of these terms to (1) is then $z_2 P(E_2)$. By continuing in this way we see that (1) and therefore $E(Z)$ can be written as

$$E(Z) = z_1 \cdot P(E_1) + z_2 \cdot P(E_2) + \dots,$$

or equivalently as

(2) $$E(Z) = z_1 P(Z = z_1) + z_2 P(Z = z_2) + \dots.$$

When the probability distribution of Z is known, formula (2) is usually more convenient than formula (1). Furthermore, (2) shows that the expected value of a random variable depends only on the distribution of the random variable, that is, the values it can take on and the probabilities of taking on these values, and not on the random variable itself. (For an example of the distinction, see Problem 2.8.) For some purposes however, (1) is very convenient, as it does not require us to know the distribution of Z but only the model and the definition of Z.

EXAMPLE 1. *Gambling systems.* The expectation $E(G)$ of Example 3.4 can be computed by the use of (2) instead of (1). Since G takes on the values 1 and -7 with probabilities $P(G = 1) = \tfrac{7}{8}$ and $P(G = -7) = \tfrac{1}{8}$, we find $E(G) = 1 \cdot \tfrac{7}{8} - 7 \cdot \tfrac{1}{8} = 0$, as before.

EXAMPLE 2. *Indicators.* Let I be an indicator; that is, a random variable whose only values are 0 and 1. Then

$$E(I) = 0 \cdot P(I = 0) + 1 \cdot P(I = 1),$$

so that

$$E(I) = P(I = 1).$$

In words, the expected value of an indicator is the probability of the indicated event.

The expected value of a random variable Z is often used to represent the *center* of the distribution of Z. The interpretation of $E(Z)$ as a central value of the distribution is supported by two considerations.

(i) The expected value is exactly analogous to the physical concept of *center of gravity* of a mass distribution. Let us imagine that the z axis is a weightless rod with mass $P(Z = z_1)$ located at z_1, mass $P(Z = z_2)$ located at z_2, etc. Thus a unit of mass is distributed along the rod in the same way as the unit of probability is distributed along the z axis. The point at which the z axis would then be in balance is known as its center of gravity, and as we shall show below, this point is always at $E(Z)$. This is illustrated in Figure 1a for the distribution of the random variable D of Example 2.1, and in Figure 1b for the number B of heads that appear when three fair pennies are tossed (see Problem 5). In each case the center of gravity is marked by $\triangle$.

0   1   2   3   0   1   2   3

(a)   (b)

FIGURE 1.   CENTER OF GRAVITY

(ii) We shall say that the distribution of Z is *symmetric* about a point μ if it assigns equal probabilities to points equally distant from μ in both directions; that is, if

(3) $$P(Z = \mu + x) = P(Z = \mu - x) \qquad \text{for every } x.$$

(Thus in Figure 1b the distribution is symmetric about $\mu = 1.5$.) It can be shown (Problem 10) that then $E(Z) = \mu$, so that the expected value of a symmetrically distributed random variable is its "center of symmetry." The result is intuitively plausible from (i); for if the mass distribution is symmetric about μ, we would expect the rod to balance at μ.

In spite of its role as center of the distribution, $E(Z)$ need not be a typical, nor even a possible, value of Z (see for example Figure 1). Furthermore, if a distribution is highly asymmetric, it can happen that almost all of the probability lies on one side of the expected value. For example, if Z can take on only the two values 0 and 100 with probabilities $P(Z = 0) = .99$ and $P(Z = 100) = .01$, then $E(Z) = 1$, so that 99% of the probability lies to the left of $E(Z)$. Again, suppose one very rich family has a summer cottage in a village of poor fishermen. If Z denotes the wealth of a family selected at random from this village, then $E(Z)$ will give a rather distorted picture of the prosperity of the village.

To avoid this difficulty, the *median* is sometimes proposed as an alternative value for the center of a distribution. Roughly speaking, the median is the value which has half of the distribution on either side of it.

The equation

(4) $E(Z) = z_1 P(E_1) + z_2 P(E_2) + \ldots$

is valid (and useful) under somewhat more general conditions than those leading
to (2). Suppose that E_1, E_2, ... are exclusive events such that every simple event
belongs to one of the E's. If $Z(e)$ has the same value z_1 for all simple events e in
E_1, the same value z_2 for all simple events in E_2, and so on, then the argument leading to (2) shows (4) to hold even though z_1, z_2, ... may not all be distinct.

For readers acquainted with elementary statics, we now give a proof of the
relationship between expectation and center of gravity stated above. We have
to show that the sum of the torques tending to turn the rod about the point $E(Z)$,

$$[z_1 - E(Z)]P(Z = z_1) + [z_2 - E(Z)]P(Z = z_2) + \ldots,$$

is zero. Since the probabilities of $(Z = z_1)$, $(Z = z_2)$, ... add up to one, we have

$$E(Z) = E(Z)P(Z = z_1) + E(Z)P(Z = z_2) + \ldots.$$

Subtracting this equation from (2) gives the desired result.

PROBLEMS

1. Use formula (2) to find the expected value of a ticket in the lottery of Problem
3.7(i) and 3.7(ii).

2. Under the assumptions of Problem 2.6, find the expected number of rotten
eggs in the sample.

3. Find the expected number of keys that must be tried to open the door of
Problem 1.5.7.

4. Use (2) to find
  (i) the expectation required in Problem 3.5;
  (ii) the expected value of the random variable T whose distribution is given by
     (2.1).

5. Calculate the distribution, and use (2) to obtain the expectation, of the number
B of heads that appear when three fair pennies are tossed. (See Figure 1b.)

6. Let I be an indicator random variable. Can you find any relationship between
$E(I)$ and $E(I^2)$? Between I and I^2? Generalize to higher powers of I.

7. Check for each of the following distributions whether it is symmetric, and if so
find the point of symmetry.
  (i) The distribution of T given by (2.1).
  (ii) The distribution of D in Example 2.1.
  (iii) The distribution of G in Example 3.4.
  (iv) The distribution of the number of keys that must be tried to open the door
     of Problem 1.5.7.
  (v) The distribution of B in Problem 5.

8. Let Z be a random variable which takes on the values $1, 2, \ldots, N$ each with probability $1/N$. Show that this distribution is symmetric about the value $\frac{1}{2}(N + 1)$ and hence that $E(Z) = \frac{1}{2}(N + 1)$. Use (2) to derive the identity

$$(5) \qquad 1 + 2 + \ldots + N = \frac{N(N + 1)}{2},$$

which will be used in Section 6.8.

9. Find the expected gain for the gambling schemes of (i) Problem 4.3.8(i), (ii) Problem 4.3.9(i).

10. If Z is symmetric about μ, show that
  (i) the random variables $Z - \mu$ and $\mu - Z$ have the same distributions;
  (ii) $E(Z) = \mu$.
[Hint: (i) $P(\mu - Z = x) = P(Z - \mu = -x)$; apply (3). (ii) By (i), $E(Z - \mu) = E(\mu - Z)$.]

5.5 LAWS OF EXPECTATION

In this section we shall develop several useful laws connecting the expected values of certain random variables which are defined on the same model. These laws often permit us to calculate expectations by expressing them in terms of other expectations that we already know, and thus to avoid the necessity of using formulas (1) or (2) of the preceding section. With their aid we shall obtain the expectations of several important random variables.

The simplest kind of random variable is one capable of assuming only a single value, say c, so that $Z(e) = c$, for all e in $\mathcal{E}$. Such a random variable, which does not vary at all, is called a *constant* random variable. Since it is always equal to c, it will clearly be equal to c on the average, and so its expected value must also be c. This may be expressed by

$$(1) \qquad E(c) = c$$

and proved formally by reference to equation (2) of the preceding section. In fact, if c is the only possible value of Z, $P(Z = c) = 1$, so that

$$E(Z) = c \cdot P(Z = c) = c \cdot 1 = c.$$

If Z is any random variable, and c is any constant, we can obtain a new random variable by adding c to the value of Z. Let us denote the new random variable by $Z + c$. For example, if Z denotes the random amount a salesman will earn through commissions during a month and if c is his fixed monthly salary, then $Z + c$ will be his total monthly income. The expectation of the random variable $Z + c$ is related to that of Z by equation

$$(2) \qquad E(Z + c) = E(Z) + c.$$

In words, when a constant c is added to a random variable, the same constant is added to its expected value. This relation is just what one would expect: if Z is increased by c in each case, it will be increased by c on the average. A formal proof will be given following the proof of equation (4) below.

Relation (2) concerns the effect of adding a constant; analogously, multiplication by a constant gives

(3) $$E(cZ) = c \cdot E(Z).$$

This is again intuitively plausible since if the value of Z is multiplied by the constant c in each case, its average value will be multiplied by the same constant. (The proof of this is left as an exercise. See Problem 1.)

We now come to the most important law, the *addition law of expectation:* for any two random variables Z and W,

(4) $$E(Z + W) = E(Z) + E(W).$$

In words, the expectation of the sum of two random variables is the sum of their expectations. To get an intuitive understanding of the addition law, let us imagine a gambler who is paid an amount Z by the casino, depending on the roll of a die. In addition, the gambler makes a side-bet with a colleague, which pays him W. Then $Z + W$ is the total amount he receives on a play of the game. The expectation $E(Z + W)$ stands for the average of his total receipts in a long series of plays. Clearly the average value of his total winnings from both sources will equal the sum of his average winnings from the two sources separately. If we replace average by expectation, this statement becomes (4).

To obtain a formal proof of (4), we note that for the simple event e_1 the random variable $Z + W$ takes on the value $Z(e_1) + W(e_1)$, for e_2 the value $Z(e_2) + W(e_2)$, etc. Therefore, from formula (3.1),

$$E(Z + W) = [Z(e_1) + W(e_1)]P(e_1) + [Z(e_2) + W(e_2)]P(e_2) + \ldots.$$

By rearranging terms, the right-hand side may be rewritten

$$[Z(e_1)P(e_1) + Z(e_2)P(e_2) + \ldots] + [W(e_1)P(e_1) + W(e_2)P(e_2) + \ldots];$$

but this is of course equal to $E(Z) + E(W)$, which completes the proof.

If in (4) we take for W the constant random variable c, then (4) reduces to $E(Z + c) = E(Z) + E(c)$. By (1), this is equal to $E(Z) + c$, which proves (2).

It is easy to extend the addition law to more than two random variables. Thus, we may regard $Z + W + V$ as the sum of the random variable $(Z + W)$ and the random variable V. Therefore, by (4),

$$E(Z + W + V) = E(Z + W) + E(V).$$

Now we may apply (4) again to break up $E(Z + W)$ into $E(Z) + E(W)$, showing

$$E(Z + W + V) = E(Z) + E(W) + E(V).$$

More generally, if $Z_1, Z_2, \ldots, Z_n$ are any n random variables,

(5) $E(Z_1 + Z_2 + \ldots + Z_n) = E(Z_1) + E(Z_2) + \ldots + E(Z_n).$

This *general addition law* is useful when we can express a complicated random variable as the sum of several simple ones whose expectations are easier to compute.

EXAMPLE 1. *Dice.* Let T be the total number of points showing when two dice are thrown. If X_1 and X_2 denote the numbers on the two dice separately, then $T = X_1 + X_2$, and hence $E(T) = E(X_1) + E(X_2)$. By Example 3.1, $E(X_1) = E(X_2) = \frac{7}{2}$, so that $E(T) = 7$. The same answer can be obtained less simply by a direct evaluation of $E(T)$ (see Problem 4.4(ii)).

EXAMPLE 2. *Lottery.* Recall Example 3.5. We shall now modify it by supposing that two tickets are drawn from the box, without replacement. Let Y_1 denote the amount written on the first ticket drawn, while Y_2 denotes the amount on the second ticket drawn. The total amount paid in prizes is $Y_1 + Y_2$, and by (4) we have $E(Y_1 + Y_2) = E(Y_1) + E(Y_2)$.

To evaluate this sum, we shall use the model for ordered sampling developed in Section 2.3, with $s = 2$. According to the equivalence law, on each of the two draws each ticket has probability $1/N$ of appearing. Therefore Y_1 and Y_2 each has the same distribution as the random variable Y considered in Example 3.5. It follows from (3.2) that $E(Y_1) = E(Y_2) = \bar{v}$, and hence the expected total paid out is $E(Y_1 + Y_2) = \bar{v} + \bar{v} = 2\bar{v}$. (Notice that the same would be true if the sampling were with replacement, since in that case Y_1 and Y_2 would again have the same distribution as Y.)

An extension of the argument shows that if $s > 2$ tickets are drawn (with or without replacement), the expected total paid out is $s\bar{v}$.

EXAMPLE 3. *Stratified sampling.* In a survey of a three-block district, one dwelling is to be sampled from each block. Some of the dwellings are apartment houses, as shown below:

Block	1	2	3
Number of apartment houses	2	5	1
Number of private residences	11	4	9

What is the expected value of the number A of apartment houses in the sample?

Let I_1 denote the number of apartment houses drawn from Block 1. Clearly, I_1 will be either 0 or 1, and in fact $I_1 = 1$ indicates that the dwelling drawn from Block 1 is an apartment house. Similarly, let I_2 and I_3 denote the numbers of apartment houses drawn from Blocks 2 and 3. Thus $I_1 + I_2 + I_3 = A$ is the total number of apartment houses in the sample.

By the addition law (5),

$$E(A) = E(I_1) + E(I_2) + E(I_3).$$

We know (Example 4.2) that the expected value of an indicator is just the probability of the indicated event. Therefore $E(I_1)$ is the probability that the dwelling drawn from Block 1 is an apartment house, so that $E(I_1) = \frac{2}{13} = .154$. Similarly, $E(I_2) = \frac{5}{9} = .556$ and $E(I_3) = \frac{1}{10} = .100$. Finally therefore

$$E(A) = .154 + .556 + .100 = .810.$$

The method used in this example is widely applicable. Often the number of occurrences of some event may be represented as a sum of indicators, each of which specifies whether the event occurred on one occasion. The reader may convince himself of the usefulness of the *method of indicators* by considering how difficult it would be to calculate $E(A)$ by the methods of Section 4.

EXAMPLE 4. *Matching.* A box contains five tickets numbered from 1 to 5. They are drawn out one by one. What is the expected value of the number M of occasions when the number on the ticket matches the ordinal number of the draw (e.g., ticket number 2 obtained on second draw)?
  Let $I_1, \ldots, I_5$ indicate that a match occurs on draws one, $\ldots$, five. (Thus $I_2 = 1$ if and only if the second ticket drawn bears number 2, etc.) Clearly $M = I_1 + \ldots + I_5$. Let us compute $E(I_2)$. Since each ticket has the same probability of appearing on the second draw (equivalence law of ordered sampling), $P(I_2 = 1) = \frac{1}{5} = E(I_2)$. Similarly $E(I_1) = E(I_3) = E(I_4) = E(I_5) = \frac{1}{5}$, and hence $E(M) = 1$.
  The method applies equally well with any number of tickets; the expected number of correct matchings is always 1.

It is natural to ask whether there is a multiplication law of expectation analogous to the addition law: is the expected value of the product of two random variables equal to the product of their expectations? That this is not always true may be seen by a simple example. Let Z be the number of heads, and W be the number of tails, observed when a fair penny is tossed. Then $E(Z) = \frac{1}{2}$ and $E(W) = \frac{1}{2}$, so that $E(Z) \cdot E(W) = \frac{1}{4}$. But the product ZW is always equal to 0, so that $E(ZW) = 0 \neq \frac{1}{4}$.
  There is however an important case in which the multiplication law does hold. Suppose that the random variables are defined on a product model with two factors, and that Z refers only to the first and W only to the second factor model. (For example, the random variables X_1 and X_2 of Example 1 refer to the throws of two different dice, for which a product model is used.)

We then have the following *multiplication law of expectation:*

(6) $E(ZW) = E(Z) \cdot E(W)$ if Z and W are defined on different factors.

The proof of (6) rests on the definition (3.1.4) of probabilities in a product model. Consider the value of the product ZW corresponding, for example, to the simple event $(e_1$ and $f_2)$ of the product model. Since Z refers only to the first factor, Z in this case has the value $Z(e_1)$ while W has the value $W(f_2)$, so that ZW has the value $Z(e_1)W(f_2)$. By (3.1.4), the probability of this event is p_1q_2. Thus the contribution to the expectation of ZW is $Z(e_1)W(f_2)p_1q_2$. The contributions of the other simple events are obtained analogously and hence, by the definition (3.1) of expectation, $E(ZW)$ equals

$$Z(e_1)W(f_1)p_1q_1 + Z(e_1)W(f_2)p_1q_2 + \ldots$$
$$+ Z(e_2)W(f_1)p_2q_1 + Z(e_2)W(f_2)p_2q_2 + \ldots$$
$$+ \ldots.$$

Taking out the factor $Z(e_1)p_1$ from the first row, $Z(e_2)p_2$ from the second row, etc., we find

$$E(ZW) = [Z(e_1)p_1 + Z(e_2)p_2 + \ldots][W(f_1)q_1 + W(f_2)q_2 + \ldots]$$
$$= E(Z)E(W).$$

The multiplication law of expectation is in fact true for any independent random variables Z and W (Problem 17); however, we shall have occasion to use it only in the special case proved above.

PROBLEMS

1.   Prove that $E(cZ) = cE(Z)$.

2.   Let Y denote the amount you will win in a gambling game and suppose that $E(Y) = \$2.00$.
   (i) If you have to pay $\$2.50$ to be allowed to play, what is your total expected gain or loss?
   (ii) State what law you have used in part (i).

3.   How many points may we expect
   (i) when three dice are thrown?
   (ii) when n dice are thrown?

4.   From a half-dozen eggs of which two are rotten, four are selected at random. Find the expected value of the number R of rotten eggs in the sample using the answer to Problem 4.2 by representing R as $R = 2 - D$ where D is the number of rotten eggs not included in the sample.

5.   Prove that
$$E(Z - W) = E(Z) - E(W).$$
[Hint: Write $Z - W = Z + (-1) \cdot W$.]

6. Prove that

$$E(cZ + dW) = cE(Z) + dE(W)$$

where c and d are constants.

7. If $Z_1, Z_2, \ldots, Z_n$ are any n random variables having a common expectation ζ, and if $\overline{Z}$ denotes their average, prove that $E(\overline{Z}) = \zeta$.

8. Suppose that 10% of the parcels sent abroad do not reach their destination. A person wishing to send two dresses could send them either in a single parcel or in two separate parcels.

    (i) For both methods, find the value the sender can expect to reach the destination if the dresses are worth \$10 and \$15 respectively.

    (ii) For both methods find the probability that both dresses will reach their destination.

    (iii) For both methods find the probability that at least one of the dresses will reach its destination.

    (iv) For each of the criteria (i), (ii), (iii) determine which of the methods is preferable.

[Hints: (ii), (iii) Assume that different mailings are unrelated so that a product model is appropriate for the mailing of two packages.]

9. Solve the following earlier problems by the method of indicators: (i) Problem 3.2, (ii) Problem 3.5, (iii) Problem 4.2, (iv) Problem 4.3.

10. Let A be the number of aces in a five-card poker hand. Calculate $E(A)$ by the following two methods.

    (i) Letting $I_1, \ldots, I_5$ indicate the appearance of an ace on the first, $\ldots$, fifth card dealt.

    (ii) Letting J_1, J_2, J_3, J_4 indicate that the ace of spades, hearts, diamonds, clubs appears in the hand. (See Problem 2.2.12.)

11. If five dice are thrown, how many different faces may be expected to show? [Hint: Let I_1 indicate that at least one die shows an ace, etc.]

12. If three persons are seated at random at a lunch counter with six seats, how many persons may expect to have no one sitting next to them? [Hint: This problem may be worked by listing the $\binom{6}{3} = 20$ equally likely arrangements, and for each the number of isolated persons. Alternatively, one may let I_1 indicate that the first seat is occupied by an isolated person, etc.]

13. Under the assumptions of Problem 4.2.11, find

    (i) the expected rank assigned to Brand A by a single judge,

    (ii) the expected value of the sum of the ranks assigned to Brand A by the 5 judges,

    (iii) the expected average value of the ranks assigned to Brand A by the 5 judges.

14. Use the method of indicators to find the expected number of corner plots in the sample of Problem 4.2.8.

15. (i) Find the distribution of $X_1 \cdot X_2$ in Example 1 by considering its value in each of the 36 equally likely cases.

(ii) Use (i) to find $E(X_1 X_2)$ and verify that it equals $E(X_1) \cdot E(X_2) = (\frac{7}{2})^2$.

16. Use (6) to prove

$$P(E \text{ and } F) = P(E)P(F)$$

if E and F relate to different factors of a product model.

[Hint: Let Z indicate E and let W indicate F, and note that then ZW is also an indicator random variable.]

17. Prove that (6) holds whenever Z and W are independent.

[Hint: Compute the left-hand side of (6) using (4.4) where $E_1, \ldots$ are the events $(Z = z_1 \text{ and } W = w_1)$, etc.]

5.6 VARIANCE

We noted in Section 4 that the expected value of a random variable can be used to specify the center of the distribution of the random variable. However, two distributions with the same expectation, and hence centered at the same point, may still be very different. Thus $E(Z) = 0$ if Z takes on the values -1, 0, 1 with probabilities $\frac{1}{4}$, $\frac{1}{2}$, $\frac{1}{4}$ respectively; but also $E(W) = 0$ if W takes on the values -5, 0, 5 with probabilities $\frac{1}{4}$, $\frac{1}{2}$, $\frac{1}{4}$ respectively (see Figure 1). A much more complete idea of a distribution is obtained if in addition to knowing its expectation, which tells us where it

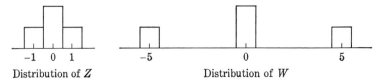

Distribution of Z Distribution of W

FIGURE 1.

is centered, we also know the extent to which the distribution is dispersed away from this center. In this section we shall study the quantity that is most commonly used to specify the dispersion of a distribution.

To simplify the writing, we shall denote the expected value $E(Z)$ of the random variable Z by the Greek letter ζ. It is customary to use, as a measure of dispersion, the expected value of $(Z - \zeta)^2$. This is known as the *variance* of Z, and is denoted by $\text{Var}(Z)$.

Definition. The variance of the random variable Z is

(1) $$\text{Var}(Z) = E(Z - \zeta)^2.$$

In words, the variance of a random variable is the expectation of the square of the difference between Z and its expectation. (This measure of dispersion was introduced by K. F. Gauss (1777–1855).)

To see in what sense (1) measures the dispersion of the distribution of Z, note that if the distribution is widely dispersed, Z will with high probability differ greatly from ζ, so that $(Z - \zeta)^2$ will probably be large, and hence will be large "on the average." Thus if the distribution of Z is widely dispersed, $\text{Var}(Z)$ will be large. (Variance is the analog of the physical concept of the *moment of inertia* of a mass distribution about its center of gravity.)

The reader may wonder why the difference $Z - \zeta$ is squared in defining variance. Suppose that instead we had tried to define a measure of dispersion by using the expected value of $Z - \zeta$ itself. Since $E(Z - \zeta) = E(Z) - \zeta$, we see that $E(Z - \zeta) = 0$, so that as our measure of dispersion we would always get zero. The reason for this is that $Z - \zeta$ is sometimes positive and sometimes negative, as Z happens to fall to the right or to the left of ζ, the positive and negative values just balancing out on the average. This difficulty is avoided by squaring, since $(Z - \zeta)^2$ can never be negative. There are other ways of making $Z - \zeta$ positive; for example, one might use $E|Z - \zeta|$ as a measure of dispersion, where the absolute value $|Z - \zeta|$ means the quantity $Z - \zeta$ always taken with positive sign. This measure was proposed by P. S. Laplace (1749–1827). Laplace's measure is also reasonable but it turns out that Gauss' measure is easier to work with and has nicer mathematical properties.

EXAMPLE 1. *Throwing a die.* We shall calculate the variance of the number X of points showing when a fair die is thrown. In Example 3.1 the expected value of X was computed to be $E(X) = \frac{7}{2}$. The table below lists each possible value x of X, the corresponding probability, and the value of $(x - \frac{7}{2})^2$. (For example, when $x = 2$, $(x - \frac{7}{2})^2 = (2 - \frac{7}{2})^2 = \frac{9}{4}$.)

x	1	2	3	4	5	6
$P(X = x)$	$\frac{1}{6}$	$\frac{1}{6}$	$\frac{1}{6}$	$\frac{1}{6}$	$\frac{1}{6}$	$\frac{1}{6}$
$(x - \frac{7}{2})^2$	$\frac{25}{4}$	$\frac{9}{4}$	$\frac{1}{4}$	$\frac{1}{4}$	$\frac{9}{4}$	$\frac{25}{4}$

Using formula (1) and recalling the definition of expectation (formula 3.1), we find

$$\text{Var}(X) = E(X - \tfrac{7}{2})^2 = \tfrac{25}{4}\cdot\tfrac{1}{6} + \tfrac{9}{4}\cdot\tfrac{1}{6} + \tfrac{1}{4}\cdot\tfrac{1}{6} + \tfrac{1}{4}\cdot\tfrac{1}{6} + \tfrac{9}{4}\cdot\tfrac{1}{6} + \tfrac{25}{4}\cdot\tfrac{1}{6}$$
$$= \tfrac{70}{24} = \tfrac{35}{12}.$$

As further illustrations, the reader may check that the distributions of Figure 1 have $\text{Var}(Z) = \frac{1}{2}$ and $\text{Var}(W) = \frac{25}{2}$.

There is an alternative to formula (1) which is sometimes more convenient for computing variances. Squaring out $(Z - \zeta)^2$ gives $Z^2 - 2Z\zeta + \zeta^2$. Using the laws of expectation, we then find $\text{Var}(Z) = E(Z^2) - 2\zeta E(Z) + \zeta^2$. Since $E(Z) = \zeta$, we see that $2\zeta E(Z) = 2\zeta^2$, and hence

(2) $$\text{Var}(Z) = E(Z^2) - \zeta^2.$$

Formula (2) is more convenient than (1) in that it dispenses with the differences $Z - \zeta$. Thus, in Example 1,

$$E(X^2) = 1 \cdot \tfrac{1}{6} + 4 \cdot \tfrac{1}{6} + 9 \cdot \tfrac{1}{6} + 16 \cdot \tfrac{1}{6} + 25 \cdot \tfrac{1}{6} + 36 \cdot \tfrac{1}{6} = \tfrac{91}{6}$$

so that by formula (2), $\text{Var}(X) = \tfrac{91}{6} - (\tfrac{7}{2})^2 = \tfrac{35}{12}$ which agrees with the value found earlier with the aid of (1).

EXAMPLE 2. *Lottery.* As in Example 3.5 suppose that a box contains N tickets, on which are written amounts $v_1, \ldots, v_N$. If Y denotes the amount written on a ticket drawn at random, we saw that $E(Y) = \bar{v}$, the arithmetic mean of $v_1, \ldots, v_N$. Let us now consider the variance of Y. By formula (1),

$$\text{Var}(Y) = (v_1 - \bar{v})^2 \cdot \frac{1}{N} + \ldots + (v_N - \bar{v})^2 \cdot \frac{1}{N}$$

$$= [(v_1 - \bar{v})^2 + \ldots + (v_N - \bar{v})^2]/N.$$

This is the arithmetic mean of the N quantities $(v_1 - \bar{v})^2, \ldots, (v_N - \bar{v})^2$, which are the squared deviations of the amounts $v_1, \ldots, v_N$ from their arithmetic mean $\bar{v}$, and is called the *mean square deviation* of the numbers $v_1, \ldots, v_N$. We shall denote it by τ^2, so that

$$(3) \qquad \tau^2 = [(v_1 - \bar{v})^2 + \ldots + (v_N - \bar{v})^2]/N,$$

and

$$(4) \qquad \text{Var}(Y) = \tau^2.$$

will be important in Section 9.1 in the discussion of sampling by variables. If the v's have the numerical values assumed in Example 3.5, we find

$$\tau^2 = [(5 - 1.1)^2 + (2 - 1.1)^2 + (2 - 1.1)^2 + (2 - 1.1)^2 $$
$$+ (0 - 1.1)^2 + \ldots + (0 - 1.1)^2]/10$$
$$= [(3.9)^2 + 3(0.9)^2 + 6(1.1)^2]/10 = 2.49.$$

There is an alternative way to compute τ^2 that is sometimes more convenient. Since $E(Y) = \bar{v}$ and $\text{Var}(Y) = \tau^2$, it follows from (2) that $\tau^2 = E(Y^2) - \bar{v}^2$ and hence

$$(5) \qquad \tau^2 = \frac{1}{N} (v_1^2 + \ldots + v_N^2) - \bar{v}^2.$$

Using this method, we find for the numerical example above

$$E(Y^2) = (5^2 + 3 \cdot 2^2 + 6 \cdot 0^2)/10 = 3.7$$

so that $\tau^2 = 3.7 - (1.1)^2 = 2.49$ as before.

The mean square deviation defined above (which is also sometimes called the "population variance") is a measure of the extent to which the numbers $v_1, \ldots, v_N$ are unequal. As the average of squares it is always greater than or equal to zero; it is zero if and only if all the v's are equal.

EXAMPLE *3*. *Indicators*. For later use we now obtain the variance of an indicator random variable. Since an indicator I takes on only the values 1 and 0, and since $1^2 = 1$ and $0^2 = 0$, it follows that $I^2 = I$ in all cases and hence that $E(I^2) = E(I)$. Thus, by formula (2),

$$\text{Var}(I) = E(I) - [E(I)]^2 = E(I)[1 - E(I)].$$

If the probability of the event indicated by I is p (that is, $P(I = 1) = p$), we have

(6) $$\text{Var}(I) = p(1 - p).$$

PROBLEMS

1. Compute the variance of the random variable D of Example 3.2, by both formulas (1) and (2).

2. Compute the variance of
  (i) the bridge bonus of Example 3.3;
  (ii) the random variable B of Problem 3.2.

3. Compute the variance of the random variable
  (i) Y of Problem 3.4;
  (ii) Z of Problem 3.9.

4. Compute the variance of
  (i) the number of correct answers of Problem 1.5.9;
  (ii) the random variable T whose distribution is given by (2.1).

5. Compute the variance of
  (i) the number of rotten eggs in the sample of Problem 4.2;
  (ii) the random variable B of Problem 4.5.

6. Suppose that the lottery of Example 2 has an even number of tickets, half of which have the value 0 and half the value 1. Find $\text{Var}(Y)$.

7. In Problem 5.8 let Z denote the value of the dresses that reach their destination. Find $\text{Var}(Z)$ for both methods of mailing.

8. Find the variance of the value Y of a ticket drawn from the lottery of (i) Problem 3.7(i), (ii) Problem 3.7(ii).

9. Compute Laplace's measure of dispersion $E|Z - \zeta|$ if Z is
  (i) the random variable D of Example 3.2;
  (ii) the random variable Y of Problem 3.4.

5.7 LAWS OF VARIANCE

Variance is governed by laws quite analogous to the laws of expectation. Corresponding to (1)–(3) of Section 5, we have

(1) $$\text{Var}(c) = 0$$

(2) $\text{Var}(Z + c) = \text{Var}(Z)$
(3) $\text{Var}(cZ) = c^2\,\text{Var}(Z).$

These are all intuitively plausible.   If a random variable is always equal
to the constant c, clearly c will also be its expectation.   Since it therefore
never differs from its expectation, its dispersion about this expectation will
be 0.   Again, if we add the constant c to the random variable Z, the expectation ζ of Z is also increased by c (this is just the law (5.2)).   It follows that
the difference $Z - \zeta$ is unchanged, and the variance is therefore also unchanged.   Finally, multiplying a random variable by c will also multiply
its expectation by c, so that the difference $Z - \zeta$ will be c times as large as
before.   Its square is then c^2 times as large, and it follows from (5.3) that
the variance is multiplied by c^2.   As a special case of (3) we obtain by
putting $c = -1$

(4) $\text{Var}(-Z) = \text{Var}(Z).$

According to (3), multiplying a random variable by a constant multiplies
its variance by the *square* of the constant.   For example, if we convert
from measuring in feet to measuring in inches, all measurements are multiplied by 12, so that in the new units the variance of the measurement is
144 times as large as before.   For some purposes, it is more convenient
to have a measure of dispersion that changes by the same factor as the
scale, instead of its square.   This has led to the introduction of the
standard deviation of a random variable Z, denoted by $\text{SD}(Z)$ and defined
as the (positive) square root of the variance.

Definition.   The standard deviation of the random variable Z is

(5) $\text{SD}(Z) = \sqrt{\text{Var}(Z)}.$

Consider now $\text{SD}(cZ) = \sqrt{\text{Var}(cZ)}$.   It follows from (3) that this is
equal to

$$\sqrt{c^2\,\text{Var}(Z)} = c\sqrt{\text{Var}(Z)} \quad \text{if } c \text{ is positive,}$$

and hence

(6) $\text{SD}(cZ) = c\cdot\text{SD}(Z) \quad \text{if } c \text{ is positive.}$

Thus, the standard deviation of a measurement in inches is just 12 times
the standard deviation of the measurement in feet.

As was the case for expectation, the most important laws for variance
are the addition laws.   By analogy with the addition law of expectation,
one might hope for an addition law of variance that would assert that
"the variance of the sum of two random variables is the sum of their
variances."   The following examples show that such a law holds in some
cases but not in others.

(a) Recall Example 5.1 where $T = X_1 + X_2$ is the total number of points
showing when two dice are thrown.   From the distribution of T given by

(2.1) it is easy to calculate that $\text{Var}(T) = \text{Var}(X_1 + X_2) = \frac{35}{6}$ (Problem 4.4(ii)). We have seen in Example 6.1 that $\text{Var}(X_1) = \text{Var}(X_2) = \frac{35}{12}$, so that at least in this case the addition law holds.

(b) For any random variable Z it follows from (3) that $\text{Var}(Z + Z) = \text{Var}(2Z) = 4\,\text{Var}(Z)$. Since this does not equal $\text{Var}(Z) + \text{Var}(Z) = 2\,\text{Var}(Z)$, the addition law does not hold in this case.

To find the conditions under which the addition law holds, let us obtain a general formula for $\text{Var}(Z + W)$. To simplify the writing we shall denote $E(Z)$ by ζ and $E(W)$ by η. From (5.4) $E(Z + W) = \zeta + \eta$; the difference between $Z + W$ and its expectation $\zeta + \eta$ is

$$(Z + W) - (\zeta + \eta) = (Z - \zeta) + (W - \eta).$$

The square of this expression is

(7) $$(Z - \zeta)^2 + 2(Z - \zeta)(W - \eta) + (W - \eta)^2.$$

Since the variance of $Z + W$ is by definition the expectation of (7),

(8) $$\text{Var}(Z + W) = \text{Var}(Z) + \text{Var}(W) + 2E[(Z - \zeta)(W - \eta)].$$

The quantity $E[(Z - \zeta)(W - \zeta)]$ appearing on the right-hand side is known as the *covariance* of Z and W, and is denoted by $\text{Cov}(Z, W)$.

Definition. The covariance of the random variables Z and W is

(9) $$\text{Cov}(Z, W) = E[(Z - \zeta)(W - \eta)].$$

In this notation, (8) may be written as

(10) $$\text{Var}(Z + W) = \text{Var}(Z) + \text{Var}(W) + 2\,\text{Cov}(Z, W),$$

and the desired *addition law for variance* is seen to be

(11) $$\text{Var}(Z + W) = \text{Var}(Z) + \text{Var}(W) \quad \text{if} \quad \text{Cov}(Z, W) = 0.$$

A detailed discussion of the properties and meaning of covariance, which is a measure of the tendency of two random variables to vary together, is not required at this point and will be postponed to Section 7.2. However we shall here note two simple properties. By multiplying out the product indicated on the right side of (9), and then applying the addition law for expectation, we find

$$E[(Z - \zeta)(W - \eta)] = E[ZW - \zeta W - \eta Z + \zeta \eta]$$
$$= E(ZW) - \zeta E(W) - \eta E(Z) + \zeta \eta = E(ZW) - \zeta \eta.$$

Hence, (9) may be written in the alternative form

(12) $$\text{Cov}(Z, W) = E(ZW) - E(Z)E(W),$$

which is analogous to the second form for variance given by (6.2).

Recalling (5.6), we see from (12) that if Z and W are defined on different factors of a product model, then

(13) $$\text{Cov}(Z, W) = 0.$$

Combining (11) and (13) gives the useful special form of the addition law

(14) $$\mathrm{Var}(Z + W) = \mathrm{Var}(Z) + \mathrm{Var}(W)$$
$$\text{if } Z, W \text{ are defined on different factors of a product model.}$$

Extension of the argument (which is given in Section 7.2) leads to

(15) $$\mathrm{Var}(Z_1 + Z_2 + \ldots) = \mathrm{Var}(Z_1) + \mathrm{Var}(Z_2) + \ldots$$
$$\text{if } Z_1, Z_2, \ldots \text{ are defined on different factors of a product model.}$$

More generally, equations (13), (14), and (15) hold for any independent random variables (Problem 11). However, we shall have occasion to use them only for the special case for which they are stated above.

EXAMPLE 1. *Several dice.* Suppose T is the total number of points showing when n dice are thrown. Then, if $X_1, X_2, \ldots, X_n$ are the numbers showing on the n dice separately, we have $T = X_1 + X_2 + \ldots + X_n$. If a product model is used to represent the experiment, the addition law (15) applies and gives

$$\mathrm{Var}(T) = \mathrm{Var}(X_1) + \mathrm{Var}(X_2) + \ldots + \mathrm{Var}(X_n).$$

By Example 6.1, each of these n terms equals $\frac{35}{12}$, and hence $\mathrm{Var}(T) = 35n/12$.

We conclude the section by obtaining a useful identity. Consider the expected squared difference of a random variable Z from an arbitrary constant a. If $E(Z) = \zeta$ and if we put $X = Z - a$, it follows from (5.2) and (2) that

$$E(X) = \zeta - a \quad \text{and} \quad \mathrm{Var}(X) = \mathrm{Var}(Z).$$

By (6.2),

$$\mathrm{Var}(X) = E(X^2) - [E(X)]^2 = E(Z - a)^2 - (\zeta - a)^2$$

and hence

(16) $$E(Z - a)^2 = \mathrm{Var}(Z) + (\zeta - a)^2.$$

Let us now apply the identity (16) to the lottery model of Example 6.2, replacing Z by Y. The variable Y takes on the values $v_1, \ldots, v_N$ each with probability $1/N$, so that

(17) $$E(Y - a)^2 = [(v_1 - a)^2 + \ldots + (v_N - a)^2]/N.$$

Since $E(Y) = \bar{v}$ and $\mathrm{Var}(Y) = \tau^2$, it is seen from (16) that the left-hand side of (17) is equal to $\tau^2 + (\bar{v} - a)^2$. Multiplying through by N and using the expression (6.3) for τ^2, we find

(18) $$(v_1 - a)^2 + \ldots + (v_N - a)^2 = (v_1 - \bar{v})^2 + \ldots + (v_N - \bar{v})^2 + N(\bar{v} - a)^2.$$

This identity, which will be useful in proving several results later in the book, is also easily verified by direct computation (Problem 12). An important special case of (18) arises when $a = 0$, giving

(19) $v_1{}^2 + \ldots + v_N{}^2 - N\bar{v}^2 = (v_1 - \bar{v})^2 + \ldots + (v_N - \bar{v})^2.$

Relation (19) may be obtained also by comparing (6.3) and (6.5).

PROBLEMS

1. Note that the distributions of Figure 6.1 are those of two random variables, one of which is a constant multiple of the other. Check that (6) holds in this case.

2. Compute the variance of the random variable R of Problem 5.4 by the method suggested there for computing $E(R)$, and Problem 6.5.

3. Prove that if Z and W are random variables defined on different factors of a product model, and if c and d are constants, then

$$\mathrm{Var}(cZ + dW) = c^2\,\mathrm{Var}(Z) + d^2\,\mathrm{Var}(W).$$

4. If $Z_1, \ldots, Z_n$ are n unrelated random variables having a common variance σ^2, and if $\bar{Z}$ denotes their average, prove that $\mathrm{Var}(\bar{Z}) = \sigma^2/n$.

5. Let I and J be the indicators of two events E and F. Show that

$$\mathrm{Cov}(I, J) = P(E \text{ and } F) - P(E)P(F).$$

6. Find the covariance of the random variables Z and W defined in Problem 2.8.

7. Use the definition (6.1) and the laws of expectation to write out formal proofs of (1), (2), and (3).

8. If a random variable is multiplied by a negative constant, what happens to its standard deviation?

9. Find the variance of the random variable A of Example 5.3. [Hint: Use the method of indicators.]

10. Solve the following earlier problems by the method of indicators: (i) Problem 6.2(ii); (ii) Problem 6.4(i).

11. Prove that (13) and (14) hold whenever Z and W are independent. [Hint: Use the result of Problem 5.17.]

12. Prove the identity (18) by writing $v_1 - a$ as $(v_1 - \bar{v}) + (\bar{v} - a)$, and similarly for $v_2 - a, \ldots, v_N - a$, and then squaring out the terms of the left-hand side of (18).

13. Let Z be any random variable, and let ζ be its expectation. Show that the value of a which makes $E(Z - a)^2$ smallest is $a = \zeta$. [Hint: Note that the second term on the right-hand side of (16) is positive for all values of a different from ζ, and hence that for all $a \neq \zeta$ the left-hand side of (16) is greater than the first term of the right-hand side.]

14. Show that the value of a which makes $(v_1 - a)^2 + \ldots + (v_N - a)^2$ smallest is $a = \bar{v}$. [Hint: Apply the argument of the preceding problem to (18).]

15. Show that the variance of a random variable Z is always strictly positive (not only nonnegative) unless Z is constant. [Hint: If Z has at least two possible values, at least one of them must differ from $E(Z) = \zeta$. Apply (6.1).]

CHAPTER 6

SPECIAL DISTRIBUTIONS

6.1 THE BINOMIAL DISTRIBUTION

In Section 3.3 we introduced the concept of a sequence of binomial trials. These are trials on each of which there are just two possible results, conventionally called "success" and "failure." It is assumed that the various trials are unrelated, so that a product model is appropriate, and that the probability of success is the same, say p, on each trial. From these assumptions it was shown to follow that the probability of getting successes on b *specified* trials of a sequence of n trials, and failures on the remaining $n - b$ trials, is given by

$$(1) \qquad\qquad p^b q^{n-b}$$

where $q = 1 - p$ is the (constant) probability of failure on each trial.

However, in many cases we do not care on which particular trials the successes occurred, but are interested only in the total number of successes. Since this number is determined by the experimental results, it is a random variable, which we shall denote by B. Examples are the number of aces when a die is thrown ten times, the number of boys in a family of five children, the number of defectives among 20 items produced by a machine. We shall now obtain a formula for the distribution of B.

Let us begin by finding the probability that $B = 2$ when $n = 5$. In five trials, two successes occur in the following patterns of successes (S) and failures (F):

$$SSFFF, \quad SFSFF, \quad SFFSF, \quad SFFFS, \quad FSSFF,$$
$$FSFSF, \quad FSFFS, \quad FFSSF, \quad FFSFS, \quad FFFSS.$$

Since these are exclusive, the probability that $B = 2$ is the sum of the probabilities of these ten patterns. According to (1), the probability of each of these patterns is $p^2 q^3$, and hence $P(B = 2) = 10p^2 q^3$.

We could have determined the number of patterns without actually listing them.   Each pattern is specified by indicating which two of the five trials are to be successes, and the number of ways of choosing two out of the five trials is just $\binom{5}{2} = 10$.

The argument extends easily to the general case.   The number of patterns with b successes and $n - b$ failures is $\binom{n}{b}$.   These patterns are the (exclusive) ways of getting just b successes, and the probability of each pattern is $p^b q^{n-b}$, as given by (1).   Therefore the probability of getting just b successes in n binomial trials is

$$(2) \qquad\qquad P(B = b) = \binom{n}{b} p^b q^{n-b}.$$

Definition.   The number B of successes in n binomial trials each having success probability p is called a *binomial* random variable.   Its distribution (2) will be referred to as the "binomial distribution (n, p)."

For illustration, consider once more the case $n = 5$.   From formula (2) and Table A we find that the binomial distribution $(n = 5, p)$ is

(3)

b	0	1	2	3	4	5
$P(B = b)$	q^5	$5pq^4$	$10p^2q^3$	$10p^3q^2$	$5p^4q$	p^5

The term "binomial" derives from the fact that the probabilities (2) are the terms in the binomial formula for the expansion of $(q + p)^n$.   The reader may check that when $(q + p)^5$ is expanded, the successive terms are those in (3) (Problem 21).

EXAMPLE 1.   *Random digits.*   What is the distribution of the number B of zeros produced when a random digit generator is operated 5 times?   We can regard the five operations as $n = 5$ binomial trials with probability of success (i.e. getting a zero) $p = .1$.   Therefore the desired distribution is obtained by putting $p = .1$ in (3):

b	0	1	2	3	4	5
$P(B = b)$	.5905	.3280	.0729	.0081	.0005	.0000

The six entries must of course add up to 1, which gives a check on the work.

The importance of the binomial distribution is attested by the publication of several extensive tables for it.   The most notable are the tables published by the Ordnance Corps of the U.S. Army in 1952, which gives the binomial distribution to seven decimal places for all values of n up to 150, and for p at intervals of .01; and that published by Harvard University in 1955, which for these values of p gives the binomial distribution to 5 decimal places for selected values of n up to 1000.*

We give in Tables B and C at the back of the book a few examples of binomial distributions. Table B covers all values of n up to 10 for the five values $p = .05, .1, .2, .3,$ and $.4$, while Table C is for $p = .5$ and $n \leq 30$.

EXAMPLE 2. *Multiple choice examination.* An examination consists of eight multiple choice questions, each of which offers a choice between five answers of which only one is correct. To pass, it is necessary to answer at least three of the questions correctly. What is the probability that a student will pass who, being completely unprepared, for each of the questions selects one of the answers at random?

We can view the eight questions as eight unrelated trials; the probability of success (correct answer) is $p = \frac{1}{5} = .2$ for each. The desired probability is then the probability of at least three successes in eight binomial trials with $p = .2$. The probability of passing is therefore $P(B \geq 3)$ where B has the binomial distribution $(n = 8, p = .2)$. Table B gives

$$P(B \geq 3) = .1468 + .0459 + .0092 + .0011 + .0001 = .2031.$$

The reader will notice that no values of p greater than $\frac{1}{2}$ are given in our tables. Such values have been omitted, thereby cutting the size of Table B in half, because a binomial probability for $p > \frac{1}{2}$ can be reduced to one with $p < \frac{1}{2}$. To see how this is done, suppose we wish to find the probability of getting seven hits (and three misses) when firing ten times at a target, where it is assumed that the shots are unrelated and that the probability of a hit is .6 on each shot. If we call a hit a "success," the desired probability is $P(B = 7)$ for the binomial distribution $(n = 10, p = .6)$, which is not given in Table B. However, if we instead call a miss a "success," then the desired probability is $P(B = 3)$ for the binomial distribution $(n = 10, p = .4)$, which from Table B is seen to be .2150. By means of this device, which amounts to interchanging the roles of "success" and "failure," one sees that $P(B = b)$ for the binomial distribution (n, p) is equal to $P(B = n - b)$ for the binomial distribution $(n, 1 - p)$. The same identity may be proved from formula (2) (Problem 23).

In the special case when $p = \frac{1}{2}$, replacing p by $1 - p$ changes nothing, so that our identity in this special case states

$$P(B = b) = P(B = n - b) \quad \text{when} \quad p = \frac{1}{2}.$$

---

* *Table of the Cumulative Binomial Probabilities,* Ordnance Corps Pamphlet ORDP 20-1 (1952). 577 pages.
Tables of the Cumulative Binomial Probability Distribution, Harvard University Press (1955). 503 pages.

That is, when $p = \frac{1}{2}$, B has a distribution which is symmetric about $n/2$ in the sense of Section 5.4 (Problem 18). Thus, when $p = \frac{1}{2}$ it suffices to give the values of $P(B = b)$ for $b \leqq n/2$; this fact permits Table C to be half as large as would otherwise be necessary. For example, if we need $P(B = 7)$ for the binomial distribution $(n = 10, p = \frac{1}{2})$, this is the same as $P(B = 3)$ for that distribution, which from Table C is seen to be .1172.

EXAMPLE 3. *Quality control.* It is a characteristic of mass production that not all items coming off a production line will conform to specifications. Items that fail to conform may be called *defectives*. It is one of the tasks of *quality control* to seek to identify and eliminate the causes leading to defective items, but even after this has been done an occasional defective will appear as if by accident. The successive items coming off the line may in fact behave like binomial trials, with the appearance of a defective item constituting a "success." If this is the case, the process is said to be "in a state of (statistical) control."

A process which is in control may of course at any time lose this property if some part of the process deteriorates or breaks down. It is important to check, by regular inspection of the items produced, whether the process is still in control. To illustrate how this can be done, suppose that the process has been in control for some time and that observation during this period has shown the average frequency of defectives to be 5 percent. As a check, ten items of the day's production are inspected each day. If the process continues under control, it is reasonable to assume that the number B of defectives has the binomial distribution $(n = 10, p = .05)$. The distribution of B is then given by the following table (taken from Table B);

(4)

b	0	1	2	3	4	5
$P(B = b)$	.5987	.3151	.0746	.0105	.0010	.0001

with the probabilities for $b > 5$ being negligible. Suppose now that it has been agreed to institute a careful physical check of the whole process on any day on which the sample contains three or more defectives. As long as the process is in control, we see from the table that $P(B \geqq 3) = .0116$. With this inspection procedure, we would therefore on the average institute the complete check unnecessarily on about one percent of the days. A more detailed discussion of the methods used for deciding such questions is taken up in books on statistics.

EXAMPLE 4. *Size of an experiment.* It is known from past experience that on the average about 20 percent of the animals entering a certain experiment die before termination of the experiment. If we want to have probability at least .98 of having at least five animals complete the experiment, with how many animals should we start? It seems natural to regard the number B of surviving animals as the number of successes in n binomial trials with probability $p = .8$ of success, and we wish then to find the smallest number n of trials such that $P(B \geq 5) \geq .98$.

Let us first try $n = 7$. What is the probability of getting five or more successes on $n = 7$ trials with $p = .8$? Interchanging "success" and "failure" as discussed above, we see that the desired probability is the same as the probability of obtaining two or fewer successes with $n = 7$ and $p = .2$. From Table B we find this to be $.2097 + .3670 + .2753 = .8520$. Thus seven animals are not enough since the probability that five of them or more will survive is only 85%. A similar calculation shows that there is a probability $.9437$ of five or more survivors when eight animals are used, and a probability $.9804$ when nine are used. Thus nine is the smallest number of animals guaranteeing the desired result.

We conclude this section by finding the expectation and variance of the binomial random variable B. To compute the expectation of the number B of successes in n binomial trials, we could multiply each possible value b of B by its probability $\binom{n}{b} p^b q^{n-b}$, and then add all these terms. There is however a much simpler method, based on the representation of B as a sum of indicators, an idea already employed in Section 5.5. The total number of successes in n trials is the number of successes in the first trial plus the number of successes in the second trial plus . . . plus the number of successes in the nth trial. Therefore, if $I_1, I_2, \ldots, I_n$ denote the numbers of successes in the first, second, . . . , nth trial respectively, then

$$(5) \qquad\qquad B = I_1 + I_2 + \ldots + I_n.$$

This equation can also be verified in a slightly different way. The number I_1 of successes in the first trial is 1 if the first trial is a success and 0 if the first trial is a failure. It is thus an indicator random variable, indicating success in the first trial. Similarly, I_2 indicates success in the second trial, and so forth. Since each indicator equals 1 if the corresponding trial succeeds and is otherwise 0, the number of successes is the number of indicators equal to 1, which is the sum of the indicators, as was to be proved. Now by Example 5.4.2, the expected value of each of the indicators $I_1, \ldots, I_n$ is p. It follows from (5) that $E(B)$ is the sum of n terms, each equal to p, so that

$$(6) \qquad\qquad E(B) = np.$$

This elegant, important, and useful formula asserts that in a sequence of binomial trials, the expected number of successes is the product of the number of trials and the success probability.

The representation (5) of B as a sum of indicators also gives us the variance of B. Since the indicators $I_1, \ldots, I_n$ are defined on different factors of a product model, it follows from the addition law for variance (5.7.15) that

$$\mathrm{Var}(B) = \mathrm{Var}(I_1) + \ldots + \mathrm{Var}(I_n).$$

The variance of each I was seen in Example 5.6.3 to be equal to $p(1 - p) = pq$ so that

(7) $\mathrm{Var}(B) = npq.$

To illustrate formulas (6) and (7), let us recall Example 3, where $n = 10$ and $p = .05$. The number B of defectives in this example has expectation $E(B) = .5$ and variance $\mathrm{Var}(B) = .475$. The reader may check these values by computing $E(B)$ and $\mathrm{Var}(B)$ from (5.4.2) and (5.6.2), using the distribution (4).

PROBLEMS

1. Use Table C to find the probabilities $P(B = b)$ for the following values of n and b when $p = .5$: $n = 4$, $b = 2$; $n = 6$, $b = 3$; $n = 8$, $b = 4$; $n = 10$, $b = 5$; $n = 20$, $b = 10$; $n = 30$, $b = 15$.

2. Use Tables B and C to find the probabilities $P(B = b)$ for the following values of n, p, and b:
  (i) $n = 5$, $p = .2$, $b = 2$
  (ii) $n = 5$, $p = .8$, $b = 3$
  (iii) $n = 10$, $p = .6$, $b = 7$
  (iv) $n = 20$, $p = .5$, $b = 13$.

3. For $n = 6$, $p = .3$ find the probabilities of
  (i) at least three successes
  (ii) at most three successes.

4. Plot the histogram for the binomial distributions (i) $n = 10$, $p = .2$, (ii) $n = 30$, $p = .5$.

5. Each student in a class of ten is asked to write down at random one of the digits $0, 1, \ldots, 9$. The instructor believes that digits 3 and 7 are especially attractive. If the digits are really selected at random, how surprising would it be if four or more students chose one of these "attractive" digits?

6. In the preceding problem how surprising would it be if fewer than three digits were even?

7. In Example 3.3.8, what is the probability that eight or more patients receive the same drug?

8. Compute the distribution of the number B of male children in a three-child family, assuming $P(\mathrm{Male}) = .514$.

9. (i) If $n = 5$, how small must p be before $P(B = 0) > P(B = 1)$?
  (ii) Solve the problem for an arbitrary value of n.

10. What is the most probable number of successes in eight binomial trials with success probability $p = .1$?

11. In Table B, verify the entry $P(B = 2) = .2458$ when $n = 6$ and $p = .2$ from formula (2).

12. In Example 3, suppose that the process has gone out of control, so that the probability of a defective has jumped from its usual value of .05 to the value .2. How likely is it that the inspection procedure will call for a check?

13. Find the probability that the frequency f of heads in n tosses with a fair coin lies between .4 and .6 inclusive for $n = 5$, $n = 10$, and $n = 20$.

14. Use formulas (5.4.2) and (2) to check that $E(B) = np$ for the cases $n = 1, 2, 3$.

15. (i) Find formulas for the expectation and variance of the frequency B/n of success in n binomial trials.
　　(ii) What can be said about the behavior of the variance as n becomes very large?

16. Find formulas for the expectation and variance of the number of failures in n binomial trials with success probability p.

17. In Example 4, if nine animals are used, what is the expectation of the number of survivors? What is its variance?

18. Using formulas (2.2.3) and (2), show that the binomial distribution is symmetric about $E(B) = n/2$ when $p = \frac{1}{2}$.

19. Find the expectation and variance of the number of successes in n unrelated trials when the probability of success is p_1 on the first trial, p_2 on the second trial, $\ldots$, p_n on the nth trial. Are these trials binomial?

20. Certain textbooks state that np is the value of B most likely to occur. Criticize this statement.

21. Expand the binomial $(q + p)^5$ by multiplication and check the assertion made in the text about (3).

22. Use the fact that the probabilities (2) are the terms in the expansion of $(q + p)^n$ to show that these probabilities add up to one.

23. Use formula (2) to prove that $P(B = b)$ for the binomial distribution (n, p) is equal to $P(B = n - b)$ for the binomial distribution $(n, 1 - p)$.

24. If in a sequence of n unrelated trials, the success probabilities $p_1, \ldots, p_n$ are close although not equal, the binomial distribution corresponding to n trials and success probability $p = (p_1 + \ldots + p_n)/n$ will give a good approximation to the distribution of the number S of successes. Compute this approximation for the distribution of Problem 3.3.9 and compare it with the distribution found there.

6.2　THE HYPERGEOMETRIC DISTRIBUTION

We have already on several occasions considered the problem of drawing a sample from a population containing two different kinds of items: red and white marbles, defective and nondefective fuses, conservatives and liberals, etc.   To have a general terminology, let us refer to the items of one kind as *special* and the remaining items as *ordinary*.   Then the number D of special items appearing in the sample is a random variable, and we shall now obtain its distribution.

Let the size of the population be N and the size of the sample s, and suppose that the population contains r special and $N - r$ ordinary items. The distribution of D was already obtained in Example 5.2.1 for the case $N = 7$, $r = 4$, $s = 3$, if we regard the four conservatives as the special items.   A study of this example reveals the general method.   An examination of the samples giving $D = 2$ in the example shows that the samples are arranged in a tableau of three rows and six columns, or $3 \cdot 6 = 18$ samples in all.   The columns correspond to the $\binom{4}{2} = 6$ ways in which two conservatives can be selected from the four available conservative members: 45, 46, 47, 56, 57, 67.   The rows correspond to the $\binom{3}{1} = 3$ ways in which one liberal can be selected from the three available liberals: 1, 2, 3.

Let us now carry through the argument in general.   How many samples of size s can be formed to contain just d special, and hence $s - d$ ordinary, items?   There are r special items available, so that the special items for the sample may be chosen in $\binom{r}{d}$ ways.   Similarly, the $s - d$ ordinary items must be chosen from the $N - r$ such items in the population, which can be done in $\binom{N - r}{s - d}$ ways.   Each choice of the special items may be combined with each choice of the ordinary items.   Therefore the number of samples with $D = d$ is $\binom{r}{d}\binom{N - r}{s - d}$.   If all $\binom{N}{s}$ samples are assumed to be equally likely, this gives

$$(1) \qquad\qquad P(D = d) = \frac{\binom{r}{d}\binom{N - r}{s - d}}{\binom{N}{s}}.$$

Definition.   The number D of special items in a random sample of size s from a population of size N that contains r special items is called a *hypergeometric* random variable.   Its distribution (1) will be referred to as the "hypergeometric distribution (N, r, s)."   (The term has its origin in the fact that the quantities (1) appear in a series of that name studied in analysis.)

As an illustration, let us use this formula to derive the hypergeometric distribution of Example 5.2.1. Putting $N = 7$, $r = 4$, $s = 3$ in (1), we obtain the following results, which agree with those obtained earlier by direct enumeration.

d	$\binom{4}{d}$	$\binom{3}{3-d}$	$P(D = d)$
0	1	1	$\frac{1}{35}$
1	4	3	$\frac{12}{35}$
2	6	3	$\frac{18}{35}$
3	4	1	$\frac{4}{35}$
			$\overline{1}$

The hypergeometric probabilities (1) depend on four quantities: N, r, s, and d. It would be essentially impossible to publish a table covering all values that might arise in practice. A table* has been published giving the probabilities to six decimal places for populations of size $N \leqq 50$, and certain selected higher values.

To obtain the expected value of D, one might use formula (5.4.2), writing $E(D)$ as the sum of the products of the possible values d and the corresponding probabilities (1), and then simplifying the result. (This method was illustrated in Example 5.3.2.) A much simpler derivation may be based on the method of indicators, used in the preceding section for the binomial random variable. Recalling from Section 2.3 that a random sample can be obtained by drawing an ordered random sample, we may think of D as the number of special items in an ordered sample of size s. In this model, D will have the same distribution (and hence the same expectation) as before.

The total number of special items included in s draws is the number of special items obtained on the first draw plus the number of special items obtained on the second draw plus ... plus the number of special items obtained on the sth draw. Therefore, if $I_1, I_2, \ldots, I_s$ denote the number of special items obtained on the first, second, ..., sth draw respectively, then

$$(2) \qquad\qquad D = I_1 + I_2 + \ldots + I_s.$$

As in the binomial case, this equation can also be seen in a slightly different way. The number I_1 of special items on the first draw is 1 or 0 as the first draw produces a special or an ordinary item. It is thus an indicator random variable, indicating success on the first draw. Similarly I_2 indicates a special item on the second draw, and so forth. Since each indicator equals 1 if the corresponding draw produces a special item and is

---

* *Tables of the Hypergeometric Probability Distribution*, by Gerald J. Lieberman and Donald B. Owen. Stanford University Press (1961). 726 pages.

otherwise 0, the number of special items in the sample is the number of indicators equal to 1, which is the sum of the indicators, as was to be shown. To compute $E(D)$ it is now only necessary to find the expectation of each of the I's.

By Example 5.4.2, we have $E(I_1) = P(I_1 = 1)$, which is the probability that the first item drawn is special. Since all N items are equally likely to be drawn on the first draw and since r of them are special, it follows that

$$E(I_1) = \frac{r}{N}.$$

By the same argument, $E(I_2) = P(I_2 = 1)$ is the probability that the second item is special. By the equivalence law of ordered sampling (2.3.5), on each draw the probability of getting a special item is r/N and therefore $E(I_2) = \ldots = E(I_s) = r/N$. Hence by applying the addition law of expectation to (2) we find

(3) $$E(D) = s \cdot \frac{r}{N}.$$

We shall now develop an approximation for the hypergeometric distribution which is accurate when the sample constitutes only a small fraction of the population, so that the *sampling fraction* s/N is small. Suppose that a sample of s items is drawn *with replacement* from the population of N items of which r are special. On each draw the chance of getting a special item is r/N, just as it was for sampling without replacement, but now the s draws are unrelated. Therefore they form a sequence of s binomial trials, and the number of special items in the sample has the binomial distribution with $n = s$ and $p = r/N$.

As we have remarked in Example 3.3.3, when the sampling fraction s/N is small, it should make little difference whether sampling is done with or without replacement. This suggests that the distribution of D, the number of special items when sampling without replacement, will be approximately the same as the binomial distribution with $n = s$ and $p = r/N$, *provided s/N is small*. For example, if in fact D has the hypergeometric

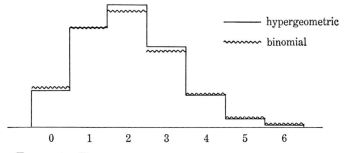

FIGURE 1. BINOMIAL APPROXIMATION TO HYPERGEOMETRIC

distribution ($N = 100$, $r = 20$, $s = 10$), we might as an approximation treat D as if it had the binomial distribution ($n = 10$, $p = .2$). Figure 1 shows the two histograms to be in reasonably good agreement. It is common practice to use the binomial tables for the computation of hypergeometric probabilities when the sampling fraction is small.

The expected value of the approximating binomial distribution with $n = s$ and $p = r/N$ is of course $np = s \cdot r/N$, which agrees exactly with $E(D)$. Thus the exact and approximate distributions are centered at the same place. The reason for this agreement is that whether we sample with or without replacement, the number of special items in the sample is the sum

$$I_1 + I_2 + \ldots + I_s$$

of the indicators of special items on the s draws. With either sampling method, each indicator has the same expectation $/N$.

The variance of the approximating binomial distribution, from formula (1.7) with $n = s$ and $p = r \ N$, is

$$(4) \qquad\qquad s \cdot \frac{r}{N} \cdot \left(1 - \frac{r}{N}\right).$$

Will this again agree exactly with $\mathrm{Var}(D)$? We should not expect this to happen, because in deriving (1.7) use was made of the unrelatedness of the indicators, which does not hold for sampling without replacement. The formula for $\mathrm{Var}(D)$ requires a correction factor, which turns out to be $(N - s)/(N - 1)$. This gives for the variance of a hypergeometric random variable

$$(5) \qquad\qquad \mathrm{Var}(D) = \frac{N - s}{N - 1} \cdot s \cdot \frac{r}{N}\left(1 - \frac{r}{N}\right).$$

This formula will be proved in Section 7.2.

We note that the correction factor is always less than 1 (unless $s = 1$ in which case there is no difference between sampling with and without replacement) but that if N is much larger than s, it is quite close to 1. That the two formulas for the variance are in close agreement when s/N is small corresponds to the fact noted earlier that in this case it makes little difference whether the sampling is with or without replacement.

In the special case when $s = N$, in which the "sample" consists of the entire population, we see that $\mathrm{Var}(D) = 0$. This is as it should be, since D has the constant value r if we take the entire population into the sample.

PROBLEMS

1. Use (1) to check the distribution of the random variable D of Problem 5.2.6.

2. Compute the distribution of the number of red cards in a poker hand, using

Table A and the value $\binom{52}{5} = 2{,}598{,}960.$ Give the probabilities to three decimals and graph the histogram.

3. A sample of size $s = 5$ is drawn from a population of $N = 20$ items. For what values of r is $P(D = 0) > P(D = 1)$?

4. A batch of 20 items contains five defectives. Find the probability that a sample of four will contain more than one defective.

5. Suppose that the sample of four houses of Example 4.2.3 is drawn at random from all 13 houses rather than by the method of stratified sampling. Find the distribution of
  (i) the number of corner houses included in the sample;
  (ii) the number of houses from the south side of the street included in the sample.

6. Suppose that in Example 3.3.8, so as to avoid the possibility that most of the ten patients receive the same drug, drug A is assigned to five of the patients at random with the other five receiving drug B. If five of the patients have a light case of the disease and five a severe case, what is the probability that at least four of the severe cases will receive drug A?

7. Using formula (1), solve (i) Problem 2.2.5, (ii) Problem 2.2.6.

8. A lot of ten items contains five defectives. Plot the histogram of the distribution of the number D of defectives in a sample of four, and that of the binomial approximation to this distribution.

9. A sample of ten items is drawn from a lot of 1000, which contains 50 defective items. Use the binomial approximation to find approximately the probability that the sample will contain two or more defectives.

10. Derive formulas for the expectation and variance of the fraction D/s of special items, when the distribution of D is given by (1).

11. A sample of size s is drawn from a population of N items, of which r are special. Derive formulas for the expectation and variance of the number of special items left in the population after the sample has been drawn. What is the distribution of this number?

12. A box contains nine marbles, three red, three white, three blue.
  (i) What is the probability that a sample of four will contain marbles of only two colors?
  (ii) How many colors do you expect in such a sample?
  (iii) What is the distribution of the number of red marbles?

13. A stratified sample is obtained by drawing unrelated samples from four blocks as follows:

Block	1	2	3	4
Private dwellings	8	10	13	7
Apartment houses	4	3	2	5
Sample size	2	2	3	2

Find the expectation and variance of the number of apartment houses included in the sample.   [Hint: Let A_1 be the number of apartment houses drawn from block 1, etc.]

14.   In the preceding problem, find the probability that the sample includes at least one apartment house from each block.

15.   In Problem 13, find the probability that no apartment house is drawn.

16.   The random variable D of equation (2) may be represented as a sum of indicators in a different way.   Number the special items from 1 to r, and let J_1 indicate that the first special item is included in the sample, etc.
   (i) Prove that $D = J_1 + J_2 + \ldots + J_r$.
   (ii) Use this representation to obtain an alternative proof of (3).

6.3   STANDARD UNITS

One of the most remarkable facts in probability theory, and perhaps in all of mathematics, is that the histograms of a wide variety of different distributions are very nearly the same when the right units are used on the horizontal axis.   We cannot present the theoretical reasons underlying this fact, but we can and shall support it by some computational evidence, and then show how it may be used to calculate, with little effort, approximate values for certain probabilities that would be very cumbersome to compute exactly.   Let us begin by considering an example.

EXAMPLE 1.   *The sum of points on several dice.*   We obtained in Problem 1.5.4 the distribution of the number, say T_2, of points showing when two dice are thrown.   By an extension of the method used there, it is possible in principle to find the distribution of the number T_n of points showing when n dice are thrown, for any value of n, although the work gets heavier as n is increased.   We present the histograms for $n = 1, 2, 4$, and 8 in Figure 1 (here T_1 denotes the number of points on a single die).
   A study of this figure will make clear the following points.   (a) As the number n of dice is increased, the distribution moves off to the right. This is not surprising since it is easily seen (Problem 5.5.3) that $E(T_n) = 7n/2$.   The distribution of T_n is centered at $E(T_n)$, which gets arbitrarily large as n gets sufficiently large.   (b) The distribution tends to get more spread out as n gets larger.   This is also reasonable, since we know (Example 5.7.1) that $SD(T_n) = \sqrt{\frac{35}{12}} \cdot \sqrt{n}$.   The standard deviation is a measure of the spread of the distribution and as n becomes large, so does $\sqrt{n}$, and hence so does $SD(T_n)$.   We note also that the minimum and maximum values of T_n are n and $6n$ respectively, so that the range of T_n is $6n - n = 5n$, which also becomes large with n.   (c) The histogram is a rectangle when $n = 1$, and roughly the shape of a triangle when $n = 2$. As n increases, the histogram appears to smooth out, though for $n = 8$ it is

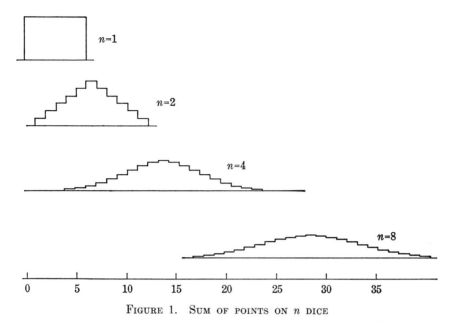

FIGURE 1. SUM OF POINTS ON n DICE

already so low and spread out that its shape cannot be seen very clearly.

In order to bring the distribution into sharper focus, we shall make a change in the units of the graphs.   To overcome the tendency of the distribution to move off to the right, let us take $E(T_n)$ as the new origin on the horizontal axis.   This can be achieved by considering the random variable $T_n - E(T_n)$, whose expected value is 0, so that its histogram is centered at 0.   Similarly, the tendency to spread out may be overcome by using $\mathrm{SD}(T_n)$ as the new unit of scale, or equivalently by considering the random variable

$$T_n^* = \frac{T_n - E(T_n)}{\mathrm{SD}(T_n)}.$$

The change of origin and scale that we have suggested for T_n may be applied to any random variable Z, and leads to the consideration of the "standardized" variable

$$(1) \qquad Z^* = \frac{Z - E(Z)}{\mathrm{SD}(Z)},$$

which is also known as the random variable Z "reduced to standard units." It is seen that

$$E(Z^*) = \frac{E[Z - E(Z)]}{\mathrm{SD}(Z)} = 0$$

and

$$\mathrm{Var}(Z^*) = \frac{\mathrm{Var}[Z - E(Z)]}{[\mathrm{SD}(Z)]^2} = \frac{\mathrm{Var}(Z)}{\mathrm{Var}(Z)} = 1,$$

so that a random variable, when it has been reduced to standard units, has expectation 0 and variance 1.

To see how to construct the histograms of standardized variables, let us recall from Section 5.2 that a histogram is a row of contiguous bars, one for each possible value of the random variable. Each bar is centered at the value it represents, and its area is equal to the probability of that value. As an example consider the number B of successes in two binomial trials with success probability $p = \frac{1}{9}$. Since

$$E(B) = \tfrac{2}{9} \quad \text{and} \quad SD(B) = \sqrt{2 \cdot \tfrac{1}{9} \cdot \tfrac{8}{9}} = \tfrac{4}{9},$$

the distributions of B and B^* are given in the following table.

b	0	1	2
b^*	$\dfrac{0 - \left(\frac{2}{9}\right)}{\frac{4}{9}} = -\dfrac{2}{4}$	$\dfrac{1 - \left(\frac{2}{9}\right)}{\frac{4}{9}} = \dfrac{7}{4}$	$\dfrac{2 - \left(\frac{2}{9}\right)}{\frac{4}{9}} = \dfrac{16}{4}$
Probability	$\frac{64}{81}$	$\frac{16}{81}$	$\frac{1}{81}$

The three bars of the histogram of B^* are centered at $-\frac{2}{4}$, at $\frac{7}{4}$, and at $\frac{16}{4}$ respectively, as shown in Figure 2. The distance between successive centers is

$$\tfrac{7}{4} - \left(-\tfrac{2}{4}\right) = \tfrac{9}{4} \quad \text{and} \quad \tfrac{16}{4} - \tfrac{7}{4} = \tfrac{9}{4}.$$

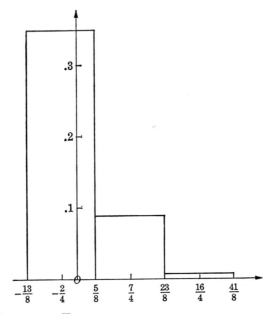

FIGURE 2. HISTOGRAM OF A STANDARDIZED BINOMIAL

Each bar must therefore have width $\frac{9}{4}$ extending half this amount on either side of the center. For example, the bar corresponding to the value $b = 0$ covers the interval from

$$-\tfrac{2}{4} - \tfrac{1}{2}\cdot\tfrac{9}{4} = -\tfrac{13}{8} \quad \text{to} \quad -\tfrac{2}{4} + \tfrac{1}{2}\cdot\tfrac{9}{4} = \tfrac{5}{8}.$$

Similarly, the second bar of the histogram covers the interval from $\frac{5}{8}$ to $\frac{23}{8}$, and the third one the interval from $\frac{23}{8}$ to $\frac{41}{8}$.

Let us next consider the height of the first bar. This is determined by the fact that

$$\text{area} = \text{height} \times \text{width}$$

and that the area (by definition of a histogram) must equal the probability, which is $\frac{64}{81}$. Since the width is $\frac{9}{4}$, we must have

$$\tfrac{9}{4} \times \text{height} = \tfrac{64}{81}$$

or

$$\text{height} = \tfrac{64}{81}\cdot\tfrac{4}{9} = \tfrac{256}{729}.$$

Similarly, the height of the second bar is found to be $\frac{64}{729}$ and that of the last bar $\frac{4}{729}$.

Let us now generalize this result. Suppose that Z is a random variable whose possible values are consecutive integers. To simplify the notation, let

$$E(Z) = \zeta \quad \text{and} \quad \text{SD}(Z) = \sigma.$$

If z is any possible value of Z, the next value is $z + 1$, and the corresponding values of Z^* are

$$\frac{z - \zeta}{\sigma} \quad \text{and} \quad \frac{z + 1 - \zeta}{\sigma}.$$

The distance between these two values is

$$(2) \qquad \frac{z + 1 - \zeta}{\sigma} - \frac{z - \zeta}{\sigma} = \frac{1}{\sigma}.$$

(This agrees with the value $\frac{9}{4}$ between successive values in the example, since there $\text{SD}(Z) = \frac{4}{9}$.) Since this is the distance between any two successive values, it follows as in the example that each bar of the histogram must have width $1/\sigma$, extending half this amount on either side of the center. The bar of the histogram corresponding to z therefore has as its base the interval

$$\left(\frac{z - \zeta}{\sigma} - \frac{1}{2}\cdot\frac{1}{\sigma}, \frac{z - \zeta}{\sigma} + \frac{1}{2}\cdot\frac{1}{\sigma}\right) \quad \text{or} \quad \left(\frac{z - \zeta - \frac{1}{2}}{\sigma}, \frac{z - \zeta + \frac{1}{2}}{\sigma}\right).$$

Since the area of the bar is $P(Z = z)$ and its width is $1/\sigma$, its height must satisfy the equation

$$\text{height} \cdot \frac{1}{\sigma} = P(Z = z),$$

so that

$$\text{height} = \sigma \cdot P(Z = z).$$

In more general notation, we have proved that the bar of the histogram of Z^* corresponding to the value $Z = z$ has as its base the interval with end points

$$(3) \qquad \frac{z - E(Z) - .5}{SD(Z)} \quad \text{and} \quad \frac{z - E(Z) + .5}{SD(Z)}$$

while its height is

$$(4) \qquad\qquad SD(Z) \cdot P(Z = z)$$

as shown in Figure 3.

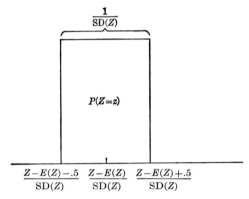

FIGURE 3. SINGLE BAR OF HISTOGRAM OF Z^*

Application of these formulas gives the histograms of T_1^*, T_2^*, T_4^*, and T_8^* shown in Figure 4. Comparing this with Figure 1, it is seen that in the new units it is much easier to perceive the shapes of the histograms and that they become smoother as n is increased.

In calculating a standard deviation, it is necessary to extract the square root of a variance. While there are arithmetic methods for extracting square roots, it is frequently quicker to use a table such as Table D. This table gives the square roots of the integers from 1 to 99, and also (as $\sqrt{10n}$) the square roots of the integers 10, 20, 30, . . . , 990. Some examples will indicate how the table is used.

(a) $\sqrt{17} = 4.1231$

(b) $\sqrt{470} = 21.679$

(c) $\sqrt{1700} = \sqrt{17 \times 100} = \sqrt{17} \times \sqrt{100} = \sqrt{17} \times 10 = 41.231$

(d) $\sqrt{.047} = \sqrt{470/10,000} = \sqrt{470}/100 = .21679$

(e) To find $\sqrt{17.3}$, we must use interpolation. The table gives $\sqrt{17} = 4.1231$ and $\sqrt{18} = 4.2426$. Since 17.3 is three-tenths of the way

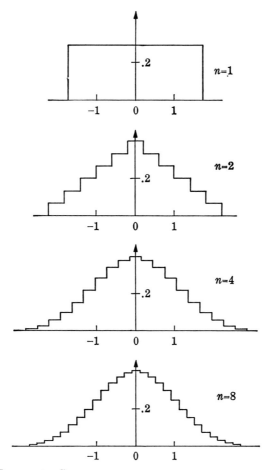

FIGURE 4.   STANDARDIZED SUM OF POINTS ON n DICE

from 17 to 18, it is natural to take $\sqrt{17.3}$ to be three-tenths of the way from 4.1231 to 4.2426.   To obtain $\sqrt{17.3}$, we therefore start with $\sqrt{17}$ and add to it three-tenths of the difference between $\sqrt{18}$ and $\sqrt{17}$, that is

$$\sqrt{17.3} = 4.1231 + .3(4.2426 - 4.1231) = 4.1231 + .3(.1195)$$
$$= 4.1590.$$

(The correct value is 4.1593.)

(f) The computation of $\sqrt{1.53}$ would seem to call for interpolation between $\sqrt{1}$ and $\sqrt{2}$; however $\sqrt{n}$ is changing too rapidly here for the interpolation to be accurate.   Since $\sqrt{1.53} = \sqrt{153}/10$, we may instead interpolate between $\sqrt{150} = 12.247$ and $\sqrt{160} = 12.649$ to obtain the result $\sqrt{1.53} = 12.368/10 = 1.2368$. (The correct value is 1.2369.)

PROBLEMS

1. Construct the histogram for B^* where B is the number of successes in 10 binomial trials with probability of success $p = .5$.

2. Let B have the binomial distribution with $n = 100, p = \frac{1}{2}$. Find the beginning and end point of the base of the bar in the histogram of B^* corresponding to the values (i) $B = 50$, (ii) $B = 47$, (iii) $B = 52$.

3. Construct the histogram for D^* where D is the random variable defined in Example 5.2.1.

4. Let D have the hypergeometric distribution with $N = 200, r = 30, s = 20$. Find the beginning and end point of the base of the bar in the histogram of D^* corresponding to the values (i) $D = 2$, (ii) $D = 3$, (iii) $D = 5$.

5. Use Table D to find the square roots of (i) 900, (ii) 47,000, (iii) .000173, (iv) .963.

6.4 THE NORMAL CURVE AND THE CENTRAL LIMIT THEOREM

In Figure 4 of the preceding section we saw that the histograms of the standardized variables T_n^* (where T_n is the sum of the number of points on n dice) appear to smooth out and take on a definite shape as n increases. In more advanced treatments of probability theory it is proved in fact that as n increases indefinitely, the histogram of T_n^* tends to the smooth curve pictured in Figure 1, which is known as the *normal curve*. Some of its properties will be discussed later in this section, but we first give another example of distributions tending to the normal curve.

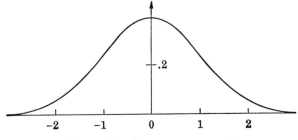

FIGURE 1. THE NORMAL CURVE

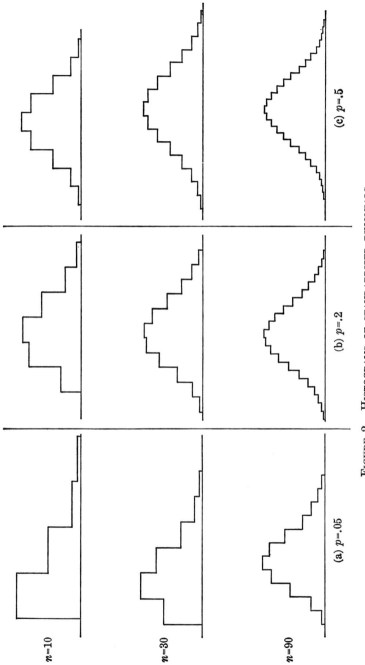

FIGURE 2. HISTOGRAMS OF STANDARDIZED BINOMIALS

EXAMPLE 1. *Binomial distributions.* In Section 1 we defined the binomial random variable B as the number of successes in n binomial trials each having success probability p. Since $E(B) = np$ and $\text{Var}(B) = npq$, where $q = 1 - p$, the variable B in standard units is

(1) $$B^* = \frac{B - np}{\sqrt{npq}}.$$

We show in Figure 2 the histograms of B^* for increasing n (10, 30, 90) and for three different values of p (.05, .2, .5). The figure shows that for each fixed value of p, as n is increased the histogram of B^* looks more and more like the normal curve. Notice that the approach to the normal curve is considerably slower for $p = .05$ than for $p = .5$. Generally, the approach to the normal curve is slower the further p is from .5; if p is close either to 0 or to 1, n must be quite large before the approximation is acceptable. As a rough rule-of-thumb, the approximation is fairly good provided npq exceeds 10.

The behavior of T_n^* and B^* illustrates a quite general phenomenon. Whenever a random variable Z is the sum of a large number of independent random variables, all of which have the same distribution,† then $Z^* = [Z - E(Z)]/\text{SD}(Z)$ will have a histogram close to the normal curve. (Thus $T_n = X_1 + \ldots + X_n$ is the sum of independent random variables representing the numbers of points on the n dice, while $B = I_1 + \ldots + I_n$ is the sum of n independent indicator random variables.) If $Z = Z_1 + \ldots + Z_n$, where the Z's are independent and have the same distribution, it can be shown that as n increases without limit, the histogram of Z^* tends to the normal curve. This result is known as the *central limit theorem.*

Since the central limit theorem tells us that certain histograms are close to the normal curve, it often justifies the use of areas under the normal curve as approximations to the corresponding areas of these histograms, and hence as approximations to certain probabilities. The details of this procedure will be explained in the next section, but first let us introduce a table of areas under the normal curve.

It is customary to denote by $\Phi(z)$ the area under the normal curve, above the horizontal axis, and to the left of the vertical line at z. Thus $\Phi(z)$ is the area of the shaded region of Figure 3. A short table of $\Phi(z)$ for positive values of z is given as Table E. Table E may be supplemented by several remarks about Φ.

(a) The total area under the normal curve equals 1. This is not surprising since the curve is a limit of histograms each having total area equal to 1.

---

† Actually this result requires a mild restriction on the distribution, which is, however, automatically satisfied when the value set of the distribution is finite, as is assumed throughout this book.

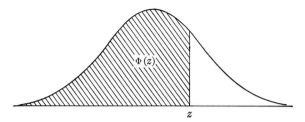

FIGURE 3.   AREA UNDER NORMAL CURVE

(b) According to Table E, $\Phi(3.90) = 1.0000$. The value of $\Phi(3.90)$ is not exactly 1, but it is 1 to four decimals of accuracy.   In fact $\Phi(3.90) = .999952$ to six decimals.

(c) An immediate consequence of (a) is that

(2)   Area to the right of $z = 1 - \Phi(z)$.

For example, the area to the right of $z = 1.2$ is $1 - \Phi(1.2) = 1 - .8849 = .1151$.

(d) The normal curve is symmetric about 0.   Since the total area under the curve is 1, it follows that the area to the left of 0 and that to the right of 0 are both $\frac{1}{2}$, which checks the entry $\Phi(0) = .5000$.   More generally, it follows from the symmetry of the curve that the area to the left of $-z$, which is $\Phi(-z)$, is equal to the area to the right of z, which by (2) is equal to $1 - \Phi(z)$, so that

(3) $\Phi(-z) = 1 - \Phi(z)$,

as illustrated in Figure 4a.   This explains why it is not necessary to extend Table E to negative values of z.   To obtain for example $\Phi(-1.3)$ one computes $\Phi(-1.3) = 1 - \Phi(1.3) = 1 - .9032 = .0968$.

(e) It is often required to find the area under the normal curve *between* two vertical lines.   Such areas can be obtained as the difference of two values of Φ.   The area between z and z', where $z < z'$, is the area to the left of z' minus the area to the left of z.   This is illustrated in Figure 4b, where the shaded region has area $\Phi(z') - \Phi(z)$.   For example, the area between .4 and 1.3 is

$$\Phi(1.3) - \Phi(.4) = .9032 - .6554 = .2478.$$

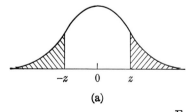
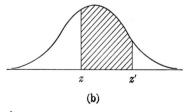

(a)   (b)

FIGURE 4.

As another example, let us find the area between $-.35$ and 1.24. The area to the left of 1.24 is $\Phi(1.24) = .8925$; that to the left of $-.35$ is $1 - \Phi(.35) = .3632$; thus, the desired area is $.8925 - .3632 = .5293$.

(f) Table E gives values of $\Phi(z)$ only for values of z that are multiples of one hundredth. Other values may be obtained by interpolation. Let us illustrate the method by finding a value for $\Phi(.364)$. The table gives $\Phi(.36) = .6406$ and $\Phi(.37) = .6443$. Since $.364$ is four-tenths of the way from $.36$ to $.37$, it is natural to take $\Phi(.364)$ to be four-tenths of the way from $.6406$ to $.6443$. To obtain $\Phi(.364)$, we therefore start with $\Phi(.36)$ and add to it four-tenths of the difference between $\Phi(.37)$ and $\Phi(.36)$, that is,

$$\Phi(.364) = .6406 + .4(.6443 - .6406) = .6406 + .4(.0037)$$
$$= .6406 + .0015 = .6421.$$

PROBLEMS

1. Find the area under the normal curve to the left of (i) $.87$, (ii) -1.46, (iii) 1.072, (iv) $-.156$.

2. Find the area under the normal curve to the right of (i) $.04$, (ii) -3.97, (iii) $.423$, (iv) -1.006.

3. Find the area under the normal curve between (i) $.41$ and 1.09, (ii) $-.26$ and 2.13, (iii) -1.41 and $-.07$, (iv) -1.237 and 1.237.

4. Find the area under the normal curve outside the interval (i) $(-1.82, 1.82)$, (ii) $(.08, 2.15)$.

5. Find the value of z such that the area under the normal curve
    (i) to the left of z is $.9732$ (v) to the left of z is $.95$
    (ii) to the right of z is $.8186$ (vi) between $-z$ and z is $.5$
    (iii) to the left of z is $.2912$ (vii) between z and $2z$ is $.1$.
    (iv) between $-z$ and z is $.6826$

6.5 THE NORMAL APPROXIMATION

Let us now consider some examples of the use of the normal curve in obtaining approximate values of probabilities.

EXAMPLE 1. *The sum of points on three dice.* What is the probability that the number T_3 of points showing on three dice is equal to 15? The desired probability is the area of the corresponding bar of the histogram of T_3^*. From Example 3.1 we know that $E(T_3) = 3(\frac{7}{2}) = 10.5$ and $SD(T_3) = \sqrt{3(\frac{35}{12})} = 2.958$. According to (3.3), this bar covers the interval from $(15 - 10.5 - .5)/2.958 = 1.352$ to $(15 - 10.5 + .5)/2.958 = 1.690$. The normal approximation to the probability is the area under the normal curve above this interval, or $\Phi(1.690) - \Phi(1.352) = .9545 - .9118 = .0427$, as illustrated in Figure 1a. For comparison, the true value of $P(T_3 = 15)$ is $\frac{10}{216} = .0463$. The approximation is thus in error by $.0427 - .0463 = -.0036$; it is too small by 8% of the true value. For many purposes this degree of accuracy would suffice.

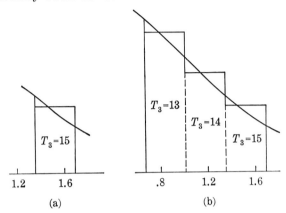

FIGURE 1. NORMAL APPROXIMATION TO DISTRIBUTION OF T_3

The method extends readily to the sum of the probabilities of several consecutive values. As an example, let us compute the probability $P(13 \leq T_3 \leq 15)$ that T_3 lies between 13 and 15 inclusive. By the addition law, this is

$$P(T_3 = 13) + P(T_3 = 14) + P(T_3 = 15),$$

which is the sum of the areas of the adjacent bars covering the intervals (12.5, 13.5), (13.5, 14.5), and (14.5, 15.5). Together, these bars cover the interval (12.5, 15.5). When we go over to standard units, this becomes the interval from $(12.5 - 10.5)/2.958 = .676$ to $(15.5 - 10.5)/2.958 = 1.690$, as shown in Figure 1b. The normal curve area above this interval is

$$\Phi(1.690) - \Phi(.676) = .9545 - .7505 = .2040$$

which may be compared with the exact value

$$P(13 \leq T_3 \leq 15) = \tfrac{46}{216} = .2130.$$

The approximation is low by .0090 which is 4% of the true value.

Let us now generalize the foregoing results. Suppose Z is any random variable taking on consecutive integers as its possible values, and let a and b be any of these values, with $a < b$. We are interested in obtaining an approximation for the probability

$$P(a \leq Z \leq b) = P(Z = a) + P(Z = a + 1) + \ldots + P(Z = b).$$

This probability is the sum of the areas of the bars in the Z histogram that cover the interval $(a - .5, b + .5)$. The corresponding bars in the Z^* histogram extend from

$$[a - .5 - E(Z)]/\text{SD}(Z) \quad \text{to} \quad [b + .5 - E(Z)]/\text{SD}(Z).$$

The desired approximation is therefore

$$(1) \quad P(a \leqq Z \leqq b) = \Phi\left(\frac{b + .5 - E(Z)}{\text{SD}(Z)}\right) - \Phi\left(\frac{a - .5 - E(Z)}{\text{SD}(Z)}\right)$$

EXAMPLE 2. *Male births.* Of the 5000 births from New York State represented in Figure 1.2.3c, 2641 or 52.8% were boys. A twenty-year record of over two million births from New York State gives 51.4% boys. Is the higher frequency of boys in our 5000 cases evidence that they really differ in this regard from the general experience? Let us see how likely would be so large or larger a number of boys, if in fact $p = P(\text{Male}) = .514$.

To compute $P(B \geqq 2641)$ when the number B has the binomial distribution with $n = 5000$, $p = .514$ exactly from formula (1.2) would be tedious, and no binomial table covers so large a value of n. To obtain an approximation for this probability, we apply (1) with B instead of Z and $E(Z) = 5000 \times .514 = 2570$, $\text{SD}(Z) = \sqrt{5000 \times .514 \times .486} = 35.34$, $a = 2641$ and $b = 5000$. Substitution in (1) gives for the desired probability the approximate value

$$\Phi\left(\frac{5000.5 - 2570}{35.34}\right) - \Phi\left(\frac{2640.5 - 2570}{35.34}\right) = \Phi(68.77) - \Phi(1.995)$$

$$= 1 - .9770 = .0230.$$

This probability is small enough to cast some doubt on the hypothesis that these 5000 births are in accord with the general experience in New York State.

When in (1) the value of b is the largest value that Z can take on, so that the left-hand side of (1) can be written as $P(Z \geqq a)$, as was the case in the preceding example, a simplification of (1) is possible. The value of $\Phi\left(\frac{b + .5 - E(Z)}{\text{SD}(Z)}\right)$ (in the preceding example it was $\Phi(68.77)$), is then usually so close to 1 that one may simplify (1) to

$$(2) \quad P(a \leqq Z) = 1 - \Phi\left(\frac{a - .5 - E(Z)}{\text{SD}(Z)}\right).$$

Similarly, when a is the smallest possible value of Z, $\Phi\left(\frac{a - .5 - E(Z)}{\text{SD}(Z)}\right)$ will be nearly 0, and we get

$$(3) \qquad\qquad P(Z \leqq b) = \Phi\left(\frac{b + .5 - E(Z)}{\mathrm{SD}(Z)}\right).$$

While many random variables have a representation as a sum of independent terms with the same distribution, this is by no means true of all random variables. The central limit theorem, however, has many extensions to sums of independent random variables not all having the same distribution, and also to certain sums of dependent variables. The following two examples illustrate the latter possibility.

EXAMPLE 3. *Hypergeometric.* The hypergeometric random variable D, introduced in Section 2, is seen by formula (2.2) to be the sum of s indicators; these all have the same distribution but are not independent. It is shown in more advanced treatments of probability theory that the histogram of D, expressed in standard units, is close to the normal curve provided $\mathrm{Var}(D)$ is not too small. Figure 2 shows the histogram of D^* for the hypergeometric distribution ($N = 20$, $r = 8$, $s = 7$), with the normal curve superimposed.

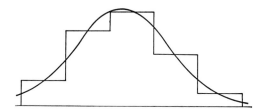

FIGURE 2.   NORMAL APPROXIMATION TO HYPERGEOMETRIC DISTRIBUTION

Experience has shown that a great many variable quantities encountered in nature are distributed in a shape closely resembling the normal. For example, if we measure the heights of a large number of men and plot the frequencies with which various heights are observed, we obtain an *empirical histogram* whose shape is nearly of the normal form. We may give a theoretical argument to explain this phenomenon. The height of any individual is the resultant of the action of a large number of more or less unrelated genetic and environmental effects, so that the central limit theorem would lead us to expect a normal form. It should not however be thought that all distributions encountered in nature are normal. For example, in certain regions of central Africa, the distribution of heights of adult males would resemble Figure 3a: one factor (whether the man is or is not a pygmy) in this case dominates the other factors. Another non-normal distribution is that of individual income: a few individuals have

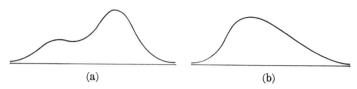

(a)   (b)

FIGURE 3. DISTRIBUTIONS NOT RESEMBLING THE NORMAL CURVE

incomes far larger than the rest, so that the distribution (Figure 3b) has a long "tail" to the right.

PROBLEMS

1. Suppose B has the binomial distribution ($n = 100$, $p = .2$). Calculate the normal approximations to (i) $P(B = 20)$, (ii) $P(B < 18)$, (iii) $P(B \leq 17)$, (iv) $P(24 < B \leq 29)$, (v) $P(B > 29)$.

2. Suppose B has the binomial distribution ($n = 10$, $p = .6$). Calculate the normal approximations to (i) $P(B = 1)$, (ii) $P(B = 3)$, (iii) $P(B = 5)$ and compare them with the exact values.

3. Let B be the number of successes in 100 binomial trials with probability $p = \frac{1}{5}$ of success. Use the normal approximation to find a number c such that the probability $P(B < c)$ is approximately (i) .95, (ii) .8, (iii) .5. [Hint: (i) use the approximate formula

$$P(B < c) = \Phi\left(\frac{c - 20.5}{4}\right)$$

and the fact that $\Phi(1.645) = .95$ to get an equation for c.]

4. Let B be the number of successes in 300 trials with probability $\frac{3}{4}$ of success. Use the method of the preceding problem to find a number c such that $P(B < c)$ is approximately (i) .95, (ii) .9, (iii) .75.

5. Under the assumptions of the preceding problem find c such that $P(B > c)$ is approximately (i) .95, (ii) .7.

6. Under the assumptions of Problem 3 find a number c such that $P(|B - 20| \leq c)$ is approximately (i) .95, (ii) .8, (iii) .5. [Hint: $|B - 20| \leq c$ means that $20 - c \leq B \leq 20 + c$. Use formula (4.3).]

7. A college has invited 800 guests to a charter-day picnic. For the purpose of ordering the picnic baskets, it is assumed that the decisions of the guests are unrelated, and that each has a probability $\frac{2}{3}$ of accepting the invitation. With this assumption, how many baskets should be ordered if the college wishes to be (approximately) 99% certain that there will be a basket for each guest who comes?

8. If A is the number of apartment houses in the stratified sample of Problem 2.13, calculate the normal approximation to $P(A \geq 5)$.

9. A random digit generator is operated n times. Find the approximate probability that the frequency of even digits lies between .4 and .6 when (i) $n = 50$, (ii) $n = 250$, (iii) $n = 50,000$.

10. A bag contains a two-headed penny and a two-tailed penny. A penny is chosen at random from the bag and is then tossed five times.
   (i) Obtain the distribution of the number H of heads and plot its histogram.
   (ii) Calculate $E(H)$ and $\text{Var}(H)$, and show that the normal approximation is not satisfactory in this case.
   (iii) Would the normal approximation be better if the coin were tossed many times rather than only five times?
   (iv) Would the normal approximation be better if the coin were returned to the bag and a fresh draw were made before each toss?
[This problem uses the concepts and results of Sections 4.3 and 4.4.]

6.6 THE POISSON APPROXIMATION FOR $np = 1$

As was pointed out in Section 4, the normal approximation to the binomial distribution does not work very well if p is near 0 unless n is quite large. Since $q = 1 - p$ is then close to 1, the rule of thumb given in Example 4.1 suggests that the normal approximation could be relied upon for small p only if np is greater than or equal to 10. We would not, for example, expect it to work well when $p = .01$ and $n = 100$, in which case $np = 1$. Fortunately there is available a quite different method, the *Poisson approximation*, which gives good results when p is near 0. (By the device of relabeling failures as successes, the same method can also be used for values of p near 1.)

To explain the Poisson approximation, let us at first fix the expected number of successes, $E(B) = np$, at the value 1. Table 1 shows five different binomial distributions, corresponding to $n = 2, 5, 10, 20,$ and 40, with p respectively $\frac{1}{2}, \frac{1}{5}, \frac{1}{10}, \frac{1}{20},$ and $\frac{1}{40}$, so that in each case $np = 1$.

TABLE 1. BINOMIAL DISTRIBUTIONS WITH $np = 1$

	$n = 2$ $p = \frac{1}{2}$	$n = 5$ $p = \frac{1}{5}$	$n = 10$ $p = \frac{1}{10}$	$n = 20$ $p = \frac{1}{20}$	$n = 40$ $p = \frac{1}{40}$	$\cdots$	Poisson approximation: n very large $p = 1/n$
$b = 0$	.2500	.3277	.3487	.3585	.3632		.3679
1	.5000	.4096	.3874	.3774	.3725		.3679
2	.2500	.2048	.1937	.1887	.1863		.1839
3		.0512	.0574	.0596	.0605		.0613
4		.0064	.0112	.0133	.0143		.0153
5		.0003	.0015	.0022	.0026		.0031
6			.0001	.0003	.0004		.0005
7							.0001

If the first two rows of the table are compared, it is apparent that the values of $P(B = 0)$ and $P(B = 1)$ come closer together as n is increased and correspondingly p is decreased. When $n = 2$, $P(B = 1)$ is twice as large as $P(B = 0)$, but by the time $n = 40$, the ratio of $P(B = 1)$ to $P(B = 0)$ is only $.3725/.3632 = 1.026$. This suggests that, when n is very large, $P(B = 1)/P(B = 0)$ might be very close to 1, so that to a good approximation the same value could be used for both $P(B = 1)$ and $P(B = 0)$.

It is easy to verify this suggestion. It follows from the formula for binomial probabilities (1.2) and the fact that $\binom{n}{0} = 1$ and $\binom{n}{1} = n$, that

$$P(B = 0) = q^n \quad \text{and} \quad P(B = 1) = npq^{n-1}.$$

Since for the present we are only dealing with the case $np = 1$, this means that

$$\text{(1)} \qquad \frac{P(B = 1)}{P(B = 0)} = \frac{1}{q}.$$

If p is close to 0, then $q = 1 - p$ is close to 1, and therefore so is $1/q$. This proves the suggestion that the ratio (1) will be near 1 if p is near 0. Therefore, if n is large and $p = 1/n$ is correspondingly small, we have

$$P(B = 1) \doteq P(B = 0)$$

where $\doteq$ means that the two expressions are approximately equal.

In a precisely similar way, it can be shown that $P(B = 2)/P(B = 1)$ will be close to $\frac{1}{2}$ when n is large and p small and $np = 1$ (see Problem 1). Since $P(B = 2)$ is about half as large as $P(B = 1)$, which in turn is close to $P(B = 0)$, we have the approximation

$$P(B = 2) \doteq \tfrac{1}{2}P(B = 0).$$

Continuing in the same way, we find

$$P(B = 3) \doteq \tfrac{1}{3} \cdot \tfrac{1}{2}P(B = 0) = \tfrac{1}{6}P(B = 0)$$
$$P(B = 4) \doteq \tfrac{1}{4} \cdot \tfrac{1}{3} \cdot \tfrac{1}{2}P(B = 0) = \tfrac{1}{24}P(B = 0)$$

and so forth. But of course the probabilities of all possible values of B must add up to 1, so that

$$
\begin{aligned}
1 = \ & P(B = 0) + P(B = 1) + P(B = 2) \\
& \qquad + P(B = 3) + P(B = 4) + \ldots \\
\doteq \ & P(B = 0) + P(B = 0) + \tfrac{1}{2}P(B = 0) \\
& \qquad + \tfrac{1}{6}P(B = 0) + \tfrac{1}{24}P(B = 0) + \ldots \\
= \ & P(B = 0)[1 + 1 + \tfrac{1}{2} + \tfrac{1}{6} + \tfrac{1}{24} + \ldots]
\end{aligned}
$$

(2)

where in the last step the quantity $P(B = 0)$ has been factored out.

The factor $1 + 1 + \tfrac{1}{2} + \tfrac{1}{6} + \tfrac{1}{24} + \ldots$ can be calculated numerically to any desired degree of accuracy. The work is shown in Table 2, where the factor is computed to four decimal places, giving the value 2.7183. We have added up only eight terms, and could have continued to add as many more as we wished, but the remaining ones are so small that they do not amount to much even when taken all together. (This fact is proved rigorously in theoretically more advanced books.) The number we have computed to four decimals is a very important one in mathematics, and is denoted by the letter e, in honor of the Swiss mathematician Leonhard Euler (1707–1783).

TABLE 2. CALCULATION OF $1 + 1 + \frac{1}{2} + \frac{1}{6} + \frac{1}{24} + \ldots = e$

$$1 = 1.0000$$
$$1 = 1.0000$$
$$\tfrac{1}{2} = .5000$$
$$1/2\cdot3 = \tfrac{1}{6} = .1667$$
$$1/2\cdot3\cdot4 = \tfrac{1}{24} = .0417$$
$$1/2\cdot3\cdot4\cdot5 = \tfrac{1}{120} = .0083$$
$$1/2\cdot3\cdot4\cdot5\cdot6 = \tfrac{1}{720} = .0014$$
$$1/2\cdot3\cdot4\cdot5\cdot6\cdot7 = \tfrac{1}{5040} = .0002$$

$$2.7183$$

Now let us substitute this result in (2), to find

$$1 \doteq P(B = 0)2.7183.$$

Dividing, we get for $P(B = 0)$ the approximate value $1/2.7183 = .3679$. That is to say, if n is large, so that $p = 1/n$ is small, the probability that there will be no successes is approximately .3679, regardless of the precise values of n and $p = 1/n$. This approximation is already reasonably good when $n = 40$ and $p = \tfrac{1}{40}$, where the correct value is .3632, and the larger n is, the better the approximation will be. Since $P(B = 1) \doteq P(B = 0)$, the same value .3679 may be used to approximate $P(B = 1)$; since $P(B = 2) \doteq \tfrac{1}{2}P(B = 0)$, the value $\tfrac{1}{2}(.3679) = .1839$ may be used to approximate $P(B = 2)$, and so forth. The approximate values are shown as the last column of Table 1.

EXAMPLE 1. *Triplets.* It is stated that the chance of triplets in human births is 1/10,000. What is the probability of observing at least 4 sets of triplets in a record of 10,000 human births?

Let us regard the births as unrelated, so that the number B of sets of triplets has the binomial distribution corresponding to $n = 10,000$ and $p = 1/10,000$. Since $np = 1$ and n is very large, we may use the Poisson approximation shown in the last column of Table 1. Thus

$$P(B \geq 4) = P(B = 4) + P(B = 5) + P(B = 6) + \dots$$
$$\doteq .0153 + .0031 + .0005 + .0001$$
$$= .0190.$$

There is a little less than a 2% chance of observing so many sets of triplets.

PROBLEMS

1. (i) Show that $P(B = 2) = \dfrac{n(n - 1)}{2} p^2 q^{n-2}$. [Hint: Problem 2.2.14].

(ii) In the case $np = 1$, show that the preceding formula reduces to $P(B = 2)$
$$= \frac{1}{2}\left(1 - \frac{1}{n}\right) q^{n-2}.$$

(iii) Use result (ii) to establish that when $np = 1$,

$$P(B = 2)/P(B = 1) = \frac{1}{2}\left(1 - \frac{1}{n}\right) \cdot \frac{1}{q}.$$

(iv) Use result (iii) to explain why $P(B = 2) \doteq \frac{1}{2}P(B = 1)$, when n is large and $p = 1/n$ is small.

2. By steps parallel to those of Problem 1, explain why $P(B = 3) \doteq \frac{1}{3}P(B = 2)$ when n is large and $p = 1/n$ is small.

3. Calculate the Poisson approximation for the following binomial probabilities:
(i) $P(B > 4)$ when $n = 300$ and $p = 1/300$,
(ii) $P(3 \leq B \leq 5)$ when $n = 80$ and $p = 1/80$,
(iii) $P(B \leq 1)$ when $n = 50$ and $p = 1/50$.

4. A machine is claimed on the average to produce only one defective in a hundred. If the claim is true, how surprising would it be to find five or more defectives in a lot of 100?

5. Refine the computations in Table 2 to obtain a five-decimal value for e.

6.7 THE POISSON APPROXIMATION: GENERAL CASE

For simplicity of exposition, in the preceding ection we considered only the case $np = 1$, but the method is applicable to any fixed value of $E(B) = np$. Suppose we consider the binomial distributions with np fixed at the value

(1) $$np = \lambda.$$

We shall be interested in obtaining an approximation to these distributions when p is close to 0 and hence n is very large.   Just as in the case $np = 1$, we have
$$P(B = 0) = q^n \quad \text{and} \quad P(B = 1) = npq^{n-1}$$
and hence
$$\frac{P(B = 1)}{P(B = 0)} = \frac{np}{q}.$$

Since q is close to 1, and np is equal to λ, we have for large n

$$\frac{P(B = 1)}{P(B = 0)} \doteq \lambda$$

or

(2) $P(B = 1) \doteq \lambda P(B = 0).$

By an exactly analogous argument we find

$$\frac{P(B = 2)}{P(B = 1)} \doteq \tfrac{1}{2}\lambda$$

(3) $\dfrac{P(B = 3)}{P(B = 2)} \doteq \tfrac{1}{3}\lambda$

$$\frac{P(B = 4)}{P(B = 3)} \doteq \tfrac{1}{4}\lambda, \quad \text{etc.}$$

To see how these relations can be used to obtain approximate probabilities, suppose that $\lambda = 2$. Then it is found by exactly the same method as for the case $\lambda = 1$ in the preceding section that

(4) $P(B = 2) \doteq \tfrac{1}{2}4P(B = 0), \quad P(B = 3) \doteq \tfrac{1}{6}8P(B = 0),$

$$P(B = 4) \doteq \tfrac{1}{24}16P(B = 0)$$

and so forth. Adding the probabilities and factoring out the common factor $P(B = 0)$ gives, in analogy to (6.2),

$$1 = P(B = 0)[1 + 2 + \tfrac{1}{2}4 + \tfrac{1}{6}8 + \ldots].$$

The factor in brackets can be calculated to any desired degree of accuracy. Taking only the first 12 terms gives to it the value 7.3891 and hence gives $P(B = 0) \doteq .1353$. The probabilities of the other values can now be computed from (2) and (4).

This method can be used to obtain the Poisson approximation corresponding to any given value of λ. Table F shows the results for 20 different values of λ ranging from .1 to 10. The Poisson approximation applies not only to the binomial random variable B, but also to a more general random variable S to be defined below, and for this reason the headings of Table F are in terms of S rather than B. A much more extensive table is available giving to eight decimal places the probabilities for values of λ ranging from .0000001 to 205.*

As an illustration of the use of Table F, let us find $P(B \leq 3)$ when B has the binomial distribution corresponding to $n = 120$ and $p = .04$. Here $E(B) = np = 4.8$, which is too small to permit safe use of the normal approximation. But, since n is large and p is small, we may use the Poisson approximation. By adding the four entries for $\lambda = 5$ and $S = 0, 1, 2, 3$

---

* *Tables of the Individual and Cumulative Terms of Poisson Distribution,* D. Van Nostrand Co., Inc. (1962). 202 pages.

from Table F, we find that $P(B \leq 3)$ is about .2650 when $E(B) = 5$. Similarly $P(B \leq 3)$ is about .4335 when $\lambda = E(B) = 4$. As $E(B) = 4.8$ in the present case, it is necessary to interpolate to find $P(B \leq 3) \doteq .2987$. (The correct value, computed from the binomial formula, is .2887.)

As another illustration, let us find an approximation for $P(B = 60)$ when $n = 60$ and $p = \frac{19}{20}$. In this case, p is near 1, while the Poisson approximation requires that p be near 0. We can make the method applicable by looking at failures rather than successes. The chance of a failure is $\frac{1}{20}$, and 60 successes means 0 failures. The desired probability is therefore the same as $P(B = 0)$ when $n = 60$ and $p = \frac{1}{20}$. For this problem $np = 3$, and the result .0498 may be read directly from Table F. (The correct value computed from the binomial formula is .0461.)

We have developed the Poisson approximation for use with the binomial distribution, but it has in fact much wider application. Let S be the number of successes on n unrelated trials with success probabilities $p_1, \ldots, p_n$. If each of these probabilities is small, the Poisson approximation with

$$\lambda = E(S) = p_1 + \ldots + p_n$$

works well even though the chance of success is not the same on each trial.

EXAMPLE 1. *Effect of training.* Suppose that in the training of new workers to perform a delicate mechanical operation, the probabilities that the worker will be successful on his first, second, and third attempt are $p_1 = .03$, $p_2 = .06$, $p_3 = .11$ respectively, and that the attempts may be considered to be unrelated. The distribution of the number S of successes among these three attempts, which was obtained in Problem 3.3.9, is shown below together with the Poisson approximation corresponding to $\lambda = E(S) = .03 + .06 + .11 = .20$.

s	0	1	2	3	4
$P(S = s)$	.812	.177	.011	.000	.000
Poisson approximation	.819	.164	.016	.001	.000

The approximation is fairly good, even though one trial has a success probability as high as .11.

Unrelated trials with varying but small success probabilities occur in many situations, which explains the wide applicability of the Poisson approximation. The following are two typical examples.

EXAMPLE 2. *Telephone traffic.* A telephone company anticipates that there will be, on the average, five lines in use at any given moment between two communities during the peak hours. How many lines should be built so that there is less than one chance in twenty a subscriber will find all lines in use when he makes a call?

Let S be the number of subscribers who are using their telephones for a call between the two communities at a given moment. Each subscriber is a "trial" having only a small chance of "success," i.e. of making a call at that moment. Under ordinary circumstances these trials, although certainly not having the same success probability, will be unrelated, so that the Poisson approximation can be used for the distribution of S. This will of course not be the case if some event causes many subscribers to call the other community at the same time.

From Table F we see that with $\lambda = 5$, $P(S \geq 9) = .0680$ while $P(S \geq 10) = .0317$. Thus, under the assumption that the number of lines in use at a given moment follows the Poisson distribution, the company will want to provide ten lines.

EXAMPLE 3. *Suicides.* During the week following the suicide of a film star, a newspaper columnist notes that in his city there were 12 suicides as compared with an average figure of 8 per week. He attributes the extra deaths to the suggestive effect of the star's suicide. Is this explanation convincing?

Let S be the number of suicides committed in the city during a given week. Considering each inhabitant of the city as a trial, the assumptions underlying the Poisson approximation appear not unreasonable. From Table F with $\lambda = 8$, we find $P(S \geq 12) = .1118$. Thus, if we assume the number of suicides per week to follow the Poisson distribution, there would be 12 or more suicides in about one ninth of the weeks. The observed number could well be explained as a chance event, without the necessity of invoking a suggestion effect.

In Section 6 we mentioned that when $\lambda = np = 1$, the probability $P(S = 0)$ is equal to $1/e$ where e is the number 2.7183 . . . calculated to four decimal places in Table 6.2. More generally, it is shown in more advanced treatments of the subject that in the Poisson approximation for arbitrary λ, one has $P(S = 0) = 1/e^{\lambda}$.

Each of the columns of Table F consists of a sequence of positive numbers which (except for rounding errors) add up to 1. It is natural to think of such a sequence as defining a probability distribution for a random variable whose possible values are $s = 0, 1, 2, \ldots$. This Poisson random variable, unlike those we have previously considered, has an infinite number of possible values. An interesting feature of the Poisson distribution is that its expected value and variance are equal. This fact can be seen intuitively by considering the formula for binomial variance,

$$\text{Var}(B) = np(1 - p) = E(B)(1 - p).$$

If p is very small, $1 - p$ will be very close to 1, and $\text{Var}(B)$ will nearly equal $E(B)$. Thus, if S is a Poisson random variable with $E(S) = \lambda$, then we have $\text{Var}(S) = \lambda$ and hence $\text{SD}(S) = \sqrt{\lambda}$.

Table F gives the Poisson distribution for $\lambda \leq 10$; for larger values of λ the normal approximation gives good results. That is, if λ is as large as 10, one may apply formula (5.3) to get the approximation

$$(5) \qquad P(S \leq s) \doteq \Phi\left(\frac{s + .5 - \lambda}{\sqrt{\lambda}}\right).$$

PROBLEMS

1. Verify the first approximate equation of (3) by the method of Problem 6.1.

2. Check the value 7.3891 derived in the text from (4).

3. Compare the Poisson approximation with the correct binomial probability for the following cases:

(i) $P(B = 3)$ when $n = 8$ and $p = .05$,
(ii) $P(B = 9)$ when $n = 10$ and $p = .95$,
(iii) $P(1 \leq B \leq 4)$ when $n = 10$ and $p = .1$,
(iv) $P(B = 2)$ when $n = 9$ and $p = .05$.

4. If a table such as Table F is subject to one erroneous digit out of 1000, how likely is it that Table F is error free?

5. If you buy a lottery ticket in 100 lotteries, in each of which your chance of winning a prize is $\frac{1}{200}$, what is the (approximate) probability that you will win a prize (i) at least once, (ii) exactly once, (iii) exactly twice?

6. Compute the (approximate) probabilities of the preceding problem if the probability of winning a prize is $\frac{1}{50}$ in 20 of the 100 lotteries and $\frac{1}{800}$ in the remaining 80 lotteries.

The remaining problems relate to the material of the section that is in small print.

7. If S has the Poisson distribution with $\lambda = 10$, compare the normal approximation (5) of $P(S \leq 7)$ with the correct value given by Table F.

8. Given that S has the Poisson distribution with $\lambda = .1$, check numerically from Table F that $E(S)$ and $\mathrm{Var}(S)$ are both equal to λ.

9. Obtain a formula for $E(S^2)$ when S has a Poisson distribution, using the fact that $\mathrm{Var}(S) = E(S) = \lambda$.

10. Let Z_1 and Z_2 be independent random variables having Poisson distributions with $E(Z_1) = .1$ and $E(Z_2) = .3$.

(i) The distribution of Z_1 is a good approximation to the distribution of the number B_1 of successes in 100 binomial trials with success probability $p = .001$; the distribution of Z_2 is a good approximation to the distribution of the number B_2 of successes in 300 binomial trials with success probability $p = .001$. What is the distribution of the random variable $B_1 + B_2$? By considering the Poisson approximation to this distribution, conjecture the distribution of $Z_1 + Z_2$.

(ii) Check your conjecture from Table F. [Hint: $P(Z_1 + Z_2 = 0) = P(Z_1 = 0)P(Z_2 = 0); P(Z_1 + Z_2 = 1) = P(Z_1 = 0)P(Z_2 = 1) + P(Z_1 = 1)P(Z_2 = 0)$; etc.]

(iii) Carry out the work of parts (i) and (ii) for the case $E(Z_1) = .2$ and $E(Z_2) = .3$.

6.8 THE UNIFORM AND MATCHING DISTRIBUTIONS

In this section we present two simple distributions which further illustrate the concepts of this chapter.

(a) *The uniform distribution.* Suppose that a box contains N tickets which bear the labels $1, 2, \ldots, N$. A ticket is chosen at random and the number X written on the ticket is observed. If the phrase "chosen at random" means that each ticket has the same probability $1/N$ of being chosen, then the random variable X has probability $1/N$ of assuming each of its possible values $1, 2, \ldots, N$, so that its probability distribution is

(1)

x	1	2	$\cdots$	N
$P(X = x)$	$\dfrac{1}{N}$	$\dfrac{1}{N}$	$\cdots$	$\dfrac{1}{N}$

If the events $X = 1, \ldots, X = N$ constitute the simple events of the model, the model is uniform in the sense of Section 1.5. Correspondingly the distribution of X is called the *uniform distribution* (on the integers $1, \ldots, N$). It is also known as the rectangular distribution since the histogram of X has the form of a rectangle.

We already encountered this distribution when considering the experiment of throwing a fair die. The number X of points showing when a fair die is thrown has the uniform distribution for $N = 6$. As another illustration, let X be a digit produced by a random digit generator (Example 1.2.2); then $X + 1$ has the uniform distribution for $N = 10$. The following examples illustrate some other situations in which a uniform distribution may arise.

(i) When a calculation is carried to five decimal places and then rounded off to four decimals, the digit X appearing in the fifth place must be one of $0, 1, 2, \ldots, 9$. In many types of calculation it appears that these ten digits occur about equally often; that is, we may suppose that $X + 1$ has the uniform distribution on the integers $1, \ldots, 10$. This model is often employed in studying the accumulation of rounding errors in high-speed computing machines.

(ii) Students of industrial accidents may conjecture that because of a fatigue effect accidents are more likely to occur late than early in the day, or in the week. A skeptic maintains that no such effect exists, and that

an accident is equally likely to occur on Monday, . . . , Friday. If the
days of the work week are numbered 1 to 5, he would assume a uniform
model for the number X of the day on which an accident occurs. By
observing the numbers X for several unrelated accidents, one may investigate the adequacy of the uniform model in comparison with a "fatigue
effect" model. A similar approach can be used when studying the possibility of a "birth order effect" for rare maladies which some geneticists
think more likely in later than in earlier children of a family; in the study
of a possible seasonal effect on earthquakes; etc. Methods for dealing
with such problems are discussed in books on statistics.

What is the expectation of the uniform random variable X defined by
(1)? From (5.4.2) and (1), we have

$$E(X) = 1 \cdot \frac{1}{N} + 2 \cdot \frac{1}{N} + \ldots + N \cdot \frac{1}{N} = (1 + 2 + \ldots + N)/N.$$

It is shown in elementary books on algebra that

(2) $1 + 2 + \ldots + N = \tfrac{1}{2}N(N + 1)$

from which it follows that

(3) $E(X) = \tfrac{1}{2}(N + 1)$

This formula shows, for example, that the expected number of points showing when a fair die is thrown, is $\tfrac{7}{2}$ (see Example 5.3.1). For an alternative
proof of (2) and (3), see Problem 1. In a similar way, the algebraic formula
for the sum of squares,

(4) $1^2 + 2^2 + \ldots + N^2 = \tfrac{1}{6}N(N + 1)(2N + 1)$

shows that

(5) $E(X^2) = \tfrac{1}{6}(N + 1)(2N + 1)$

and hence that

(6) $\mathrm{Var}(X) = \dfrac{N^2 - 1}{12}.$

Again, the laws of expectation provide an alternative proof of (4) and (5)
(see Problem 2).

(b) *The matching distribution.* As in case (a), consider again N tickets
labeled $1, 2, \ldots, N$, but now suppose that all N tickets are drawn at
random one at a time and are laid out in a row. Whenever the label on
the ticket agrees with the number of its position in the row, we say that a
match has occurred. Let M denote the number of such matches; then the
distribution of M is called the *matching* distribution.

For illustration, suppose that $N = 4$ and that the tickets are laid out

3   2   1   4.

Here the ticket labeled 2 is in the second position and the ticket labeled 4 is in the fourth position; hence two matches have occurred and $M = 2$.

What is the distribution of M? If "drawn at random" means that the $N!$ possible orderings of the N tickets are equally likely (see Section 2.4), it is only necessary to count the number of orderings giving each value of M to find the desired distribution. Again using $N = 4$ for illustration, we know from Table 2.3.1 that there are $4! = 24$ possible orderings. They are shown in the tableau below, grouped according to the value of M. (Here each instance of a match is indicated by italics.)

$M = 0$: 2143 2341 2413 3412 3421 3142 4321 4312 4123
$M = 1$: *1*342 *1*423 3*2*41 4*2*13 24*3*1 41*3*2 231*4* 312*4*
$M = 2$: *12*43 *1*43*2* *1*3*24* 4*23*1 3*21*4* 2*134*
$M = 4$: *1234*

Thus, when $N = 4$, the distribution of M is

m	0	1	2	3	4
$P(M = m)$	$\frac{9}{24}$	$\frac{8}{24}$	$\frac{6}{24}$	0	$\frac{1}{24}$

In general, there will always be exactly one ordering which gives a match in every place, so that $P(M = N) = 1/N!$. Since it is not possible to have all but one place matched, $P(M = N - 1) = 0$. The entire distribution for any particular value of N can in principle be worked out by listing all cases as we have done for $N = 4$ (Problem 7), but the work rapidly becomes prohibitive as N increases. In Problem 10 we present a short-cut method by means of which the entries in Table 1 were obtained. This table gives the number $C(m, N)$ of orderings of N tickets which have exactly m matches, for $N \leqq 8$.

TABLE 1. $C(m, N)$

	$N = 1$	2	3	4	5	6	7	8
$m = 0$	0	1	2	9	44	265	1854	14833
1	1	0	3	8	45	264	1855	14832
2		1	0	6	20	135	924	7420
3			1	0	10	40	315	2464
4				1	0	15	70	630
5					1	0	21	112
6						1	0	28
7							1	0
8								1
$N! = (N)_N =$	1	2	6	24	120	720	5040	40,320

EXAMPLE *1*. *Baby pictures.* A magazine prints the photographs of five movie stars, and also (in scrambled order) a baby picture of each. If a reader correctly matches at least three of them, can he justly claim to have demonstrated an ability to recognize resemblances? It might be argued that the correct matchings were just luck—after all, even if the reader matched at random, he might happen to get three or more right. But how likely would this be?

From Table 1 for $N = 5$, we see that the probability of getting three or more correct matches by luck is $(10 + 1)/120 = 0.092$. That is, about one out of every 11 persons who matches at random will do as well or better as the reader who makes three correct identifications.

As was shown in Example 5.5.4, the expected value of M is for all N equal to one,

$$(7) \qquad\qquad\qquad E(M) = 1.$$

It is a remarkable fact that we expect exactly one match, regardless of the number of tickets. The variance of M turns out to be also equal to one for all N (Problem 7.2.17),

$$(8) \qquad\qquad\qquad \mathrm{Var}(M) = 1.$$

If the sampling of the N tickets had been done with replacement, the number M of matches would have the binomial distribution corresponding to N trials with success probability $1/N$ on each trial. For large N we would therefore by Sections 6 and 7 expect the distribution of M to be approximately the Poisson distribution corresponding to $\lambda = N(1/N) = 1$. It is another remarkable fact, which unfortunately we cannot prove here, that the matching distribution is well approximated by this Poisson distribution even though the sampling is done without replacement. The reader may compare the distribution of M for $N = 8$ with the Poisson distribution with $\lambda = 1$ (Problem 9).

PROBLEMS

1. Let the distribution of X be given by (1).
   (i) Apply formula (5.4.2) to obtain expressions for $E(X^2)$ and $E(X + 1)^2$. By forming the difference of these two expressions, show that

   $$E(X + 1)^2 - E(X^2) = [(N + 1)^2 - 1]/N = N + 2.$$

   (ii) Use the fact that

   $$E(X + 1)^2 - E(X^2) = E[(X + 1)^2 - X^2] = 2E(X) + 1$$

   and the result of (i) to find $E(X)$.
   (iii) By comparing the expression (5.4.2) of $E(X)$ with its value found in (ii), prove (2).

2. (i) Using the results and methods of the preceding problem, prove (5) by taking the difference of $E(X + 1)^3$ and $E(X^3)$.
   (ii) Use the result of (i) to prove (4).

3. (i) If X has the distribution (1), what are the possible values of $Z = 2X - 1$ and what are the probabilities of these values?

(ii) By comparing the expression for $E(Z)$ obtained from (5.4.2) with the value $2E(X) - 1$ obtained from (3), prove that the sum of the first N odd integers is

$$(9) \qquad 1 + 3 + 5 + \ldots + (2N - 1) = N^2.$$

4. By applying the method of Problem 3 to $E(Z^2)$ instead of $E(Z)$, prove that

$$(10) \qquad 1^2 + 3^2 + 5^2 + \ldots + (2N - 1)^2 = N(4N^2 - 1)/3.$$

5. Let X_1, X_2 be independent random variables, each having the distribution (1), and let Y be the larger of X_1 and X_2.

(i) Show that $P(Y \leq y) = y^2/N^2$ for $y = 1, 2, \ldots, N$.

(ii) Show that $P(Y = y) = (2y - 1)/N^2$ for $y = 1, 2, \ldots, N$.

6. Let X_1, X_2 be independent random variables, each having the distribution (1). Find the distribution of $Y = X_1 + X_2$.

7. Check the value $C(2, 5)$ of Table 1 by enumeration.

8. Suppose that the magazine of Example 1 asks its readers to match the pictures of eight (instead of five) movie stars. What is the probability that by purely random matching a reader will get at least four right?

9. Compare the distribution of M for $N = 8$ with the Poisson distribution for $\lambda = 1$.

10. (i) Show that $C(2, 5) = \binom{5}{2} C(0, 3)$ by counting the number of choices of the two tickets which are to provide the matchings, and the number of orderings of the remaining tickets which will not lead to any additional matchings.

(ii) Obtain analogous formulas for $C(1, 5)$ and $C(3, 5)$, and from these formulas compute $C(1, 5)$, $C(2, 5)$, $C(3, 5)$ using the first four columns of Table 1.

(iii) Find $C(0, 5)$ by using the fact that

$$C(0, 5) + C(1, 5) + C(2, 5) + C(3, 5) + C(5, 5) = 5!$$

and compare the values $C(0, 5), \ldots, C(3, 5)$ obtained with the fifth column of Table 1.

11. Use the method of the preceding problem to extend Table 1 to the case $N = 9$.

12. Show that for all values of N, $C(N, N) = 1$, $C(N - 1, N) = 0$, and $C(N - 2, N) = \binom{N}{2}$.

6.9 THE LAW OF LARGE NUMBERS

In this section we shall derive a law which, in a sense, justifies the model for probability built in Chapter 1, by showing that this model predicts the phenomenon of long-run stability which was the conceptual basis for our notion of probability.

We begin by putting into a quantitative form the notion, introduced in Section 5.6, that a widely dispersed random variable Z must have a large variance. Let us again denote $E(Z)$ by ζ, and consider an interval centered at ζ, say $(\zeta - c, \zeta + c)$ where c is any positive number. Of the possible values of Z, some may fall outside this interval and some inside it. Denote the possible values of Z outside (or on the end points of) the interval by $z_1, z_2, \ldots$ and those inside it by $w_1, w_2, \ldots$. By the definitions (5.6.1) of variance and (5.4.2) of expectation, the variance of Z can then be written in the form

$$\mathrm{Var}(Z) = E(Z - \zeta)^2$$

(1)
$$= (z_1 - \zeta)^2 P(Z = z_1) + (z_2 - \zeta)^2 P(Z = z_2) + \cdots$$
$$+ (w_1 - \zeta)^2 P(Z = w_1) + (w_2 - \zeta)^2 P(Z = w_2) + \cdots.$$

Since the values $z_1, z_2, \ldots$ all lie outside the interval $(\zeta - c, \zeta + c)$ (or on its end points) each of the quantities $(z_1 - \zeta)^2, (z_2 - \zeta)^2, \ldots$ is at least as large as c^2. We shall therefore not increase the right side of (1) if we replace $(z_1 - \zeta)^2, (z_2 - \zeta)^2, \ldots$ each by c^2. The terms in the last row of (1) are all nonnegative, so we shall again decrease (or at least not increase) the right side of (1) if we eliminate these terms. Consequently

(2)
$$\mathrm{Var}(Z) \geq c^2 P(Z = z_1) + c^2 P(Z = z_2) + \cdots.$$

Factoring out c^2, the right-hand side can be written as $c^2[P(Z = z_1) + P(Z = z_2) + \ldots]$. Since $z_1, z_2, \ldots$ are the possible values of Z outside the interval $(\zeta - c, \zeta + c)$, the probabilities in brackets add up to the probability that Z falls outside the interval, or $P(|Z - \zeta| \geq c)$. This proves the famous *Chebyshev inequality*, that

(3)
$$\mathrm{Var}(Z) \geq c^2 P(|Z - \zeta| \geq c)$$

for any random variable Z and any positive number c.

This inequality gives quantitative expression to the idea that wide dispersion means large variance. If the distribution of Z is widely dispersed, there exists a large number c such that a substantial probability lies outside $(\zeta - c, \zeta + c)$; that is, such that $P(|Z - \zeta| \geq c)$ is substantial. Since c is large, c^2 will be very large, and the right side of (3) must be large. But by (3), the variance of Z is then still larger.

The inequality holds for any random variable Z. Let us apply it to the particular random variable B/n, where B has the binomial distribution (n, p) introduced in Section 1. The expectation and variance of B/n are $E(B/n) = p$ by (1.6) and (5.5.3), and $\mathrm{Var}(B/n) = pq/n$ by (1.7) and (5.7.3). Substituting these values in (3) and dividing by c^2, we get

(4)
$$P\left(\left|\frac{B}{n} - p\right| \geq c\right) \leq \frac{pq}{nc^2}$$

for any positive number c and any binomial distribution (n, p).

The inequality (4), which is known as the *law of large numbers*, was discovered by James Bernoulli (1654-1705). This law serves to reinforce our concept of probability as long-run frequency. We began (Section 1.2) by presenting empirical evidence for the fact that when a long sequence of unrelated trials is performed under similar conditions, the frequency of a specified result (a "success") tends to be stable. Conceptually, the probability p of success represents in the model this stable frequency. The binomial trials model (Section 3.3) was constructed to represent a sequence of unrelated trials under constant conditions, and in this model B/n represents the frequency of success. If the model is realistic, it should then turn out that within the model B/n is in some sense close to p, at least if n is large.

The law of large numbers expresses a sense in which B/n is close to p when n is large enough. For let c be a small number, so that the interval $(p - c, p + c)$ is a narrow interval centered at p. Since c is small, c^2 will be very small and hence pq/c^2 will be very large. In spite of this, by taking n large enough, we can make pq/nc^2 as small as we please, and by (4), $P(|B/n - p| \geq c)$ will then be still smaller; that is, by taking n large enough we can make sure that B/n is very unlikely to differ from p by as much as c. In other words, if the number of trials is large enough, it is unlikely that the frequency B/n of success will differ much from the probability p of success. (It is actually this fact, which is a simple consequence of inequality (4), that is usually called "the law of large numbers," rather than (4) itself.

It is important to realize that the law of large numbers does not "prove" experimental long-run frequencies to be stable. The real world is not under the sway of mathematical arguments; rather, mathematical models are realistic only to the extent that their conclusions correspond to observation. Long-run stability is an empirical fact. The law of large numbers merely asserts that our model for probability is sufficiently realistic to agree with this fact. A model for probability that led to an opposite conclusion would presumably not be sufficiently realistic to be of much use.

While the law (4) is of great conceptual interest and theoretical value, the bound provided by the right side is usually very crude. (This is only to be expected in view of the wholesale reductions involved in passing from (1) to (2).) To illustrate this, consider the special case $p = \frac{1}{2}$. Table 1 provides a comparison of the actual probability $P(|B/n - \frac{1}{2}| \geq c)$ with the bound (4), which in the present case is $pq/nc^2 = 1/4nc^2$, for several values of n and c. The last column of Table 1 shows the normal approximation (6.5.1) for $P(|B/n - p| \geq c)$. We see that the normal approximation is good, but that the bound (4) is often far larger than the true value. Thus, B/n tends to be actually much closer to p than is guaranteed by the law of large numbers.

TABLE 1.   ILLUSTRATION OF THE BOUND FOR $p = \frac{1}{2}$

c	n	$P\left(\left\|\dfrac{B}{n} - \dfrac{1}{2}\right\| \geq c\right)$	$\dfrac{1}{4nc^2}$	normal approx.
.1	50	.203	.5	.203
	100	.0567	.25	.0574
	200	.00568	.0125	.00582
.05	100	.368	1	.368
	200	.179	.5	.179
	400	.0510	.25	.0512
	800	.00518	.125	.00522

The law of large numbers given in (4) may easily be generalized to deal with averages rather than frequencies. Recall that, in Section 5.3, the expectation of a random variable Z was motivated as representing the long-run average value of many unrelated observations on the quantity that Z represents. Let these observations be represented by random variables $Z_1, Z_2, \ldots, Z_n$ which are defined on different factors of a product model, and each of which has expectation ζ and variance σ^2. Let the average of these random variables be denoted by

$$\overline{Z} = (Z_1 + Z_2 + \ldots + Z_n)/n.$$

It is then easy to see that $E(\overline{Z}) = \zeta$ and $\mathrm{Var}(\overline{Z}) = \sigma^2/n$ (Problem 5.7.4). If we now apply (3) to $\overline{Z}$, we find

(5) $$P(|\overline{Z} - \zeta| \geq c) \leq \sigma^2/nc^2.$$

This is a more general version of the law of large numbers; in fact (4) is the special case of (5) that arises when $Z_1, Z_2 \ldots$ are indicators (see (1.5)). The more general law (5) asserts that it is unlikely that $\overline{Z}$ will be far from its expected value ζ, if n is sufficiently large. This theorem supports the common practice of averaging many unrelated observations on a quantity when one wishes to determine it with high precision.

PROBLEMS

1. For $p = 1/2$, $n = 30$ and three suitable values of c, compare the right side of (4) with the corresponding probabilities from Table C.

2. Verify the entry .0574 of Table 1, using Table E.

3. Let Z be a random variable, with $E(Z) = 0$ and $\mathrm{Var}(Z) = 1$, whose distribution is adequately described by the normal curve. Use Table E to find the value of c for which the right side of (3) is largest.

4. Try to find values of n and c for which the bound provided by the right side of (4) is close to the value on the left side, for $p = \frac{1}{2}$.

5. (i) Find a distribution for Z and a value of c for which the two sides of (3) are equal.

(ii) Describe all distributions of Z for which this can occur.

[Hint: Equality requires that nothing is thrown away in passing from (1) to (2).]

6. (i) Show that $pq = p(1 - p)$ is equal to $\frac{1}{4} - (p - \frac{1}{2})^2$.

(ii) Use (i) to prove that $pq \leq \frac{1}{4}$ for all values of p.

(iii) Use (ii) to prove the *uniform* law of large numbers

$$P\left(\left|\frac{B}{n} - p\right| \geq c\right) \leq 1/4nc^2$$

in which the right side no longer depends on p.

7. Consider n unrelated trials with success probabilities $p_1, p_2, \ldots, p_n$.

(i) If $\bar{p} = (p_1 + \ldots + p_n)/n$, and S denotes the number of successes in the n trials, show that

$$P\left(\left|\frac{S}{n} - \bar{p}\right| \geq c^2\right) \leq 1/4nc^2.$$

(ii) What does this inequality tell us about the behavior of the success frequency S/n for large n?

[Hint (i): In (3), use the variance for S found in Problem 1.19, and apply the inequality obtained in part (ii) of the preceding problem.]

8. If Z^* denotes the random variable Z reduced to standard units as defined in (3.1), show that

(6) $P(|Z^*| \geq d) \leq 1/d^2.$

[Hint: In (5), replace c by $d\sigma/\sqrt{n}$.]

9. Let Z have the uniform distribution on the integers $1, \ldots, 9$. Compare the left and right sides of (3) for $c = 1, 2, 3$ and 4. [Hint: Use the results of Section 6.8.]

6.10 SEQUENTIAL STOPPING

In deriving the binomial distribution for the number B of successes in n binomial trials (Section 1), we assumed that the number n of trials was fixed in advance, regardless of how the trials would turn out. When the trials are performed *sequentially*, with the outcome of each trial known before the next trial is performed, it is possible to let the number of trials depend on the results obtained. A medical experiment may, for example, be abandoned if there are too many failures; the length of the world series in baseball depends on the outcomes of the successive games; the number of attempts needed to reach a person by telephone depends on the number of times the line is found busy; and so on. In such situations, the number of trials becomes a random variable, and the number of successes no longer has a binomial distribution. A model for sequential binomial trials will depend not only on the success probability p for single trials, but also on the *stopping rule* which specifies when observation is discontinued.

EXAMPLE 1. *World Series.* In matches between two contestants or teams, the rules often specify that the number of games played to determine the winner will depend on the outcomes. The baseball world series, for example, continues until one of the two teams has won four games. (Other examples occur in bridge, tennis, yacht races, etc.) It is of interest in such a series to know how many games will be played, and what is the chance that a given team will win.

Let us treat the successive games as a series of binomial trials, in which Team A has fixed probability p of winning any one game (which we shall call a "success"). The stopping rule is: continue the trials until a total of four successes or four failures has occurred and then stop. The record of play can be represented by a sequence of the letters S and F, where for example FSSFSFS would mean that Team A won the second, third, fifth and seventh games and hence the series. Under the assumptions made, the probability of this pattern is $qppqpqp = p^4q^3$. There are in fact 70 possible patterns, which may be grouped according to the numbers N_S and N_F of successes and failures, as shown in tableau (1):

	n_S	n_F	$P(N_S = n_S \text{ and } N_F = n_F)$
	4	0	p^4
	4	1	$4p^4q$
	4	2	$10p^4q^2$
(1)	4	3	$20p^4q^3$
	3	4	$20p^3q^4$
	2	4	$10p^2q^4$
	1	4	$4pq^4$
	0	4	q^4

Here, for example, the second line reflects the fact that four patterns (FSSSS, SFSSS, SSFSS, SSSFS) give the result ($N_S = 4$ and $N_F = 1$), and each pattern has probability p^4q. Notice that in this case the four patterns correspond to the four possible positions of the one failure among the first four trials. Similarly, the coefficient 10 in $P(N_S = 4, N_F = 2)$ represents the $\binom{5}{2} = 10$ ways of placing two F's among the first five symbols, and so forth.

From tableau (1) it is possible to obtain answers to various questions related to the series. For example, the number $N = N_S + N_F$ of games played has the distribution shown below, which is also given numerically for several values of p.   As one might expect, the series tends to be longer when the teams are evenly matched than when one team is superior to the other.

n	$P(N = n)$	$p = .5$	$p = .6$	$p = .7$
4	$p^4 + q^4$	.1250	.1552	.2482
5	$4pq(p^3 + q^3)$	.2500	.2688	.3108
6	$10p^2q^2(p^2 + q^2)$	.3125	.2995	.2558
7	$20p^3q^3$	.3125	.2765	.1852

The probability that Team A wins can also be obtained from (1), but even more simply by another method.   Imagine a different rule of play, under which the teams always play seven games with victory going to the team that wins four or more.   It is clear that this rule would always result in the same outcome as that actually used, since the team winning four or more out of seven games is also the first team to win four.   Under the new rule, however, the number of trials is fixed at $n = 7$, so that the number B of games won by Team A has the binomial distribution ($n = 7$, p).   Thus, Table B gives as the probability of Team A winning the series for several values of p:

p	.5	.6	.7	.8	.9	.95
P(Team A wins series)	.5	.7102	.8740	.9667	.9973	.9998

EXAMPLE 2. *Sequentially stopped families.*   Parents sometimes have a preference with regard to the sexes of their children, and may then base the decision whether to have another child on the sexes of their present children.   If the sexes of successive children are regarded as binomial trials with fixed probability p of a boy on any given birth, the exercise of such a decision amounts to a sequential stopping rule.   What influence would parental favoritism for children of one sex or the other have on the frequencies of the sexes in the population?   In particular, could the observed slight excess of boys be explained by a favoritism for boys?

In an attempt to throw some light on these questions, let us consider the extreme case in which the parents are insistent on having a son, but otherwise want as small a family as possible.   Then their rule will be: continue having children until a son is born, and then stop.   Since we do not wish to consider families of indefinitely large size, let us fix a maximum number of children in the family, say t.   Then possible family patterns, the associated number B of boys, G of girls, and C of children, and the probabilities of the patterns, are shown in tableau (2):

	Pattern	b	g	c	Probability
	M	1	0	1	p
	FM	1	1	2	qp
(2)	FFM	1	2	3	q^2p
	$\ldots$				
	FF$\cdots$FM	1	$t-1$	t	$q^{t-1}p$
	FF$\cdots$FF	0	t	t	q^t

What will be the frequency of boys in a large population of families generated according to (2)? Suppose there are k such families, the first family having B_1 boys, G_1 girls and $C_1 = B_1 + G_1$ children; the second family having B_2 boys, G_2 girls, and $C_2 = B_2 + G_2$ children; and so forth. The frequency of boys is the total number of boys divided by the total number of children, or

$$f(\text{boys}) = \frac{B_1 + \ldots + B_k}{C_1 + \ldots + C_k} = \frac{(B_1 + \ldots + B_k)/k}{(C_1 + \ldots + C_k)/k}.$$

By the law of large numbers, if k is large, $(B_1 + \ldots + B_k)/k$ will probably be close to $E(B)$, the expected number of boys in a single family. Similarly $(C_1 + \ldots + C_k)/k$ will probably be close to $E(C)$. Therefore, it is probable that $f(\text{boys})$ will be close to $E(B)/E(C)$.

From (2) it is seen that $E(B) = 1 - q^t$. It can be shown (Problem 5) that $E(C) = (1 - q^t)/p$, so that $E(B)/E(C) = p$. This equation shows that the frequency of boys in a large population of families generated by our rule is likely to be close to p, the probability of a boy on a single birth. Thus, even an extreme stopping rule does not alter the frequency of boys in a large population.

The fact that even a stopping rule that favors boys in such an extreme way does not alter the frequency of boys suggests that this frequency would also remain constant with less extreme rules. An intuitive argument can be given for this conjecture. Suppose that the probability of a boy is p, and that the sexes of children are unrelated. Suppose that each family determines its size in its own way, which may differ from one family to another. Then regardless of how family sizes are decided, the frequency of males in the population will be near p. To see this, consider the analogous problem of a group of gamblers who are tossing a penny for which the probability of heads is p. The first gambler tosses it, using the stopping rule of the first family (identify "heads" with "boy"). When he has stopped, he passes the penny to the second gambler, who uses the stopping rule of the second family, etc. From the point of view of the coin, which is indifferent to who is doing the tossing, there is one long sequence of tosses, and the long-run frequency of heads will be close to the probability p of heads on a single toss. Analogously, the frequency of males in the population will be near the probability of a male on a single birth, regardless of the stopping rules used by the various families.

The situation is different, however, if the chance of a male varies from family to family, as some biologists believe. In this case, paradoxically, the effect of the assumptions leading to (2), which were motivated by a preference for boys, increase the frequency of girls. This can be seen intuitively by noting that under the assumed rules, girl-prone families will tend to be larger than boy-prone families. (This phenomenon is illustrated in Problem 7.)

PROBLEMS

1. Two teams continue playing until one of them has won (i) two games, (ii) three games. For each of these cases obtain a tableau analogous to (1).

2. If the probability of team A winning a single game is $p = .7$, find the probability of team A winning the series under the assumptions (i) and (ii) of the preceding problem, and compare your results with the corresponding one of Example 1.

3. Discuss the relation of Example 2 with the gambling system of Problem 5.3.8.

4. Using the fact that the probabilities in the last column of (2) must add up to one, show that

$$1 + q + q^2 + \ldots + q^{t-1} = (1 - q^t)/p.$$

5. In a family generated according to (2), let C denote the total number of children, and let I_1 indicate that $C \geq 1$, I_2 indicate that $C \geq 2, \ldots, I_t$ indicate that $C = t$. Show that
   (i) $C = I_1 + I_2 + \ldots + I_t$.
   (ii) $E(I_1) = 1$, $E(I_2) = q, \ldots, E(I_t) = q^{t-1}$.
   (iii) $E(C) = (1 - q^t)/p$.
[Hint (iii): Combine (ii) with the result of Problem 4.]

6. Give a formula for the expected number of girls in a family generated according to (2). [Hint: $G = C - B$.]

7. Suppose that a population consists of 1000 families with $p = .4$ and 1000 families with $p = .6$. Find the expected number of boys and of girls in this population if
   (i) each family has three children,
   (ii) each family is generated according to (2) with $t = 4$.
[Hint: the number of boys in the population is the sum of the numbers of boys in the 2000 families; use the addition theorem of expectation.]

8. Calculate the expected number of children in the family (2) when $p = \frac{1}{2}$ and $t = 2, 4, 8, 16$. What do you think happens to $E(C)$ when t becomes indefinitely large? Suggest an approximation for $E(C)$ in model (2) if t is large.

CHAPTER 7

MULTIVARIATE DISTRIBUTIONS

7.1 JOINT DISTRIBUTIONS

We have defined a random quantity as a quantity whose value is determined by the result of a random experiment. Actually, an experiment usually will determine the values of many different quantities. For example, when two dice are thrown the experiment determines the number of points on the first die, the number of points on the second die, the total number of points, the number of dice showing an odd number of points, etc. All of these quantities are random quantities determined by one and the same trial of the experiment. Again, when a random sample of items is drawn from a population, one usually observes two or more quantities for each item in the sample. Thus, for each child in a sample drawn from a school, the investigator may record both age and IQ; when a sample is drawn from a lot of ball bearings, the inspector may measure both diameter and hardness of each bearing in the sample. In many cases one is interested in the joint behavior of two or more random quantities relating to the same experiment, which are represented in the model by random variables.

EXAMPLE 1. *Two dice.* In a throw of two dice let F denote the maximum of the numbers of points on the two dice and G the number of dice showing an even number of points. Let us list all possible pairs of values F and G and calculate the probability for each pair of values, assuming the dice to be fair. These probabilities can be found by listing the 36 equally likely results, as was done in Example 1.5.3, and can be exhibited conveniently in a table, whose rows correspond to the possible values of G and columns correspond to the possible values of F, and whose entries are the probabilities.

Thus the result ($G = 0$ and $F = 2$) is impossible, since if the maximum of the numbers showing on the two dice is two (i.e. $F = 2$), at least one of

g＼f	1	2	3	4	5	6	Total
0	$\frac{1}{36}$	0	$\frac{3}{36}$	0	$\frac{5}{36}$	0	$\frac{9}{36}$
1	0	$\frac{2}{36}$	$\frac{2}{36}$	$\frac{4}{36}$	$\frac{4}{36}$	$\frac{6}{36}$	$\frac{18}{36}$
2	0	$\frac{1}{36}$	0	$\frac{3}{36}$	0	$\frac{5}{36}$	$\frac{9}{36}$
Total	$\frac{1}{36}$	$\frac{3}{36}$	$\frac{5}{36}$	$\frac{7}{36}$	$\frac{9}{36}$	$\frac{11}{36}$	$\frac{36}{36} = 1$

the dice must show an even number of points $(G > 0)$. The entry $\frac{2}{36}$ at $(G = 1$ and $F = 2)$ is obtained by noting that the only results with just one die showing an even number and with the maximum of the two numbers being 2, are $(1, 2)$ and $(2, 1)$.

The table above shows the *joint distribution* of the random variables G and F. In general, the joint distribution of two random variables Z and W gives, for each pair of possible values z of Z and w of W, the probability

$$(1) \qquad P(Z = z \text{ and } W = w)$$

of these values occurring on the same trial of the experiment. If Z can take on the values $z_1, z_2, \ldots$ and W the values $w_1, w_2, \ldots$, the joint distribution can be exhibited in a table as follows.

	w_1	w_2	$\ldots$
(2)　z_1	$P(Z = z_1 \text{ and } W = w_1)$	$P(Z = z_1 \text{ and } W = w_2)$	$\ldots$
z_2	$P(Z = z_2 \text{ and } W = w_1)$	$P(Z = z_2 \text{ and } W = w_2)$	$\ldots$
.	.	.	
.	.	.	
.	.	.	

EXAMPLE 2. *Double lottery.* An important general class of problems is obtained by generalizing the lottery model (Examples 5.3.5, 5.5.2, 5.6.2). In this model, a ticket is chosen at random from N tickets bearing the numbers $v_1, \ldots, v_N$. If the number on the chosen ticket is denoted by Y, then the distribution, expectation, and variance of Y can be expressed in terms of the numbers $v_1, \ldots, v_N$.

Let us now suppose that each ticket bears two numbers, say v and w. Thus, on the first ticket are written the numbers v_1 and w_1, on the second ticket the numbers v_2 and w_2, etc. A ticket is drawn at random, and as before Y denotes the v number on the ticket while the w number on the same ticket is denoted by Z. Then Y and Z are jointly distributed random variables. In fact, $P(Y = v \text{ and } Z = w)$ is just the fraction of the N tickets which bear the numbers v and w. This model arises whenever we draw an item at random from a population and are concerned with two characteristics of the items.   This model may be illustrated by the following example.

EXAMPLE 3.   *Distribution of boys and girls.* Suppose that 100 families are classified according to the number of male and female children as follows.

Boys \ Girls	0	1	2	3	4	Total
0	7	11	4	4	2	28
1	6	12	12	6	1	37
2	7	9	8	4	0	28
3	3	2	1	1	0	7
Total	23	34	25	15	3	100

A family is drawn at random and we observe the number B of boys and G of girls in the family.   Here we may represent each of the 100 families by a ticket on which is written the number of boys and girls in that family. The random variables B and G correspond to the variables Y and Z of the general discussion above.   The joint distribution of B and G may be obtained by dividing each entry of the table by 100.   Thus, $P(B = 2$ and $G = 1) = \frac{9}{100} = .09$, since just 9 of the 100 equally likely families have these values for B and G.

EXAMPLE 4.   *Items of several types.* We considered in Section 6.2 the problem of drawing a random sample of s from a population of N items of two types, called ordinary and special.   The number D of special items in the sample is a random variable having the hypergeometric distribution. Let us now see how this distribution generalizes when the items are of several types and we are interested in the numbers of each type that appear in the sample.   These numbers will be jointly distributed random variables.

To be specific, suppose that a lot of $N = 20$ manufactured items consists of 2 having major defects, 5 having minor (but no major) defects, and 13 which are without defects.   As a check on the lot, a sample of $s = 4$ is drawn at random.   The numbers D_1 of items with major defects and D_2 with minor defects have a joint distribution which can be read from the table on page 199.

The table shows the number of different samples having d_1 items with major and d_2 with minor defects, and the probability $P(D_1 = d_1$ and $D_2 = d_2)$ is found by dividing the appropriate entry of the table by the total number of samples, which is $\binom{20}{4} = 4845$.

d_1 \ d_2	0	1	2	3	4	Total
0	715	1430	780	130	5	3060
1	572	780	260	20	0	1632
2	78	65	10	0	0	153
Total	1365	2275	1050	150	5	4845

To see how the table was computed, let us find the entry for $d_1 = 0$ and $d_2 = 2$. The number of ways of selecting two items with minor defects for the sample from the five items with minor defects in the lot is $\binom{5}{2} = 10$. The remainder of the sample must consist of two nondefective items, and these can be chosen in $\binom{13}{2} = 78$ ways so that the total number of samples with $D_1 = 0$ and $D_2 = 2$ is $10 \cdot 78 = 780$.

As another example consider the entry $d_1 = 1$ and $d_2 = 2$. We must now choose two items with minor defects, $\binom{5}{2} = 10$ possibilities; one item with major defects, $\binom{2}{1} = 2$ possibilities; and one nondefective item, $\binom{13}{1} = 13$ possibilities. Altogether, there are therefore $10 \cdot 2 \cdot 13 = 260$ possible samples with $D_1 = 1$ and $D_2 = 2$.

In a situation in which the joint distribution of two random variables Z and W is given, it may be of interest to find the distribution of each random variable separately, the so-called *marginal distributions* of Z and W. How can we, from (2), obtain the marginal distribution of Z, that is the probabilities $P(Z = z_1)$, $P(Z = z_2)$, ... ? The event $Z = z_1$ occurs when Z takes on the value z_1 and W any one of the values $w_1, w_2, \ldots$, so that

$$(Z = z_1) = [(Z = z_1 \text{ and } W = w_1) \text{ or } (Z = z_1 \text{ and } W = w_2) \text{ or.} \ldots].$$

Since the events on the right-hand side of this equation are exclusive, it follows that

(3) $P(Z = z_1) = P(Z = z_1 \text{ and } W = w_1) + P(Z = z_1 \text{ and } W = w_2) + \ldots$.

The probability $P(Z = z_1)$ is therefore obtained from (2) by adding all the probabilities in the row corresponding to z_1. Similarly $P(Z = z_2)$ is the sum of the probabilities in the row corresponding to z_2, etc. The same argument also shows that $P(W = w_1)$ is the sum of the probabilities in the column corresponding to w_1 and analogously for the other values of W.

The term "marginal distribution" derives from the fact that the sum of the probabilities of each row and column is frequently shown in the margin of the table, as was done in the examples above. Thus in Example 1, we read off the marginal distribution of G from the right-hand margin of the table as

$$P(G = 0) = \tfrac{9}{36}, \quad P(G = 1) = \tfrac{18}{36}, \quad P(G = 2) = \tfrac{9}{36}$$

and similarly that of F from the bottom margin of the table. Analogously, in Example 3, the marginal distribution of the number G of girls is seen to be

$$P(G = 0) = .23, \quad P(G = 1) = .34, \quad P(G = 2) = .25,$$
$$P(G = 3) = .15, \quad P(G = 4) = .03.$$

The marginal probability distribution of W gives us the probabilities that W takes on the values $w_1, w_2, \ldots$. What can we say about these probabilities if we are given the value of Z? The probability that $W = w$ given that $Z = z$ is the conditional probability $P(W = w|Z = z)$ (see Section 4.2). Thus for example, if z is any given value of Z, the conditional probability that $W = w_1$, given $Z = z$, is

$$P(W = w_1|Z = z) = \frac{P(W = w_1 \text{ and } Z = z)}{P(Z = z)}.$$

It is easy to check (Problem 5) that the conditional probabilities

(4) $P(W = w_1|Z = z), \quad P(W = w_2|Z = z), \ldots$

add up to one, and thus constitute a distribution.

Definition. The distribution which assigns to $w_1, w_2, \ldots$ the probabilities (4) is called the *conditional distribution of W given Z = z*.

This distribution has of course an expectation, known as the *conditional expectation* of W given $Z = z$, and denoted by $E(W|Z = z)$.

Illustrations of conditional distributions are provided by each of the rows and columns of Examples 1, 3, and 4. In Example 1, for instance, the conditional distribution of G given that $F = 3$ is obtained by dividing the entries of the column $f = 3$ by the total of that column:

$$P(G = 0|F = 3) = \tfrac{3}{5}, \quad P(G = 1|F = 3) = \tfrac{2}{5}, \quad P(G = 2|F = 3) = 0.$$

The joint distribution of Z and W is particularly simple if Z and W are independent (Section 5.2), i.e. if

(5) $P(Z = z \text{ and } W = w) = P(Z = z) \cdot P(W = w)$ for all z, w.

In this case, the conditional distribution of W, given that $Z = z$, is the same as the marginal distribution of W, for all z (Problem 12).

The concepts of this section extend in a natural way to more than two variables. For example, if Z, W, and V are any three random variables, their joint distribution is given by the probabilities

(6) $$P(Z = z, \quad W = w, \quad \text{and} \quad V = v)$$

that Z, W, and V take on any particular values z, w, and v. The marginal distribution of Z is obtained by summing the probabilities (6) over all possible pairs of values w and v; the joint marginal distribution of Z and W is obtained by summing the probabilities (6) over all possible values v. The conditional distribution of V given $Z = z$ and $W = w$ is given by the probabilities

$$P(V = v_1 | Z = z \text{ and } W = w), \quad P(V = v_2 | Z = z \text{ and } W = w), \ldots$$

etc.

PROBLEMS

1. Let Z and W be the minimum and maximum of the numbers of points showing when two fair dice are thrown. Find the joint distribution of Z and W.

2. A sample of five items is drawn at random from a population of 25 items, of which six have major defects and four have minor defects (but no major ones). Find the joint distribution of the numbers of items in the sample having major defects and having minor defects.

3. Let Z and W denote the number of ones and the number of twos appearing when three fair dice are thrown. Find the joint distribution of Z and W.

4. Find the marginal distribution of the random variable D_2 of Example 4 from formula (6.2.1) and check this against the marginal distribution of D_2 read from the table of Example 4.

5. Check that the probabilities (4) add up to one. [Hint: Use formula (4.4.5).]

6. Find the following conditional distributions:
  (i) the distribution of F given $G = 1$ in Example 1;
  (ii) the distribution of B given $G = 3$ in Example 3.

7. Find the conditional distribution of D_2 given $D_1 = 1$ in Example 4
  (i) from the table of Example 4;
  (ii) using the fact that this conditional distribution is hypergeometric.

8. In Example 1,
  (i) find the conditional expectation of the random variable F, given each of the possible values of G ($G = 0$, $G = 1$, $G = 2$);
  (ii) show that
$$P(G = 0)E(F|G = 0) + P(G = 1)E(F|G = 1) + P(G = 2)E(F|G = 2) = E(F).$$

9. (i) Find the conditional expectation of the random variable G of Example 3, given each of the possible values of B.

(ii) In analogy to Problem 8(ii), show that $E(G)$ can be computed by adding the conditional expectations of part (i) each multiplied by the probability of the corresponding value of B.

10.   For any two random variables Z and W, let $\varphi(w) = E(Z|W = w)$. Then $E\varphi(W) = E(Z)$. Prove this result for the case that Z can take on three values z_1, z_2, z_3, and W two values w_1, w_2.

11.   Check the conditional distribution of G given $F = 3$ given in the text by enumerating all possible simple events (pairs of values of the two dice) and constructing a conditional model (given the event $F = 3$) using (4.1.1).

12.   Prove that if Z and W are independent, then the conditional distribution of W given that Z has any particular value z agrees with the marginal distribution of W.

13.   Let the joint distribuion of Z, W, and V be given by

$\frac{1}{4} = P(Z = 0 \text{ and } W = 0 \text{ and } V = 0) = P(Z = 0 \text{ and } W = 1 \text{ and } V = 1)$
$\quad = P(Z = 1 \text{ and } W = 0 \text{ and } V = 1) = P(Z = 1 \text{ and } W = 1 \text{ and } V = 0).$

(i) Find the joint marginal distribution of Z and W and show that Z and W are independent.
(ii) Show that Z and V are independent and that W and V are independent.
(iii) Find the conditional distribution of V given $Z = 0$ and $W = 0$. Determine whether this is equal to the marginal distribution of V.

7.2   COVARIANCE AND CORRELATION

When developing a formula for the variance of the sum of two random variables Z and W in Section 5.7, we were led to define the covariance of Z and W by

$$(1) \qquad \mathrm{Cov}(Z, W) = E[(Z - \zeta)(W - \eta)]$$

where $\zeta = E(Z)$ and $\eta = E(W)$. We shall now discuss and illustrate the meaning of covariance, derive certain laws of covariance, and use these to obtain certain results for variance. In particular, these will provide proofs of formulas (5.7.15) and (6.2.5).

As mentioned in Section 5.7, the covariance of two random variables is a measure of their tendency to vary in the same way. Suppose in fact that the joint distribution of Z and W is such that large values of Z and W usually occur together, and that small values tend to occur together. This would be the case for example if Z and W were the grades on the midterm and final examinations of a randomly selected student, or if they were the ages of husband and wife of a randomly selected couple. When this happens, the quantities $Z - \zeta$ and $W - \eta$ will usually both be positive or both negative, so that the product

$$(2) \qquad\qquad (Z - \zeta)(W - \eta)$$

will usually be positive, and its expectation (1) will therefore typically also be positive (but see Problem 6).

On the other hand, suppose that large values of Z tend to go together with small values of W and vice versa (for example, if Z is the number of cigarettes smoked between the ages of 20 and 25 and W is the age at time of death, or if Z denotes the number of hours spent watching TV and W the number of books read). Then if one of the factors of (2) is positive, the other factor, and hence the product, will usually be negative. The covariance (1) will then typically also be negative.

EXAMPLE 1. *Two pennies.* Suppose that two fair pennies are tossed. Let Z denote the number of heads on the first penny and W the total number of heads on the two pennies. Here large values of Z and W, and small values of Z and W, tend to occur together, so that we expect the covariance to be positive. The joint distribution of Z and W is shown in the following table. The covariance of Z and W is therefore

Event	Probability	z	w	$z - \zeta$	$w - \eta$	$(z - \zeta)(w - \eta)$
HH	$\frac{1}{4}$	1	2	$\frac{1}{2}$	1	$\frac{1}{2}$
HT	$\frac{1}{4}$	1	1	$\frac{1}{2}$	0	0
TH	$\frac{1}{4}$	0	1	$-\frac{1}{2}$	0	0
TT	$\frac{1}{4}$	0	0	$-\frac{1}{2}$	-1	$\frac{1}{2}$

$$\text{Cov}(Z, W) = \tfrac{1}{4} \cdot \tfrac{1}{2} + \tfrac{1}{4} \cdot 0 + \tfrac{1}{4} \cdot 0 + \tfrac{1}{4} \cdot \tfrac{1}{2} = \tfrac{1}{4},$$

which is positive as we expected.

If instead we consider the covariance of Z with the total number of tails on the two tosses, we would expect a negative result (Problem 1).

EXAMPLE 2. *Double lottery.* As a second example let us obtain an expression for the covariance of the numbers Y and Z appearing on the randomly selected ticket of the double lottery discussed in Example 1.2, which we shall denote by

$$(3) \qquad\qquad \lambda = \text{Cov}(Y, Z).$$

Since each of the N tickets has probability $1/N$ of being drawn, and since $E(Y) = \bar{v}$ and $E(Z) = \bar{w}$, we see from (1) and the definition of expectation that

$$(4) \qquad \lambda = [(v_1 - \bar{v})(w_1 - \bar{w}) + \ldots + (v_N - \bar{v})(w_N - \bar{w})]/N.$$

The quantity on the right side of (4) is known as the "population covariance." Equations (3) and (4) are analogous to (5.6.3) and (5.6.4) concerning the population variance.

Covariance obeys a number of simple laws, somewhat analogous to the laws of variance. Two of these were developed in Section 5.7:

(5)$$\text{Cov}(Z, W) = E(ZW) - E(Z)E(W)$$

and

(6) $\text{Cov}(Z, W) = 0$ if Z and W are defined on different factors of a product model.

From the definition it is clear that covariance is commutative; that is, that

(7)$$\text{Cov}(Z, W) = \text{Cov}(W, Z).$$

It is also easily seen from (1) that the covariance of any random variable with a constant is zero,

(8)$$\text{Cov}(Z, c) = 0.$$

As further consequences of (1) we find that the covariance of Z and W is unchanged if any constants are added to Z and W,

(9)$$\text{Cov}(Z + a, W + b) = \text{Cov}(Z, W);$$

while multiplication by constants gives

(10)$$\text{Cov}(aZ, bW) = ab\,\text{Cov}(Z, W).$$

Finally, we have an *addition law* for covariance:

(11)$$\text{Cov}(Z + W, V) = \text{Cov}(Z, V) + \text{Cov}(W, V).$$

The proofs of these laws are left to the reader (Problem 7).

As mentioned in Section 5.7, equation (6) holds quite generally for any independent random variables Z and W. Thus, independent random variables always have zero covariance. The converse, however, is not true. Two random variables may be completely dependent, in the sense that the value of one is determined by the value of the other, but still have covariance equal to zero. For example, let Z take on the values $-1, 0, 1$ with probabilities $\frac{1}{4}, \frac{1}{2}, \frac{1}{4}$ and let $W = Z^2$. Here W is very strongly dependent on Z, being in fact known as soon as Z is known. On the other hand, since $E(Z) = 0$, it follows from (5) that

$$\text{Cov}(Z, W) = E(ZW) = \tfrac{1}{4}(-1) + \tfrac{1}{2}(0) + \tfrac{1}{4}(1) = 0.$$

Equations (9) and (10) show that covariance is unchanged by addition of arbitrary constants to the two variables, but not if the variables are multiplied by constants. A measure of the tendency of the two variables to vary together, which is unchanged both by addition and by multiplication with *positive* constants, is the *correlation coefficient* defined by

(12)$$\rho(Z, W) = \frac{\text{Cov}(Z, W)}{\sqrt{\text{Var}(Z) \cdot \text{Var}(W)}}.$$

(The correlation coefficient is undefined if either $\mathrm{Var}(Z)$ or $\mathrm{Var}(W)$ is zero.) Since the denominator of (12) is always positive, the correlation coefficient always has the same sign as the covariance. It follows that typically ρ is positive if Z and W tend to vary in the same direction, and is negative if they tend to vary in opposite directions. It is seen from (6) and (12) that

(13) $\rho(Z, W) = 0$ if Z and W are defined on different factors of a product model

and indeed (13) holds also if Z and W are independent. Two random variables whose correlation coefficient is zero are said to be *uncorrelated*.

It is important to realize that the correlation coefficient is not, as is frequently believed, a measure of how strongly the variables Z and W depend on each other, but only of the extent to which they vary together or in opposite direction. As shown above, two variables may be very strongly dependent without varying either together or in opposite directions, and the correlation coefficient in such a situation may be zero.

We must still show that $\rho(Z, W)$ is unchanged if arbitrary constants are added to Z and W, or if Z and W are multiplied by positive constants. The first statement is immediate since $\mathrm{Cov}(Z, W)$, $\mathrm{Var}(Z)$, and $\mathrm{Var}(W)$ are all unchanged if Z and W are replaced by $Z + a$ and $W + b$. To see the second, we compute

$$\rho(aZ, bW) = \frac{\mathrm{Cov}(aZ, bW)}{\sqrt{\mathrm{Var}(aZ) \cdot \mathrm{Var}(bW)}} = \frac{ab\,\mathrm{Cov}(Z, W)}{\sqrt{a^2\,\mathrm{Var}(Z) \cdot b^2\,\mathrm{Var}(W)}} = \rho(Z, W).$$

The correlation coefficient has the further property that it always lies between -1 and $+1$ so that for any two random variables Z, W

(14) $-1 \leqq \rho(Z, W) \leqq 1.$

For a proof of this statement see Problem 12.

As an application of the laws of covariance, we shall now extend the addition law for variance (5.7.10),

(15) $\mathrm{Var}(Z + W) = \mathrm{Var}(Z) + \mathrm{Var}(W) + 2\,\mathrm{Cov}(Z, W)$

to obtain a formula for the variance of three random variables, say Z, W, and V. If we think of $Z + W + V$ as the sum of $Z + W$ and V, then (15) shows that

$$\mathrm{Var}(Z + W + V) = \mathrm{Var}[(Z + W) + V] = \mathrm{Var}(Z + W) + \mathrm{Var}(V)$$
$$+ 2\,\mathrm{Cov}(Z + W, V).$$

Now apply (15) again and (11) to find

(16) $\mathrm{Var}(Z + W + V) = \mathrm{Var}(Z) + \mathrm{Var}(W) + \mathrm{Var}(V)$
$$+ 2[\mathrm{Cov}(Z, W) + \mathrm{Cov}(Z, V) + \mathrm{Cov}(W, V)].$$

The argument leading to (16) may be extended to more than three summands (Problem 13). One then obtains the *general addition law of variance:*

$$\operatorname{Var}(Z_1 + \ldots + Z_s) = \operatorname{Var}(Z_1) + \ldots + \operatorname{Var}(Z_s)$$

(17) $+ 2$ [the sum of the covariances of the $\binom{s}{2}$ pairs of the random variables $Z_1, \ldots, Z_s$].

In the particular case when the random variables $Z_1, \ldots, Z_s$ are defined on different factors of a product model (or indeed when they are independent), each of the covariances is zero and (17) implies (5.7.15).

As a further application of (17) we shall now derive the correction factor $(N - s)/(N - 1)$ for the variance of a hypergeometric random variable, encountered in Section 6.2. Consider first a somewhat more general problem.

EXAMPLE 3. *Variance in the lottery model.* Recalling the lottery model of Examples 5.3.5, 5.5.2, and 5.6.2, suppose that s tickets are drawn without replacement from a box containing N tickets labeled with values $v_1, \ldots, v_N$. Let the numbers appearing on the s successively drawn tickets be $Y_1, \ldots,$ Y_s. These are jointly distributed random variables, and by the equivalence law of ordered sampling, each of the Y's has the distribution of the random variable Y of Example 5.6.2. Thus in particular

$$\operatorname{Var}(Y_1) = \ldots = \operatorname{Var}(Y_s) = \tau^2,$$

where τ^2 is defined in (5.6.3). Similarly, each of the $\binom{s}{2} = \frac{1}{2}s(s - 1)$ pairs of the Y's has the same joint distribution, and hence the same covariance, which we shall for the moment denote by γ. From (17), it then follows that

(18) $\operatorname{Var}(Y_1 + \ldots + Y_s) = s\tau^2 + s(s - 1)\gamma.$

There remains the problem of determining the value of γ, which can be solved by means of a trick. Since formula (18) is valid for any value of $s \leqq N$, let us consider the special case $s = N$, which gives

$$\operatorname{Var}(Y_1 + \ldots + Y_N) = N\tau^2 + N(N - 1)\gamma.$$

But $Y_1 + \ldots + Y_N$ is the sum of the v values on all tickets and hence is equal to $v_1 + \ldots + v_N$, which is a constant, and which therefore by (5.7.1) has variance zero. Therefore

$$0 = N\tau^2 + N(N - 1)\gamma \quad \text{or} \quad \gamma = -\tau^2/(N - 1).$$

Substitution in (18) gives

$$\operatorname{Var}(Y_1 + \ldots + Y_s) = s\tau^2 - s(s - 1)\tau^2/(N - 1)$$

and hence

$$(19) \qquad \text{Var}(Y_1 + \ldots + Y_s) = \frac{N - s}{N - 1} s\tau^2.$$

We recognize the factor $(N - s)/(N - 1)$ as the correction factor for sampling without replacement discussed in Section 6.2. In fact, if the s tickets were drawn with replacement, the s drawings would be unrelated, so that a product model would be appropriate. In this model each of the random variables $Y_1, \ldots, Y_s$ would have variance τ^2, and by (5.7.15) we would have $\text{Var}(Y_1 + \ldots + Y_s) = s\tau^2$, which differs from (19) by just the factor in question.

Since the covariance γ of any two Y's is $-\tau^2/(N - 1)$ and the variance of each Y is τ^2, it is seen as a by-product of the above argument that the correlation coefficient of any two Y's is

$$(20) \qquad \rho = -1/(N - 1),$$

provided only that all tickets do not bear the same number. It is remarkable that this value is independent of the values $v_1, \ldots, v_N$ marked on the tickets.

EXAMPLE 4. *Variance of the hypergeometric distribution.* The hypergeometric distribution may be viewed as the special case of the lottery model when r of the tickets have v values one and the remaining $N - r$ tickets have v value zero. In this special case, $\bar{v} = r/N$ and

$$v_1^2 + \ldots + v_N^2 = r.$$

Hence, by (5.6.5),

$$\tau^2 = r(N - r)/N^2.$$

Since the random variable D of Section 6.2 is equal to $Y_1 + \ldots + Y_s$, we see from (19) that

$$(21) \qquad \text{Var}(D) = \frac{N - s}{N - 1} \cdot s \frac{r}{N}\left(1 - \frac{r}{N}\right),$$

which agrees with (6.2.5).

PROBLEMS

1. If U denotes the total number of tails on the two tosses of Example 1, find $\text{Cov}(U, Z)$.

2. A sample of size $s \geq 2$ is drawn without replacement from a population consisting of r special and $N - r$ ordinary items. If I_1 indicates that a special item is obtained on the first draw and I_2 that a special item is obtained on the second draw, find $\text{Cov}(I_1, I_2)$ using formula (5).

3. Apply (5) to show that the population covariance λ of Example 2 can be written as

$$(22) \qquad \lambda = \frac{1}{N}(v_1 w_1 + \ldots + v_N w_N) - \bar{v} \cdot \bar{w}.$$

4. Find the covariance of the random variables F and G of Example 1.1.

5. Find the covariance of the random variables Z and W of Problem 1.3.

6. Consider the four-point bivariate distribution, which assigns probability $\frac{1}{2}(1 - p)$ to each of the points $(1, 1)$ and $(-1, -1)$ in the (z, w)-plane, and probability $\frac{1}{2}p$ to each of the points $(10, -10)$ and $(-10, 10)$. Show that p may be chosen so that (2) is positive with high probability but (1) is negative.

7. Write out formal proofs of laws (9), (10), and (11).

8. Find the correlation coefficient of the pair of random variables whose covariance was found in (i) Example 1, (ii) Problem 1, (iii) Problem 2, (iv) Problem 5.

9. For the distribution of Problem 6, obtain the correlation coefficient ρ of Z and W as a function of p.

10. What happens to the correlation coefficient ρ of two random variables Z and W
  (i) if Z is multiplied by a negative constant?
  (ii) if both Z and W are multiplied by negative constants?

11. Show that

$$\operatorname{Var}(aZ + bW) = a^2 \operatorname{Var}(Z) + 2ab \operatorname{Cov}(Z, W) + b^2 \operatorname{Var}(W).$$

12. For all random variables Z, W show that
  (i) for any constant a

$$\operatorname{Var}(Z) + 2a \operatorname{Cov}(Z, W) + a^2 \operatorname{Var}(W) \geqq 0;$$

  (ii) $[\operatorname{Cov}(Z, W)]^2 \leqq \operatorname{Var}(Z) \operatorname{Var}(W)$;
  (iii) $[\rho(Z, W)]^2 \leqq 1$, and hence (14).
[Hint: (i) Use the fact that $\operatorname{Var}(Z + aW)$ cannot be negative; (ii) apply the result of (i) with $a = -\operatorname{Cov}(Z, W)/\operatorname{Var}(W)$; (iii) use (ii).]

13. Prove (17) for the case $s = 4$. [Hint: Obtain this result from (16) by the method used to obtain (16) from (15).]

14. Why does formula (20) require the assumption that all tickets do not bear the same number?

15. Suppose that in the double lottery of Example 2, s tickets are drawn without replacement. Let (Y_1, Z_1) denote the v and w values on the first ticket, (Y_2, Z_2) the values on the second ticket, etc.
  (i) If $\mu = \operatorname{Cov}(Y_1, Z_2)$, show that μ is in fact the covariance of any Y and Z with different subscripts, and that

$$(23) \qquad \mu = -\lambda/(N - 1).$$

  (ii) If $\bar{Y} = (Y_1 + \ldots + Y_s)/s$ and $\bar{Z} = (Z_1 + \ldots + Z_s)/s$, use (i) and (3) to show that

$$(24) \qquad \operatorname{Cov}(\bar{Y}, \bar{Z}) = \frac{N - s}{N - 1} \cdot \frac{\lambda}{s}.$$

(iii) Find the correlation coefficient of $(\bar{Y}, \bar{Z})$.

[Hint for (i): Use (3), (7), and (11) to express $\text{Cov}(Y_1 + \ldots + Y_s, Z_1 + \ldots + Z_s)$ in terms of λ and μ, and put $s = N$ in the resulting expression as in Example 3.]

16. Obtain the results corresponding to the three parts of the preceding problem under the assumption that the s tickets are drawn with replacement.

17. Show that the variance of the random variable M of Section 6.8 (the number of matchings) is $\text{Var}(M) = 1$. [Hint: Use the representation $M = I_1 + \ldots + I_N$ of Section 6.8, the addition law (17), and the equivalence law of ordered sampling, to find

$$\text{Var}(M) = N\,\text{Var}(I_1) + N(N-1)\,\text{Cov}(I_1, I_2).$$

Complete the solution by finding $\text{Var}\,I_1$ and $\text{Cov}(I_1, I_2)$.]

7.3 THE MULTINOMIAL DISTRIBUTION

As we mentioned at the end of Section 3.3, the concept of binomial trials extends in a natural way to unrelated trials with more than two possible outcomes. Suppose that on each trial of a sequence there are k possible outcomes, just one of which will occur. In addition, suppose that the probability of the first outcome is the same, say p_1, on each of the trials; the probability of the second outcome is the same, say p_2, on each of the trials; etc. We must of course have $p_1 + p_2 + \ldots + p_k = 1$. These assumptions amount to representing each of the trials by a model with k simple events to which are assigned the probabilities $p_1, p_2, \ldots, p_k$. If in addition we are willing to assume that the trials are unrelated, a model for the whole experiment may be formed as the product of the models for the separate trials. This product will be called the *multinomial trials* model.

In deciding whether to use a multinomial trials model for a sequence of trials, two questions must be considered, just as in the binomial case:

(a) For each of the outcomes, is the chance of its occurrence the same on all trials?

(b) Are the trials unrelated; that is, are the chances on each trial unaffected by what happens on the other trials?

We shall now consider several examples, for which a multinomial trials model may be appropriate.

EXAMPLE *1.   The loaded die.* Recall model (1.3.1) for a single throw of a loaded die. In the present notation, if the outcomes of interest are "one point showing," $\ldots$, "six points showing," then $p_1 = .21$, $p_2 = \ldots = p_5 = .17$, $p_6 = .11$. For several throws of this die, the multinomial trials model may be used with $k = 6$.

EXAMPLE 2. *Random digits.* On each trial with a random digit generator (Example 1.2.2) there are ten possible outcomes, the digits 0, 1, . . . , 9. If the generator is working properly, the multinomial trials model may be used with $k = 10$ and $p_1 = \ldots = p_{10} = .1$.

EXAMPLE 3. *Quality control.* Recall Example 6.1.3, but suppose that each item coming off the production line is classified as having major defects, minor defects but no major ones, or no defects. If the process is in a state of control, we may use the multinomial model with $k = 3$. The model will be realistic provided p_1, p_2, p_3 are close to the long-run frequencies with which the three types of items are produced.

EXAMPLE 4. *Election forecasting.* Suppose that a polling organization samples the electorate to find how many voters favor Candidate A, how many favor Candidate B, and how many are undecided. Each interview with a voter may be regarded as a trial having three possible outcomes, with probabilities equal to the fractions p_1, p_2, p_3 of the electorate who favor A, favor B, or are undecided. The trials are of course related (unless the sampling is done with replacement), but if the sampling fraction is small, the degree of relationship is negligible, and a multinomial model with $k = 3$ may be used (see the discussion in Example 3.3.3).

   As in the binomial case, the interest in a sequence of multinomial trials is often centered on the numbers of occurrences of each possible outcome. In a sequence of n multinomial trials, let $B_1, B_2, \ldots, B_k$ be the numbers of occurrences of the k possible outcomes, where of course $B_1 + B_2 + \ldots + B_k = n$. (Thus, in Example 4, n would be the number of voters interviewed, and B_1, B_2, B_3 would be the numbers of them who favor Candidate A, who favor Candidate B, and who are undecided.) The random variables $B_1, B_2, \ldots, B_k$ are known as *multinomial* random variables. Since the k random variables have the fixed sum n, it is enough to consider any $k - 1$ of them, for example $B_1, B_2, \ldots, B_{k-1}$; their values determine the value of the remaining one.
   In a multinomial model, the marginal distribution of any one of the B's, for example B_1, is binomial. This may be seen by labeling the first outcome "success" and lumping the other $k - 1$ outcomes together as "failure." Since the trials are unrelated, and since on each trial the probability of "success" is p_1, it follows that B_1 has the binomial distribution (n, p_1). It follows that

(1) $$\begin{aligned} E(B_1) &= np_1, & \ldots, & \quad E(B_k) = np_k \\ \mathrm{Var}(B_1) &= np_1(1 - p_1), & \ldots, & \quad \mathrm{Var}(B_k) = np_k(1 - p_k). \end{aligned}$$

Furthermore, it is easy to verify (Problems 4 and 5) that

(2) $$\text{Cov}(B_1, B_2) = -np_1p_2$$

and similarly for the other pairs.

The joint distribution of any $k - 1$ of the random variables $(B_1, B_2, \ldots, B_k)$ is known as a *multinomial* distribution, or more specifically as a *k-nomial* distribution. In the special case $k = 2$, there are only two possible results, and one is dealing with a sequence of binomial trials; then either of the random variables B_1 or B_2 has a 2-nomial or binomial, distribution, in agreement with our earlier terminology. When $k = 3$, the joint distribution of any pair of (B_1, B_2, B_3) is 3-nomial, or *trinomial*. To keep the discussion simple we shall treat only this case.

Let us denote by S_1, S_2, S_3 that a trial results in the first, second, or third of the three possible outcomes. (Thus $S_2S_1S_1S_3$, for example, indicates that the first trial results in outcome 2, the second and third in outcome 1, and the fourth in outcome 3). Then the probability of getting b_1 results S_1, b_2 results S_2, and $b_3 = n - b_1 - b_2$ results S_3 in some specified order (such as for example $S_1S_1 \ldots S_1S_2S_2 \ldots S_2S_3S_3 \ldots S_3$) is

(3) $$p_1^{b_1}p_2^{b_2}p_3^{b_3}.$$

(This corresponds to formula (3.3.1) in the binomial case.)

Let us denote by $\binom{n}{b_1, \, b_2}$ the number of ways to choose b_1 of the trials for S_1 and b_2 other trials for S_2. Then $P(B_1 = b_1 \text{ and } B_2 = b_2)$ is the sum of $\binom{n}{b_1, \, b_2}$ terms, each equal to (3), and hence

(4) $$P(B_1 = b_1 \text{ and } B_2 = b_2) = \binom{n}{b_1, \, b_2} p_1^{b_1}p_2^{b_2}p_3^{b_3}.$$

The number $\binom{n}{b_1, \, b_2}$ can easily be expressed in terms of numbers of combinations. There are $\binom{n}{b_1}$ ways to choose the b_1 trials for S_1. For each such choice there remain $n - b_1$ trials, of which b_2 may be chosen in $\binom{n - b_1}{b_2}$ ways for S_2. Therefore

(5) $$\binom{n}{b_1, \, b_2} = \binom{n}{b_1}\binom{n - b_1}{b_2}.$$

EXAMPLE 1. *The loaded die (continued)*. Suppose that the die is loaded so that the face with one point (ace) appears .2 of the time and the opposite face (six) only .1 of the time. The other faces together then appear .7 of the time. The die is thrown $n = 10$ times and the numbers B_1 of aces and B_2 of sixes are observed. The joint (trinomial) distribution of B_1 and B_2 is shown in the table (where only those entries are given that are at least .0001 to four decimal accuracy).

b_2 \ b_1	0	1	2	3	4	5	6	7	Total
0	.0282	.0807	.1038	.0791	.0395	.0136	.0032	.0005	.3486
1	.0404	.1038	.1186	.0791	.0339	.0097	.0018	.0002	.3875
2	.0259	.0593	.0593	.0339	.0121	.0028	.0004		.1937
3	.0099	.0198	.0169	.0081	.0023	.0004			.0574
4	.0025	.0042	.0030	.0012	.0002				.0111
5	.0004	.0006	.0003	.0001					.0014
6	.0001								.0001
Total	.1074	.2684	.3019	.2015	.0880	.0265	.0054	.0007	

As an illustration, let us check one of the entires, say that corresponding to $b_1 = 2$ and $b_2 = 3$. According to (4),

$$P(B_1 = 2 \text{ and } B_2 = 3) = \binom{10}{2,\,3}(.2)^2(.1)^3(.7)^5$$

where

$$\binom{10}{2,\,3} = \binom{10}{2}\binom{8}{3} = 45 \cdot 56 = 2520$$

and on carrying through the calculation, the desired probability is seen to be .0169.

It is an interesting property of the multinomial distribution that all of the marginal and conditional distributions associated with it are again multinomial. For example, if $k = 5$, the *joint* marginal distribution of B_1 and B_2 is trinomial with n trials and probabilities p_1, p_2; while the conditional distribution of B_3, B_4 given $B_1 = b_1$ and $B_2 = b_2$ is trinomial with $n - b_1 - b_2$ trials and probabilities $p_3/(p_3 + p_4 + p_5)$ and $p_4(p_3 + p_4 + p_5)$ (Problem 11).

Just as the binomial distribution has been generalized to the multinomial distribution, so the hypergeometric distribution may be generalized to the *multiple hypergeometric* distribution, providing a model for a more precise analysis of experiments such as that of Example 4 where a sample is drawn without replacement from a population of items of more than two types (see Example 7.1.4 and Problems 12–16).

PROBLEMS

1. Check the entry .1186 in the table of Example 1.

2. Suppose that in a production line on the average 3% of the items have irreparable defects while 10% hare reparable defects. In a day's production of 100 items, let B_1 and B_2 be the numbers of items with irreparable and reparable defects.
   (i) Use (1) and (2) to find $E(B_1)$, $E(B_2)$, $\text{Var}(B_1)$, $\text{Var}(B_2)$, $\text{Cov}(B_1, B_2)$.

(ii) Suppose that it costs $10 to repair an item, and there is a $50 loss when an item is irreparable. Let L be the loss due to defects in the day's production. Find $E(L)$, $Var(L)$. [Hint: See Problem 7.2.11.]

(iii) Use the normal approximation to find the probability that L exceeds $350.

3. In a multinomial model, what is the distribution of $B_1 + B_2$? [Hint: Use an argument analogous to that showing the marginal distribution of B_1 to be binomial.]

4. Find $Var(B_1 + B_2)$ from Problem 3, and use this result together with the addition law of variance to verify (2).

5. Verify (2) by representing B_1 and B_2 as sums of indicators.

6. In how many ways can ten councilmen be distributed among three committees so that just two councilmen are put on Committee A, three others on Committee B, and the remaining five on Committee C? [Hint: See derivation of (5).]

7. Generalize (5) to obtain a formula for the number $\begin{pmatrix} n \\ b_1, b_2, b_3 \end{pmatrix}$ of ways to choose b_1 trials for S_1, b_2 trials for S_2, b_3 trials for S_3 in a sequence of n quadrinomial trials.

8. In generalization of (4) and (5), let $k = 4$ and find the quadrinomial distribution of B_1, B_2, B_3.

9. Using the table of Example 1 and Table B,
(i) Check the distribution of B_1 against the binomial distribution ($n = 10$, $p = .2$).
(ii) Find the distribution of B_3 and check it against the binomial distribution ($n = 10$, $p = .7$).

10. Let B_1 and B_2 have the trinomial distribution (4). Using (5) and (4.2.1), show that the conditional distribution of B_2, given that $B_1 = b_1$, is binomial $(n - b_1, p_2/(p_2 + p_3))$. Check this result on the table of Example 1 for the case $b_1 = 4$.

11. Show that in a multinomial distribution with $k = 5$ and probabilities $p_1, p_2, \ldots, p_5$
(i) the joint marginal distribution of B_1 and B_2 is trinomial with n trials and probabilities p_1, p_2;
(ii) the conditional distribution of B_3, B_4 given $B_1 = b_1$, $B_2 = b_2$ is trinomial with $n - b_1 - b_2$ trials and probabilities $p_3/(p_3 + p_4 + p_5)$, $p_4/(p_3 + p_4 + p_5)$.

Problems 12–16 are concerned with the multiple hypergeometric distribution.

12. In a population of N items there are r_1, r_2, r_3 items of types 1, 2, 3 respectively ($r_1 + r_2 + r_3 = N$). If a random sample of s items is drawn and D_1, D_2, D_3 denote the numbers of items of the three types in the sample, show that

$$P(D_1 = d_1 \text{ and } D_2 = d_2) = \begin{pmatrix} r_1 \\ d_1 \end{pmatrix} \begin{pmatrix} r_2 \\ d_2 \end{pmatrix} \begin{pmatrix} r_3 \\ d_3 \end{pmatrix} \Big/ \begin{pmatrix} N \\ S \end{pmatrix}.$$

13. In the preceding problem
(i) what are the marginal distributions of D_1, D_2, D_3?
(ii) what is $E(D_1)$ and $Var(D_1)$?

14. In Problem 12, what is the conditional distribution of D_2 given $D_1 = d_1$?

15. In Problem 12, what is the distribution of $D_1 + D_2$?

16. Find $\text{Cov}(D_1, D_2)$
   (i) by specializing formula (2.4);
   (ii) in analogy with Problem 4, using Problem 15.
[Hint for (i): For items of type 1, set $v = 1$, $w = 0$; for items of type 2, set $v = 0$, $w = 1$; for items of type 3, set $v = w = 0$.]

TABLES

TABLE A. NUMBER OF COMBINATIONS $\binom{N}{s}$ OF N THINGS TAKEN s AT A TIME

s / N	2	3	4	5	6	7	8	9	10	11	12	13
2	1											
3	3	1										
4	6	4	1									
5	10	10	5	1								
6	15	20	15	6	1							
7	21	35	35	21	7	1						
8	28	56	70	56	28	8	1					
9	36	84	126	126	84	36	9	1				
10	45	120	210	252	210	120	45	10	1			
11	55	165	330	462	462	330	165	55	11	1		
12	66	220	495	792	924	792	495	220	66	12	1	
13	78	286	715	1,287	1,716	1,716	1,287	715	286	78	13	1
14	91	364	1,001	2,002	3,003	3,432	3,003	2,002	1,001	364	91	14
15	105	455	1,365	3,003	5,005	6,435	6,435	5,005	3,003	1,365	455	105
16	120	560	1,820	4,368	8,008	11,440	12,870	11,440	8,008	4,368	1,820	560
17	136	680	2,380	6,188	12,376	19,448	24,310	24,310	19,448	12,376	6,188	2,380
18	153	816	3,060	8,568	18,564	31,824	43,758	48,620	43,758	31,824	18,564	8,568
19	171	969	3,876	11,628	27,132	50,388	75,582	92,378	92,378	75,582	50,388	27,132
20	190	1,140	4,845	15,504	38,760	77,520	125,970	167,960	184,756	167,960	125,970	77,520
21	210	1,330	5,985	20,349	54,264	116,280	203,490	293,930	352,716	352,716	293,930	203,490
22	231	1,540	7,315	26,334	74,613	170,544	319,770	497,420	646,646	705,432	646,646	497,420
23	253	1,771	8,855	33,649	100,947	245,157	490,314	817,190	1,144,066	1,352,078	1,352,078	1,144,066
24	276	2,024	10,626	42,504	134,596	346,104	735,471	1,307,504	1,961,256	2,496,144	2,704,156	2,496,144
25	300	2,300	12,650	53,130	177,100	480,700	1,081,575	2,042,975	3,268,760	4,457,400	5,200,300	5,200,300
26	325	2,600	14,950	65,780	230,230	657,800	1,562,275	3,124,550	5,311,735	7,726,160	9,657,700	10,400,600

TABLE B. $P(B = b)$ FOR THE BINOMIAL DISTRIBUTION (n, p)

n	b	$p = .05$	$p = .1$	$p = .2$	$p = .3$	$p = .4$
2	0	.9025	.8100	.6400	.4900	.3600
	1	.0950	.1800	.3200	.4200	.4800
	2	.0025	.0100	.0400	.0900	.1600
3	0	.8574	.7290	.5120	.3430	.2160
	1	.1354	.2430	.3840	.4410	.4320
	2	.0071	.0270	.0960	.1890	.2880
	3	.0001	.0010	.0080	.0270	.0640
4	0	.8145	.6561	.4096	.2401	.1296
	1	.1715	.2916	.4096	.4116	.3456
	2	.0135	.0486	.1536	.2646	.3456
	3	.0005	.0036	.0256	.0756	.1536
	4		.0001	.0016	.0081	.0256
5	0	.7738	.5905	.3277	.1681	.0778
	1	.2036	.3280	.4096	.3602	.2592
	2	.0214	.0729	.2048	.3087	.3456
	3	.0011	.0081	.0512	.1323	.2304
	4		.0005	.0064	.0284	.0768
	5			.0003	.0024	.0102
6	0	.7351	.5314	.2621	.1176	.0467
	1	.2321	.3543	.3932	.3025	.1866
	2	.0305	.0984	.2458	.3241	.3110
	3	.0021	.0146	.0819	.1852	.2765
	4	.0001	.0012	.0154	.0595	.1382
	5		.0001	.0015	.0102	.0369
	6			.0001	.0007	.0041
7	0	.6983	.4783	.2097	.0824	.0280
	1	.2573	.3720	.3670	.2471	.1306
	2	.0406	.1240	.2753	.3176	.2613
	3	.0036	.0230	.1147	.2269	.2903
	4	.0002	.0026	.0287	.0972	.1935
	5		.0002	.0043	.0250	.0774
	6			.0004	.0036	.0172
	7				.0002	.0016

n	b	$p = .05$	$p = .1$	$p = .2$	$p = .3$	$p = .4$
8	0	.6634	.4305	.1678	.0576	.0168
	1	.2793	.3826	.3355	.1977	.0896
	2	.0515	.1488	.2936	.2965	.2090
	3	.0054	.0331	.1468	.2541	.2787
	4	.0004	.0046	.0459	.1361	.2322
	5		.0004	.0092	.0467	.1239
	6			.0011	.0100	.0413
	7			.0001	.0012	.0079
	8				.0001	.0007
9	0	.6302	.3874	.1342	.0404	.0101
	1	.2985	.3874	.3020	.1556	.0605
	2	.0629	.1722	.3020	.2668	.1612
	3	.0077	.0446	.1762	.2668	.2508
	4	.0006	.0074	.0661	.1715	.2508
	5		.0008	.0165	.0735	.1672
	6		.0001	.0028	.0210	.0743
	7			.0003	.0039	.0212
	8				.0004	.0035
	9					.0003
10	0	.5987	.3487	.1074	.0282	.0060
	1	.3151	.3874	.2684	.1211	.0403
	2	.0746	.1937	.3020	.2335	.1209
	3	.0105	.0574	.2013	.2668	.2150
	4	.0010	.0112	.0881	.2001	.2508
	5	.0001	.0015	.0264	.1029	.2007
	6		.0001	.0055	.0368	.1115
	7			.0008	.0090	.0425
	8			.0001	.0014	.0106
	9				.0001	.0016
	10					.0001

TABLE C. $P(B = b)$ FOR THE BINOMIAL DISTRIBUTION $(n, .5)$

n	b	p = .5	n	b	p = .5	n	b	p = .5	n	b	p = .5	n	b	p = .5
2	0	.2500	13	0	.0001	18	0	.0000	23	2	.0000	27	3	.0000
	1	.5000		1	.0016		1	.0001		3	.0002		4	.0001
3	0	.1250		2	.0095		2	.0006		4	.0011		5	.0006
	1	.3750		3	.0349		3	.0031		5	.0040		6	.0022
4	0	.0625		4	.0873		4	.0117		6	.0120		7	.0066
	1	.2500		5	.1571		5	.0327		7	.0292		8	.0165
	2	.3750		6	.2095		6	.0708		8	.0584		9	.0349
5	0	.0312	14	0	.0001		7	.1214		9	.0974		10	.0629
	1	.1562		1	.0009		8	.1669		10	.1364		11	.0971
	2	.3125		2	.0056		9	.1855		11	.1612		12	.1295
6	0	.0156		3	.0222	19	1	.0000	24	2	.0000		13	.1494
	1	.0938		4	.0611		2	.0003		3	.0001	28	3	.0000
	2	.2344		5	.1222		3	.0018		4	.0006		4	.0001
	3	.3125		6	.1833		4	.0074		5	.0025		5	.0004
7	0	.0078		7	.2095		5	.0222		6	.0080		6	.0014
	1	.0547	15	0	.0000		6	.0518		7	.0206		7	.0044
	2	.1641		1	.0005		7	.0961		8	.0438		8	.0116
	3	.2734		2	.0032		8	.1442		9	.0779		9	.0257
8	0	.0039		3	.0139		9	.1762		10	.1169		10	.0489
	1	.0312		4	.0417	20	1	.0000		11	.1488		11	.0800
	2	.1094		5	.0916		2	.0002		12	.1612		12	.1133
	3	.2188		6	.1527		3	.0011	25	2	.0000		13	.1395
	4	.2734		7	.1964		4	.0046		3	.0001		14	.1494
9	0	.0020	16	0	.0000		5	.0148		4	.0004	29	4	.0000
	1	.0176		1	.0002		6	.0370		5	.0016		5	.0002
	2	.0703		2	.0018		7	.0739		6	.0053		6	.0009
	3	.1641		3	.0085		8	.1201		7	.0143		7	.0029
	4	.2461		4	.0278		9	.1602		8	.0322		8	.0080
10	0	.0010		5	.0667		10	.1762		9	.0609		9	.0187
	1	.0098		6	.1222	21	1	.0000		10	.0974		10	.0373
	2	.0439		7	.1746		2	.0001		11	.1328		11	.0644
	3	.1172		8	.1964		3	.0006		12	.1550		12	.0967
	4	.2051	17	0	.0000		4	.0029	26	3	.0000		13	.1264
	5	.2461		1	.0001		5	.0097		4	.0002		14	.1445
11	0	.0005		2	.0010		6	.0259		5	.0010	30	4	.0000
	1	.0054		3	.0052		7	.0554		6	.0034		5	.0001
	2	.0269		4	.0182		8	.0970		7	.0098		6	.0006
	3	.0806		5	.0472		9	.1402		8	.0233		7	.0019
	4	.1611		6	.0944		10	.1682		9	.0466		8	.0055
	5	.2256		7	.1484	22	1	.0000		10	.0792		9	.0133
12	0	.0002		8	.1855		2	.0001		11	.1151		10	.0280
	1	.0029					3	.0004		12	.1439		11	.0509
	2	.0161					4	.0017		13	.1550		12	.0806
	3	.0537					5	.0063					13	.1115
	4	.1208					6	.0178					14	.1354
	5	.1934					7	.0407					15	.1445
	6	.2256					8	.0762						
							9	.1186						
							10	.1542						
							11	.1682						

TABLE D. SQUARE ROOTS

n	$\sqrt{n}$	$\sqrt{10n}$	n	$\sqrt{n}$	$\sqrt{10n}$	n	$\sqrt{n}$	$\sqrt{10n}$
1	1.0000	3.1623	34	5.8310	18.439	67	8.1854	25.884
2	1.4142	4.4721	35	5.9161	18.708	68	8.2462	26.077
3	1.7321	5.4772	36	6.0000	18.974	69	8.3066	26.268
4	2.0000	6.3246	37	6.0828	19.235	70	8.3666	26.458
5	2.2361	7.0711	38	6.1644	19.494	71	8.4261	26.646
6	2.4495	7.7460	39	6.2450	19.748	72	8.4853	26.833
7	2.6458	8.3666	40	6.3246	20.000	73	8.5440	27.019
8	2.8284	8.9443	41	6.4031	20.248	74	8.6023	27.203
9	3.0000	9.4868	42	6.4807	20.494	75	8.6603	27.386
10	3.1623	10.000	43	6.5574	20.736	76	8.7178	27.568
11	3.3166	10.488	44	6.6332	20.976	77	8.7750	27.749
12	3.4641	10.954	45	6.7082	21.213	78	8.8318	27.928
13	3.6056	11.402	46	6.7823	21.448	79	8.8882	28.107
14	3.7417	11.832	47	6.8557	21.679	80	8.9443	28.284
15	3.8730	12.247	48	6.9282	21.909	81	9.0000	28.460
16	4.0000	12.649	49	7.0000	22.136	82	9.0554	28.636
17	4.1231	13.038	50	7.0711	22.361	83	9.1104	28.810
18	4.2426	13.416	51	7.1414	22.583	84	9.1652	28.983
19	4.3589	13.784	52	7.2111	22.804	85	9.2195	29.155
20	4.4721	14.142	53	7.2801	23.022	86	9.2736	29.326
21	4.5826	14.491	54	7.3485	23.238	87	9.3274	29.496
22	4.6904	14.832	55	7.4162	23.452	88	9.3808	29.665
23	4.7958	15.166	56	7.4833	23.664	89	9.4340	29.833
24	4.8990	15.492	57	7.5498	23.875	90	9.4868	30.000
25	5.0000	15.811	58	7.6158	24.083	91	9.5394	30.166
26	5.0990	16.125	59	7.6811	24.290	92	9.5917	30.332
27	5.1962	16.432	60	7.7460	24.495	93	9.6437	30.496
28	5.2915	16.733	61	7.8102	24.698	94	9.6954	30.659
29	5.3852	17.029	62	7.8740	24.900	95	9.7468	30.822
30	5.4772	17.321	63	7.9373	25.100	96	9.7980	30.984
31	5.5678	17.607	64	8.0000	25.298	97	9.8489	31.145
32	5.6569	17.889	65	8.0623	25.495	98	9.8995	31.305
33	5.7446	18.166	66	8.1240	25.690	99	9.9499	31.464

TABLE E. AREA $\Phi(z)$ UNDER THE NORMAL CURVE TO THE LEFT OF z

z	.00	.01	.02	.03	.04	.05	.06	.07	.08	.09
.0	.5000	.5040	.5080	.5120	.5160	.5199	.5239	.5279	.5319	.5359
.1	.5398	.5438	.5478	.5517	.5557	.5596	.5636	.5675	.5714	.5753
.2	.5793	.5832	.5871	.5910	.5948	.5987	.6026	.6064	.6103	.6141
.3	.6179	.6217	.6255	.6293	.6331	.6368	.6406	.6443	.6480	.6517
.4	.6554	.6591	.6628	.6664	.6700	.6736	.6772	.6808	.6844	.6879
.5	.6915	.6950	.6985	.7019	.7054	.7088	.7123	.7157	.7190	.7224
.6	.7257	.7291	.7324	.7357	.7389	.7422	.7454	.7486	.7517	.7549
.7	.7580	.7611	.7642	.7673	.7704	.7734	.7764	.7794	.7823	.7852
.8	.7881	.7910	.7939	.7967	.7995	.8023	.8051	.8078	.8106	.8133
.9	.8159	.8186	.8212	.8238	.8264	.8289	.8315	.8340	.8365	.8389
1.0	.8413	.8438	.8461	.8485	.8508	.8531	.8554	.8577	.8599	.8621
1.1	.8643	.8665	.8686	.8708	.8729	.8749	.8770	.8790	.8810	.8830
1.2	.8849	.8869	.8888	.8907	.8925	.8944	.8962	.8980	.8997	.9015
1.3	.9032	.9049	.9066	.9082	.9099	.9115	.9131	.9147	.9162	.9177
1.4	.9192	.9207	.9222	.9236	.9251	.9265	.9279	.9292	.9306	.9319
1.5	.9332	.9345	.9357	.9370	.9382	.9394	.9406	.9418	.9429	.9441
1.6	.9452	.9463	.9474	.9484	.9495	.9505	.9515	.9525	.9535	.9545
1.7	.9554	.9564	.9573	.9582	.9591	.9599	.9608	.9616	.9625	.9633
1.8	.9641	.9649	.9656	.9664	.9671	.9678	.9686	.9693	.9699	.9706
1.9	.9713	.9719	.9726	.9732	.9738	.9744	.9750	.9756	.9761	.9767
2.0	.9772	.9778	.9783	.9788	.9793	.9798	.9803	.9808	.9812	.9817
2.1	.9821	.9826	.9830	.9834	.9838	.9842	.9846	.9850	.9854	.9857
2.2	.9861	.9864	.9868	.9871	.9875	.9878	.9881	.9884	.9887	.9890
2.3	.9893	.9896	.9898	.9901	.9904	.9906	.9909	.9911	.9913	.9916
2.4	.9918	.9920	.9922	.9925	.9927	.9929	.9931	.9932	.9934	.9936
2.5	.9938	.9940	.9941	.9943	.9945	.9946	.9948	.9949	.9951	.9952
2.6	.9953	.9955	.9956	.9957	.9959	.9960	.9961	.9962	.9963	.9964
2.7	.9965	.9966	.9967	.9968	.9969	.9970	.9971	.9972	.9973	.9974
2.8	.9974	.9975	.9976	.9977	.9977	.9978	.9979	.9979	.9980	.9981
2.9	.9981	.9982	.9982	.9983	.9984	.9984	.9985	.9985	.9986	.9986
3.0	.9987	.9987	.9987	.9988	.9988	.9989	.9989	.9989	.9990	.9990
3.1	.9990	.9991	.9991	.9991	.9992	.9992	.9992	.9992	.9993	.9993
3.2	.9993	.9993	.9994	.9994	.9994	.9994	.9994	.9995	.9995	.9995
3.3	.9995	.9995	.9995	.9996	.9996	.9996	.9996	.9996	.9996	.9997
3.4	.9997	.9997	.9997	.9997	.9997	.9997	.9997	.9997	.9997	.9998

The entries from 3.49 to 3.61 all equal .9998.
The entries from 3.62 to 3.89 all equal .9999.
All entries from 3.90 and up equal 1.0000.

TABLE F. THE POISSON APPROXIMATION $P(S = s)$

s	$E(S) = \lambda$ .1	.2	.3	.4	.5	.6	.7	.8	.9	1.0
0	.9048	.8187	.7408	.6703	.6065	.5488	.4966	.4493	.4066	.3679
1	.0905	.1637	.2222	.2681	.3033	.3293	.3476	.3595	.3659	.3679
2	.0045	.0164	.0333	.0536	.0758	.0988	.1217	.1438	.1647	.1839
3	.0002	.0011	.0033	.0072	.0126	.0198	.0284	.0383	.0494	.0613
4		.0001	.0003	.0007	.0016	.0030	.0050	.0077	.0111	.0153
5				.0001	.0002	.0004	.0007	.0012	.0020	.0031
6							.0001	.0002	.0003	.0005
7										.0001

s	$E(S) = \lambda$ 1	2	3	4	5	6	7	8	9	10
0	.3679	.1353	.0498	.0183	.0067	.0025	.0009	.0003	.0001	.0000
1	.3679	.2707	.1494	.0733	.0337	.0149	.0064	.0027	.0011	.0005
2	.1839	.2707	.2240	.1465	.0842	.0446	.0223	.0107	.0050	.0023
3	.0613	.1804	.2240	.1954	.1404	.0892	.0521	.0286	.0150	.0076
4	.0153	.0902	.1680	.1954	.1755	.1339	.0912	.0572	.0337	.0189
5	.0031	.0361	.1008	.1563	.1755	.1606	.1277	.0916	.0607	.0378
6	.0005	.0120	.0504	.1042	.1462	.1606	.1490	.1221	.0911	.0631
7	.0001	.0034	.0216	.0595	.1044	.1377	.1490	.1396	.1171	.0901
8		.0009	.0081	.0298	.0653	.1033	.1304	.1396	.1318	.1126
9		.0002	.0027	.0132	.0363	.0688	.1014	.1241	.1318	.1251
10			.0008	.0053	.0181	.0413	.0710	.0993	.1186	.1251
11			.0002	.0019	.0082	.0225	.0452	.0722	.0970	.1137
12			.0001	.0006	.0034	.0113	.0264	.0481	.0728	.0948
13				.0002	.0013	.0052	.0142	.0296	.0504	.0729
14				.0001	.0005	.0022	.0071	.0169	.0324	.0521
15					.0002	.0009	.0033	.0090	.0194	.0347
16						.0003	.0014	.0045	.0109	.0217
17						.0001	.0006	.0021	.0058	.0128
18							.0002	.0009	.0029	.0071
19							.0001	.0004	.0014	.0037
20								.0002	.0006	.0019
21								.0001	.0003	.0009
22									.0001	.0004
23										.0002
24										.0001

INDEX*

* For further entries see the Index of Examples, page 229.

INDEX OF EXAMPLES